D. B. C. Scott,
    Woodbourne.
        Banchory.
            Kincardineshire.
Botany II.

McGRAW-HILL PUBLICATIONS IN THE
BOTANICAL SCIENCES

EDMUND W. SINNOTT, Consulting Editor

FUNDAMENTALS OF CYTOLOGY

McGRAW-HILL PUBLICATIONS IN THE BOTANICAL SCIENCES

EDMOND W. SINNOTT, *Consulting Editor*

There are also the related series of McGraw-Hill Publications in the Zoological Sciences, of which E. J. Boell is Consulting Editor, and in the Agricultural Sciences, of which R. A. Brink is Consulting Editor.

FUNDAMENTALS

of

CYTOLOGY

BY

LESTER W. SHARP

Professor of Botany, Cornell University

McGRAW-HILL BOOK COMPANY, Inc.

NEW YORK AND LONDON

1943

VII

To my wife

MABEL GUNTHER SHARP

PREFACE

THIS book is intended for use in connection with college and university courses in the biological sciences. It is not a new edition of the author's "Introduction to Cytology," which was designed to serve both as a reference work, of which plant cytology was in need, and as a general textbook. This is a textbook only. Although it deals again with various principal topics of the older work and uses some of its illustrations along with many new ones, the present text is much briefer, simpler in treatment, and, it is hoped, better adapted to the needs of students whose curiosity concerning cytology has been newly aroused in elementary courses in animal and plant science. The title of the older book, in fact, might well have been reserved for this one. Where subjects not essential to an introductory treatise are included, it is not with the thought that they should be mastered now, but rather to indicate further fields of inquiry open to students of cytology.

No attempt has been made to maintain the connection between statement and source characteristic of the "Introduction to Cytology." Each chapter has, however, been provided with a short list of books and recent papers for the use of those who wish to begin an examination of the literature, but to avoid distraction the text has been left unencumbered by specific references to them. Anyone who prepares a book of this kind knows well that he is presenting mainly the work of authors whose names do not appear on the title page, and he only trusts that he does this with accuracy and fairness.

The selection, arrangement, and treatment of the various topics have been determined by experience in cytology courses having a genetical and phylogenetical bearing. In the interest of simplicity, emphasis has been placed upon "typical" cytological phenomena. Care has been taken, however, to suggest the great diversity in cytological constitution and behavior exhibited by plants and animals and to indicate the many uncertainties in a field where growth is rapid and opinions are subject to change with new evidence. It is unfortunate that the terminology could not be further simplified without impairing the usefulness of the book for those preparing to consult the literature. As every experienced teacher of natural science is aware, the student's actual knowledge of the subject is gained primarily in the field and laboratory. It is there, by thoughtful observation and discussion, that his comprehension is developed; hence, a textbook such as this one should be regarded as an adjunct to this process and never as a substitute for it.

It is a pleasant duty to acknowledge indebtedness to authors and commercial firms who have so generously contributed illustrations. The author is especially grateful to his associates at Cornell University for their willing help: to Professors Lewis Knudson, Arthur J. Eames, Lowell F. Randolph, Robert T. Clausen, and Dr. Victor M. Cutter for criticisms of certain chapters, to Miss Louise Raynor for executing the original drawings and preparing the index, and to Miss Lillian Pieper for her assistance with the manuscript.

LESTER W. SHARP.

ITHACA, NEW YORK,
June, 1943.

CONTENTS

FUNDAMENTALS OF CYTOLOGY

CHAPTER I

THE POSITION OF CYTOLOGY IN BIOLOGICAL SCIENCE

Man has been led by his native curiosity and his desire to understand the world in which he lives to examine ever smaller natural objects. Rocks, animals, plants, and even the stars themselves he has regarded first as wholes, then as organizations of visible parts, later as systems of invisible molecules and atoms, and eventually as vast arrays of subatomic units. In the earlier stages of his investigations, he depended solely upon his unaided senses, whereas the later steps were possible only after he had devised special instruments, such as the microscope, telescope, spectroscope, chemical balance, vacuum tube, and cyclotron. With these powerful aids, he has been able to extend his observations into the realms of the infinitely remote and the infinitely small; and despite the indirectness of approach involved, they have led him to knowledge of the utmost significance.

Biology.—Animals and plants must have engaged primitive man's attention from his earliest days. In his struggle to keep alive, he was inevitably led to the discovery that certain constituent parts of these organisms would serve him well as food, clothing, and fibers. Even his superstitions may have contributed something to his knowledge, for in practicing the art of divination he could scarcely have failed to observe much in the anatomy of animals that was new to him.

A more scientific interest in the constitution of organisms had become well developed in Greece by the fourth century B.C., when Aristotle and Theophrastus produced, respectively, their famous treatises on animals and plants. One can well imagine the wish of these men for keener vision. In Aristotle's work on the generation of animals it is all too evident that without more trustworthy information regarding minute structures further speculation could hardly lead him nearer to a true solution of the fundamental biological problems that held his interest.

It was not until many centuries later that the small tissue elements lying beyond the reach of unaided vision could be investigated. Simple

lenses were probably first used seriously as optical instruments sometime
in the eleventh century, while the first compound microscopes (and
telescopes) were devised at the end of the sixteenth and the beginning of
the seventeenth century. A number of models of simple and compound
instruments soon became available, and these in the hands of many men,
professional and amateur, made possible a number of researches on the
minute anatomy of living beings that still excite our admiration.

Even when aided by the microscope, however, vision is limited. As
long as the objects studied lie within the visible range, direct observation
with or without the aid of lenses may suffice, but when they are smaller
than this, one must employ the very different analytical methods familiar to the chemist and physicist. With these methods have been developed clear concepts of minute structure in terms of molecules and atoms.

Obviously the organism confronts the worker with many problems
which require more than one mode of approach. For example, in the
study of the development of an embryo or the process of secretion in a
cell one encounters structural alterations visible with the microscope,
while accompanying these are invisible alterations in functional activity
that must be investigated by chemical means. The question of the relative priority of functional and structural change is frequently debated,
but, if atoms and electrons could be as easily seen as muscles and cells, so
that every functional reaction would appear also as a visible change in
molecular structure, the question as stated would probably not arise.

Every major biological problem thus comprises several partial problems which must be solved through the use of different techniques. One
can no more solve such a major problem with a single technique than a
carpenter can build a modern house with a single tool. The fact that the
organism sets such complex problems before us began long ago to resolve
the science of biology into a number of "fields," each of them characterized by a particular class of observations to be made and hence by a
particular set of requisite techniques. Morphologists, physiologists, and
taxonomists, for example, asked the organism for three different classes of
data, and they employed three different methods of inducing the organism
to yield them. This diversification of the science, which proceeded
rapidly in the nineteenth century, gave rise to groups of specialists who
scarcely understood the language of other groups, yet all agreed in
employing one general underlying method—the scientific method of
controlled observation, formulation of hypotheses, and verification.
Upon this method they will continue to rely, for it is chiefly responsible
for the rapid increase of dependable biological knowledge in recent times.

Cytology.—Cytology as a specialized branch of biology arose from
attempts to see more clearly the microscopic structure of plants and
animals. That the tissues of organisms have a cellular organization was

demonstrated by a number of students of minute anatomy during the seventeenth and eighteenth centuries. The earliest published picture of such structure appeared in 1665 in a book by Robert Hooke. In the works of this period the term *cells* meant two things: simply cavities bounded by walls like cells in a honeycomb, or globules of numerous unrelated kinds. For the most part they were looked upon as subordinate components of tissues rather than important individualized units.

Early in the nineteenth century, attention shifted to the "juice," or "slime," which had often been observed in the cells. By the middle of

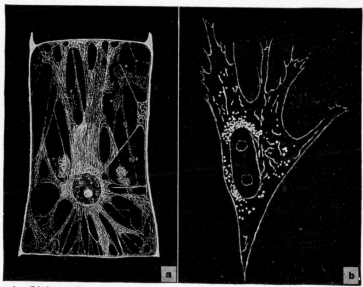

Fig. 1.—Living cells as they appear when illuminated against a dark background. *a,* cell from hair of squash plant. The cytoplasm forms a thin sheet against the cell wall, a series of streaming strands through the cell sap, and a large mass about the nucleus. (*After M. Heidenhain.*) *b,* chick-embryo cell growing on glass surface in tissue culture. In the cytoplasm are fat globules and filamentous chondriosomes. (*After T. S. P. Strangeways and R. G. Canti.*)

the century it had become evident that this unique fluid, or *protoplasm* as it came to be called, was the substance actually manifesting the phenomena of life, the thick walls observed in so many plant tissues being a product of its activity. In 1831, Robert Brown had pointed out the nucleus as a normal and characteristic constituent of cells. This made it easier to describe the typical cell as a mass of cytoplasm enclosing a nucleus, to distinguish it thus from other globules with which it had so often been confused, and to regard it as an important unit of organization. To this unit the more appropriate term *protoplast* has since been applied, although cytology's own name remains as a reminder of an earlier conception of the cell (*kytos* = hollow place).

From this point onward cytology stood out more clearly as a distinct field of study, and its own problems became more sharply defined. Among these was the task of determining to what extent the protoplast actually is "the unit of structure and function" as was claimed, a question to which we shall revert in the next chapter. It was soon discovered that many very small organisms have the structure of a single protoplast, that gametes and spores are likewise single protoplasts, and that the protoplast, whether constituting a whole organism or only a portion of one, multiplies regularly by division (Fig. 2). These discoveries, together with others that followed, made it clear that many kinds of biological problems would have to be attacked directly or indirectly

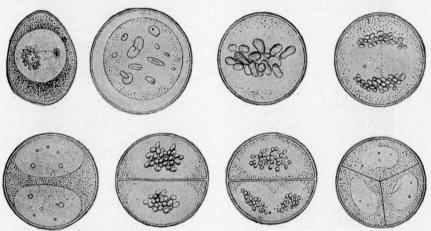

FIG. 2.—Figures of division of *Tradescantia* microsporocytes published by Wilhelm Hofmeister in 1848. This was a quarter of a century before chromosomes, shown plainly here, appeared prominently in biological literature and came to be recognized as individualized nuclear units.

through the cell unit. To the extent that such problems require this approach, they are cytological. As a matter of fact, much of the significant knowledge of the protoplast gained in recent years has developed in connection with questions that did not at first arise within the field of cytology itself.

The Classic Period of Cytology.—The latter portion of the nineteenth century witnessed striking advances in biology and the other sciences. It has become customary to refer to the last quarter of the century as the "classic period" of cytology because of its many fundamental discoveries. Some of the principal accomplishments of this period are enumerated in the following paragraphs.

Much was learned concerning the structure of cells and nuclei, their reproduction by division, and the behavior of their several components during the various phases of cell activity. Special attention was focused upon the remarkable process of mitosis, the chromosomes occupying an especially prominent place in researches of the period. Noteworthy progress was also made in studies of the physiological processes occurring in cells and the relation of these to the activities of the organism of which they are parts. As examples may be mentioned the advances in knowledge of mineral nutrition, enzymes, osmotic concentrations in cells, and the permeability of the plasma membrane.

The life cycles of various groups of plants and animals were minutely described in terms of the multiplication and differentiation of cells. The details of cell and nuclear behavior during the organism's reproductive phases were examined with special care, for it was realized that two successive generations of individuals are connected by a minute single cell—in some cases a spore, in others a fertilized egg—and that this single cell must therefore contain in its organization some kind of basis for the type of organism developing from it. A discovery of cardinal importance was that of the fusion of two nuclei, one from each parent, in the process of fertilization (1875).

It was observed further that certain organisms do not consist of cells in the usual sense, but are extensive and continuous masses of cytoplasm containing large numbers of nuclei. Notwithstanding this lack of internal cell partitions or of fixed nuclear positions, these organisms develop characteristic body forms and internal specializations. Moreover, certain organisms mainly cellular in structure pass through a noncellular stage at some period in their development or possess certain noncellular tissues in the mature body.

Discoveries like the foregoing not only furnished partial solutions to the problems originally attacked, but they also made it possible to formulate with the necessary precision those further special questions requiring answers before the problems in their broader aspects could be regarded as solved. It is thus bit by bit, rather than by one stroke, that an understanding of fundamental biological processes is reached. Even now, a century after researches on the division of cells began, we have arrived at no complete explanation of that remarkable process.

Mention should be made of technical advances made during the classic period. Far better methods for fixing and staining tissues were devised. With the aim of preserving cells with a more nearly natural appearance, careful studies were carried out on the effects of many reagents upon the various parts of the protoplast. Other investigations revealed the usefulness of coal-tar dyes which were then being produced for the first time. Formerly only a few natural dyes such as carmine and hematoxylin were employed, and although these are still extremely valuable today, the coal-tar dyes have added greatly to the variety and effectiveness of staining procedures. Vastly improved section-cutting machines, or microtomes, yielded perfect and uniformly thin sections at relatively high speed. All these aids were welcomed by cytologists and histologists whose work they greatly facilitated, though they too often had the undesirable effect of diverting attention from living material.

Compound microscopes were brought to a very high level of efficiency during the nineteenth century. During the classic period, apochromatic objectives, highly corrected against chromatic and spherical aberrations and with high resolving power, were perfected, and these, employed with newly devised eyepieces and condensers, furnished the cytologist with the finest images of highly magnified objects he had yet seen.

The closing years of the century also saw the formulation of theories that gave direction to many of the investigations yet to come. For example, there were biologists, notably August Weismann, who propounded theories of the mechanism of individual development, heredity, and evolution largely on the basis of what had recently been learned about the behavior of cells, nuclei, and chromosomes throughout the life cycles of organisms. Some of the concepts embodied in Weismann's theory of inheritance continued as a part of the framework of our modern theory, although his theory of development has been abandoned. In the field of cellular physiology the theoretical interpretations and laws pertaining to solutions, which grew out of researches on osmotic pressure and permeability in cells and nonliving systems, also continue as strong influences in the present century.

By way of summary we may say that the nineteenth century contributed to the twentieth a number of fundamental observations, certain intriguing problems, an array of useful techniques, and certain suggestive guiding theories. Observation, technical skill, and theory are all required in scientific research, and progress is surest when all three are utilized in the correct proportions.

Cytology in the Twentieth Century.—Cytology in the present century is fortunate in having several new and extremely valuable technical aids. Methods for the successful cultivation of living animal and plant tissues under controlled conditions in glass containers have been devised. For instance, there are living in flasks today (1942) healthy cells which are the descendants of similar cells removed from the heart of a chick embryo in 1912 (Fig. 3). Such cultures enable the worker to learn many things concerning the capacities of cells in a direct manner rather than by a series of inferences from fixed preparations or even from similar cells living in the complex environment within the body. Direct study is also facilitated by the micromanipulator, with which one can dissect or inject normal living cells under the best high-powered objectives (Fig. 4). Striking permanent records of observations of this character, *e.g.*, those on cell division, have been made with the motion-picture camera.

Another tool now in common use among cytologists is the X-ray tube. The irradiation of living material is now one of the best experimental means of inducing alterations in chromosomes for the purpose of analyzing

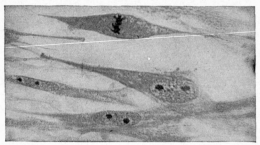

Fig. 3.—Cells (fibroblasts from heart of chick embryo) descended from a tissue culture begun by Carrel in 1912.   (*Photograph by A. Carrel; after W. Seifriz.*)

the role of these bodies in development and heredity.   X rays have also served to reveal the ultramicroscopic structure of plant cell walls. Radiations of various other types are being employed with success in connection with a number of such fundamental problems.

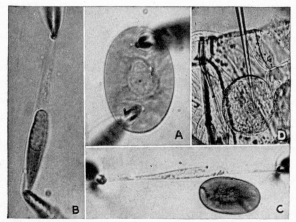

Fig. 4.—Photographs of cells being operated upon with a micromanipulator.   A, B, C, stages in the stretching of a red blood corpuscle from an amphibian between two micro-needles.   D, a micro-needle entering a living plant cell.   (*After W. Seifriz.*)

The chief advance in microscopy so far in this century is the invention of the electron microscope.   Instead of making use of visible light focused by a series of glass lenses as in the ordinary microscope (photomicroscope), this new instrument employs electron streams brought to a focus by a series of magnetic fields.   The result is a greatly increased resolving power, *i.e.*, the ability to render fine detail in an image. The photomicroscopes used for direct visual observation by cytologists reach the limit of their resolving power somewhere between 0.2 and 0.1μ,[1] two minute objects closer together than this appearing as one. A single particle somewhat below this limit may appear as a dark or light spot, depending upon the method of illumination, but its true form is not fully revealed. When ultraviolet light, quartz lenses, and photographic plates are used, the resolving power is about twice as great, for it varies with the frequency of the radiation employed. With the electron microscope, however, the resolving power is increased 20 to 50 times. The material to be examined must be dry for the best results, the interior of the instrument where it is placed for observation is occupied by a vacuum, and the image obtained is a shadow picture only; hence there are great difficulties attending the study of biological objects. Some of the results already obtained, such as those with viruses, together with the prospect of ingenious improvements, warrant the hope that the instrument will lead to further discoveries of immense importance.

Some of the fixing and staining techniques devised half a century ago still survive in the laboratory with little modification, some have been greatly altered and improved, and some have been replaced by new ones of greater value. Advances in physical chemistry and microchemistry have enabled the technician to go about his tasks with an increased understanding of what is going on in the tissues before him, even though much is still there that has not been fully explained. The cause of one of his chief perplexities has been very largely removed by the standardization of biological stains, an accomplishment of a cooperative group of biologists, manufacturers, chemists, and other interested workers.

Cytologists as well as investigators in other fields are now making increasing use of statistical methods in the evaluation of their data. Many valuable contributions have been made in past years with little conscious attention to the mathematical aspects of the problems in hand, but it is now more widely recognized that inferences drawn from observations may stand or fall with the results of mathematical analysis and that the true significance of what has been observed may not appear unless such methods are employed.

By far the most significant and encouraging development in twentieth-century cytology has been its more definite alliance with neighboring fields of biology. For many decades the various fields had given promise of becoming more mutually helpful, and now that promise is being fulfilled: the nineteenth century's subdivision of biology is being succeeded

---

[1] The symbol μ stands for micron. This equals 0.001 millimeter, or 1/25,400 inch, and is the unit of length most often used in cytology. The angstrom unit (Å), also used at times, equals 0.0001μ.

by a reunion of the parts into a more efficient whole. As each field has extended, its borders have come into contact with those of other fields from which it acquires aid for its own further development. Indeed, the regions formerly separating the fields are often found to be the most fertile of all.

The most conspicuous and so far the most profitable of such alliances is that between cytology and genetics. Although much of the foundation for this union was laid by nineteenth-century cytologists and students of heredity, modern cytogenetics dates rather definitely from 1900 and shortly thereafter, when Mendel's laws of inheritance were rediscovered and shown to have a physical basis in the known behavior of chromosomes through successive life cycles. The remarkable results of this alliance will receive special consideration in later chapters.

A second alliance now undergoing development is that between cytology and taxonomy. It has been found that characters useful in classification can often be recognized in the number and the form of the chromosomes. Not only do the chromosomal data aid in the grouping of the species and varieties, but they often furnish strong suggestions as to the manner in which certain taxonomic units have arisen during the course of evolution. The bulk of such work has so far been done with plants, although the method has proved useful with certain animal groups also.

The study of chromosomes in related plants has led to the discovery that differences in chromosome number and form sometimes show a significant correlation with differences in geographical range or ecological habitat. Here again workers in different fields—ecology, physiology, and cytology—are discovering the need for further cooperative endeavor.

Since disease is primarily an abnormal activity in cells and tissues, the close relation between cytology on the one hand and pathology and medicine on the other should be obvious. One needs only to mention the unruly growth of cancer cells or the effects of viruses on cell structure and function to indicate the importance of cooperative studies on diseased tissues.

The major problems of biology are thus joint problems, and cooperation is the modern way of solving them. The benefits of the various alliances are manifold. Cytology itself has been furnished with new and effective tools; it has become more experimental in nature; its findings have taken on new meanings. The other allied fields have been furnished by cytology with a better conception of the physical basis of the phenomena observed within their borders. The workers in all fields have been made more fully aware of their dependence upon one another and of their ignorance of much that assumes new importance for them; this all makes for tolerance and humility. Cooperation may make our individual ignorance more painfully evident, but at the same time it gives us hope of avoiding some of the consequences of ignorance.

What Cytology Is.—In view of what has been set forth above and what is to follow in later chapters, cytology may be defined as the branch of scientific biology that deals more or less directly with the structural and functional organization of protoplasm, usually in single or closely associated protoplasts, and with the relation of this organization to the phenomena of metabolism, growth, differentiation, heredity, and evolution.

Cytology thus broadly defined would appear to occupy a key position in the science of biology, since everything the organism does has a part of its cause in protoplasmic activity. This, however, does not mean that all biology must be regarded as an extension of cytology: it means rather that all biological problems have a cytological element in them. Cytology is therefore an integral part of biology, and the future progress of the science will depend very largely upon how well such integration is maintained.

CHAPTER II

THE ORGANISM AND THE CELL

The bodies of animals and plants are composed of protoplasm and its products; an organism is, in fact, an organized mass of protoplasm interacting with its environment. The protoplasm constituting the protoplast, or cell, is almost universally differentiated into two unlike portions, cytoplasm and nucleus, each of these being bounded by a definite membrane. In this chapter we shall examine the various ways in which this dual organization is manifested in the bodies of organisms. As we do so we shall point out certain general inferences which it is well to have in mind before narrowing the scope of our topics in subsequent chapters.

The Typical Protoplast.—The smallest complete example or expression of the fundamental organization of most living things—nucleated cytoplasm—is seen in the cell. This cell may exist singly or appear as one of a multitude of such units in a large body. Cells differ greatly in their internal organization and in the envelopes that may surround them, but for the present we shall limit our attention mainly to certain components common to nearly all of them, leaving further details to be dealt with in the succeeding chapter.

The cytoplasm is a mass of colorless protoplasm bounded externally by its specialized plasma membrane. It may appear as a clear viscous fluid, but often its many small inclusions give it a granular or an alveolar appearance. In plant cells it commonly encloses a considerable mass of cell sap against which it forms a limiting vacuolar membrane, and also one or more plastids in which carbohydrates are formed.

The nucleus is enclosed within the cytoplasm and is seldom normally in direct contact with any other component of the cell. It is bounded by a membrane. Usually it appears as a globule of clear matter in which numerous fine threads and one or more nucleoli are embedded.

The foregoing provisional description, very meager though it is, will serve the purposes of this chapter. The importance of structural and functional organization within the typical protoplast should be stressed at once. The cytoplasm, the nucleus, and the plastids are regions in which the protoplasm differs structurally and carries on different functional activities: they are to be regarded therefore as organs of the protoplast. The membranes, too, are such specialized regions and should be thought of not merely as barriers, but as organs of interaction

11

between cytoplasm, nucleus, and environment. Within the typical protoplast the localization of certain reactions in particular regions goes hand in hand with structural differentiations, much as it does at a higher level of organization in the various regions of a large and complex multicellular body.

As will be realized more fully later on, the concept of the cell as a fundamental organic unit has occupied a large place in biological thought. (1) It has afforded the student of organic structure a convenient concrete unit for descriptions of the minute anatomy and development of plants and animals. (2) The physiologist has often been able to gain insight into the functional activities of complex organisms by studying the activities of single cells. (3) The fact that many minute organisms have the structure of a single cell has stimulated speculation, much of it doubtless profitable, on the problem of the evolution of larger organisms. We therefore begin our cytological studies with the typical cell before us, even though our conceptions of its role may become modified as we proceed.

It is a habit of long standing to interpret a large organism in terms of its cell units. We cannot emphasize too strongly the importance of interpreting the behavior of the cell in terms of the complete organism of which it may be a small part. The relationship existing between the two individualities—the multicellular organism and the unit cell—can be made clearer through a consideration of the various arrangements assumed by cytoplasm, nuclei, and limiting membranes in particular tissues and complete organisms and by observing how these arrangements may change into one another as the development of the organism progresses.

Ontogeny, the development of an elaborate individual animal or plant from a fertilized egg, a spore, or any other small and relatively simple initial mass of protoplasm, is surely one of the most amazing phenomena on earth. The seemingly simple initial protoplast has, however, its own peculiar microscopic and submicroscopic organization. It is a major task of biologists to describe this organization and to show how it functions in the gradual transformation of the initial protoplast into a mature organism with its higher degrees of organization. This transformation involves almost innumerable structural changes and functional reactions, known and unknown. Our immediate purpose is not to describe any of these in detail, but rather to deal in a more general way with certain fundamental aspects of ontogeny, viz., growth, differentiation, and correlation. We shall then be in a better position to appreciate the relationship between the organism as a whole and the cell.

Growth.—Growth consists primarily in the synthesis of new protoplasm through the activity of that already present. It is ordinarily accompanied by an increase in size, although a cell or other mass of protoplasm may at times become much larger because of the accumulation of some nonprotoplasmic product, such as cell sap. Certain effects of growth upon the form assumed by protoplasts will now be examined.

For the sake of simplicity we shall begin with a typical cell consisting of a spherical mass of cytoplasm enclosing a spherical nucleus, these two portions being bounded by a plasma membrane and a nuclear membrane, respectively. Synthesis of new protoplasm involves interchanges of materials between cytoplasm and nucleus, the part that the nucleus can play being determined quantitatively by the area of its membrane. As the cell and nucleus increase in volume, the area of the membrane through which the interchanges must occur does not increase at the same rate; hence a point may be reached beyond which the interaction between nucleus and cytoplasm would be insufficient to support further growth of the whole protoplast. This difficulty is usually overcome in nuclear division, whereby the nuclear surface present in the protoplast is increased without a corresponding increase in the volume of any individual nucleus. Further growth can then proceed until the critical nucleocytoplasmic ratio is again reached. Sometimes a nucleus may increase its surface-volume ratio by altering its shape, the relative amount of surface being greater in nonspherical objects.

A similar limitation on the growth of a spherical cell is imposed by the area of plasma membrane through which the protoplasm interacts with the external environment. Here again the block to further growth is overcome by a division of the protoplast, or often by the assumption of a flattened or a filamentous form, as in so many algae; either of these methods leads to an increase of surface per unit volume. In large organisms like ourselves there are, of course, elaborate structural features, such as the respiratory and circulatory systems, that make possible interactions between the environment and the innermost regions of the body.

As the protoplasm continues to grow and the nuclei to multiply, the patterns assumed by the cytoplasm, nuclei, and membranes may come to differ widely in various tissues and organisms. For convenience one may refer to such patterns as *protoplasmic growth patterns*, remembering, however, that these are not always sharply distinct. In Fig. 5 there is represented diagrammatically the development of six such patterns from a typical protoplast.

1. The growth of the protoplasm and the multiplication of its nuclei may not be accompanied by the formation of partition membranes, the result being a *multinucleate mass*. Such a coenocytic condition is seen throughout the vegetative bodies of some algae and fungi and as a temporary or permanent feature of certain tissues of other plants and animals.

2. The nuclear multiplication may be accompanied regularly by the development of partition membranes, the result here being the *multicellular mass* so familiar in the tissues of most animals and plants.

3. As the nuclei multiply, the cytoplasm may not subdivide completely but gradually forms a *network*, commonly with its larger portions containing the nuclei and remaining continuous with one another through narrower strands. Such a pattern is found in some animal connective

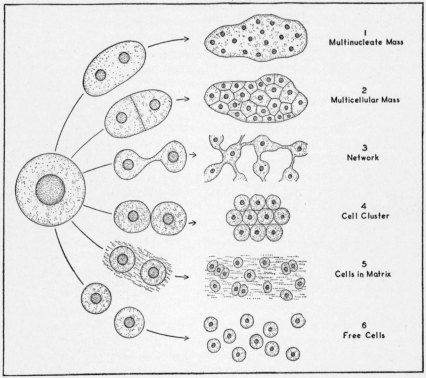

Fig. 5.—Diagram illustrating development of six different protoplasmic growth patterns from a typical protoplast. Explanation in text.

tissues (Fig. 6). The network lies embedded in a substance that may contain cells of additional types.

4. Each nuclear division may be followed by a cytoplasmic division, the resulting cells rounding up from one another but remaining in contact as a *cell cluster*. This pattern characterizes a certain stage (morula) of certain animal embryos (Fig. 94), and it is also seen in "colonial" algae (Fig. 7).

5. After nuclear and cell division the individual cells may become separated by the accumulation of an intercellular substance (matrix) secreted by the protoplasm during their formation and growth. The

secreted substance may have a firm consistency, forming with the included cells a definite tissue. Such a pattern, which is exemplified by cartilage (Fig. 8), may be termed *cells in matrix*.

6. After the individual cells are formed, they may become entirely independent *free cells*, as in the case of unicellular organisms reproducing by simple fission.

The above protoplasmic growth patterns may become transformed one into another as the structural development of the organism or tissue proceeds. The following examples will serve as illustrations. Pattern 1 changes into pattern 2 in the developing endosperm of most flowering plants and the embryos of certain gymnosperms, the appearance of walls throughout a multinucleate mass resulting in a multicellular tissue (Fig.

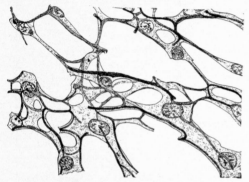
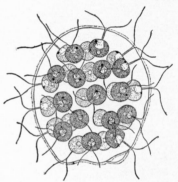

Fig. 6.—Reticular connective tissue from lymph node of cat. In the continuous cytoplasm is a network of nonelastic fibers. (*After M. Heidenhain.*)

Fig. 7.—A colonial green alga (*Eudorina*). The cells are contained in a homogeneous envelope. (*After G. M. Smith.*)

108). In developing connective tissues, pattern 3 may be derived from pattern 1 by the formation of large masses of fluid in the cytoplasm or from pattern 2 by a loosening up of the cells. Pattern 2 may give rise to pattern 4 when the cells of undifferentiated plant tissue round up from one another and form loose parenchyma. The formation of matrix characterizing cartilage (pattern 5) may begin in a multinucleate mass (pattern 1) or a multicellular mass (pattern 2). Pattern 6 develops from pattern 1 when a myxomycete plasmodium divides up into individual spores, or from pattern 2 when spores are produced in an anther or fern sporangium.

In the foregoing examples the several patterns have been described as arising either by a *subdivision* of the initial typical protoplast or by further subdivision in a pattern already formed. Similar patterns sometimes arise by an *aggregation* of free cell units or a union of tissue cells into a continuous mass of protoplasm. Thus free cells (pattern 6) may associate and form a colonial cluster (pattern 4) in certain algae. Among the slime molds there is a group of species in which free cells (pattern 6) unite in great numbers and form large pseudoplasmodia in which the original cell boundaries remain evident (pattern 2), while in another group the uniting cells lose their identity completely and form a true plasmodium (pattern 1).   In the anthers of many flowering plants the tapetum is at first a multicellular tissue (pattern 2), but while the microspores complete their development the walls in this tissue disintegrate and allow the protoplasts to flow together as a tapetal plasmodium (pattern 1).

Much interest attaches to patterns characterized by continuous cytoplasm because of the light they shed on the causes of ontogenetic develop-

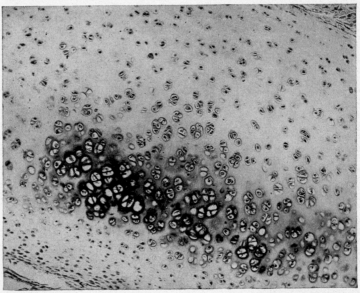

Fig. 8.—Hyaline cartilage from sternum of rabbit.   (*Courtesy of General Biological Supply House, Inc., Chicago.*)

ment in organisms with distinct cells.   When the condition has arisen as a result of nuclear division without cytoplasmic division, the resulting body or tissue is best called a *coenocyte*, whereas such a body or tissue produced by a union of previously distinct cells is known as a *syncytium*.   Evidently there are tissues, such as muscle or connective tissue, that may develop a given pattern in either of these ways.   When the mode of development in a tissue under observation is unknown, the nontechnical pattern names used in the foregoing paragraphs should suffice.

The subdivision and the aggregation of protoplasts are of interest not only from the standpoint of ontogenetic development: their relative importance in the evolution of animals and plants in general has also been a much debated point.   The true historical relationship of unicellular and multicellular organisms is at best uncertain, but that the facts set forth above have an important bearing on the question should be evident in what follows.

Differentiation.—By differentiation is meant a progressive change from a generalized and uniform condition to a more specialized and hetero-geneous condition in the protoplasmic system.   It results in the structural alteration of regions in which certain functions come to be localized, so that what is at first a mass in which all portions appear and act alike becomes a system of unlike but correlated parts, each performing one or more special functions.   In differentiation "the level of organization is raised."

Differentiation can occur in any of the proto-plasmic growth patterns reviewed above.   Even the structure of the typical protoplast is reason-ably (though not necessarily) considered to be the result of an ancient differentiation in primitive living substance, the cytoplasm, nucleus, and membranes representing specialized portions act-ing in harmony.   The astonishing extent to which differentiation can be carried in a unicellular organism is illustrated by those protozoa which have clearly specialized locomotor, digestive, excretory, and neuromotor regions (Fig. 9).   After examining such organisms as this, one can no longer accept the statement that "protozoa are simple organisms."   They are small and unicellu-lar, but considering their size and mode of life they are perhaps as well differentiated as we are. No other single cells are quite so intricately organized.

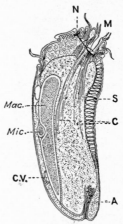

Fig. 9.—A protozoan (*Diplodinium*).   *M*, mouth; *N*, neuromotor apparatus; *Mac.*, macro-nucleus; *Mic.*, micro-nucleus; *C.V.*, contractile vacuole; *A*, anal canal; *C*, contractile region; *S*, skeletal plates. (*After R. G. Sharp.*)

A growing mass of protoplasm having any one of the "patterns," although it retains the primi-tive differentiation into cytoplasm, nucleus, and membranes, may still be regarded as generalized with respect to other expressions of differentiation that are yet to appear within it.   A mass of embryonic tissue, for example, has many nuclei, membranes, and other components, but if this same type of structure and the same general functions pervade the whole mass uniformly, it is said to be undifferentiated so far as the development of further specialized organs is concerned.

That differentiation resulting in the same general form of body or in organs having the same function may occur in protoplasmic systems of unlike pattern is shown by the following examples.   The three green algae *Stigeoclonium*, *Cladophora*, and *Vaucheria* all develop branching, filamentous bodies, although the first has numerous uninucleate cells and the second fewer and larger coenocytic compartments, while the third is completely coenocytic, having no cellular subdivisions whatever in the vegetative body. Their common body form must be developed by what is common to all of them—nucleated cytoplasm.

Even more striking are the spore-bearing organs of various plants (Fig. 10). In each of these selected cases the organ is composed of a supporting stalk and an enlarged terminal portion in which the spores are formed. In the first, a fruiting body of a slime mold, a multinucleate plasmodium grows upward into a column which enlarges at the top, becomes surrounded by a resistant outer wall, and develops an internal system of capillitium filaments, and then, only when these differentiations are practically completed, does the multinucleate protoplasm in the upper portion subdivide into spores. In the second, a fruiting body of

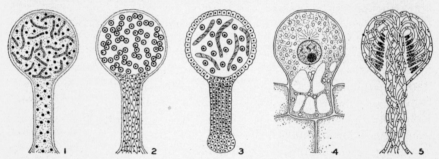

Fig. 10.—Differentiation in spore-bearing portions of various plants. Semidiagrammatic. Explanation in text. (*No. 4 redrawn from J. L. Williams.*)

another type of slime mold, a large number of separate cells become closely aggregated without actually fusing and build up a stalked structure with a slimy sheath and spore-like cysts. In the third, a sporophyte of a liverwort, a mass of multicellular tissue develops the stalked form, a sporangium wall, a system of internal filaments (elaters), and eventually spores. In the fourth, a sporangium of an alga, a single uninucleate cell elongates, projects from the body, and forms a distal globular enlargement which subdivides into spores. In the fifth example, the fruiting body of a mushroom, the organ is developed by a mass of interwoven filamentous hyphae.

Of equal interest in connection with the role of cells in structural and functional differentiation are the following observations on the development of animal eggs. The larva of a certain annelid worm develops much of its characteristic form and internal differentiation up to a certain stage even when the normal subdivision into cells is suppressed by adding KCl to the medium. In some marine animals a complete embryo may be developed by a single one of the 8 or 16 cells formed by the first 3 or 4 divisions of the fertilized egg, whereas in others the embryo lacks certain parts even after a portion of the undivided egg is removed. This indicates that subdivision into cells and differentiation are two processes that may be variously correlated in time, differentiation beginning relatively late in the first instance and relatively early in the second. In Amphibia it has been shown that, if a group of cells from one region of a sufficiently young larva be transplanted to another region, the structure into which it develops will be appropriate to the new position rather than the original one.

It appears, then, that when differentiation of regions takes place in growing protoplasm these regions need not be delimited by cell boundaries. Cellular structure is accessory, and cell division is an incident of growth rather than a cause of differentiation. The kinds of subsidiary units, present—cells, hyphae, nuclei, plastids—do, of course, share in determining the kinds of specialization that can occur, but which of these do take place in the various regions is determined by their positions in the whole system. The region behaves as it does, not because it is cells, but because it is protoplasm with a certain physicochemical constitution responding to conditions that are in some degree peculiar to that portion of the growing mass. This is strikingly illustrated by the coenocytic alga *Bryopsis*, which develops a regular and characteristic body form while the streaming cytoplasm carries the nuclei about from region to region within it. In a word, ontogenetic differentiation is to be regarded as an act of the developing system as a whole, whatever its protoplasmic growth type.

The controlling influence of the whole upon the activities of its parts in multicellular tissues has been emphasized anew in recent studies of cell behavior during the development of plant organs. In the transformation of the small ovary into the large fruit of the squash plant, it is found that growth in early stages is chiefly by cell multiplication, whereas in later stages it is entirely by cell enlargement. Meanwhile the fruit increases in size and in dry weight at constant rates, and its parts differentiate and change in relative proportions; in other words, growth and differentiation of the whole proceed uniformly whether the constituent cells are multiplying rapidly, slowly, or not at all and whether they are becoming progressively smaller (by divisions) or larger. Moreover, the rate and the time of cessation of cell division in fruits of this kind are the same regardless of cell size. In long gourds the nuclear division figures when first formed lie at various angles with respect to the long axis of the fruit, but at later stages they turn more nearly parallel to it as though in response to some polarizing force acting along the axis; hence the new partition walls develop at right angles to this axis and the number of cells along it is increased.

Similar studies of growing grass roots likewise indicate a dependence of the cell upon forces acting in the organ as a whole. In regions where the cells are elongating, it can be seen that a wave of elongation passes from the base toward the apex of the root, this wave at a given moment affecting alike whatever portions of neighboring cells occupy the same level, whether these portions are basal, median, or apical. The wave is something not dependent upon boundaries of the unit cells. Here, as in the cucurbit fruits and coenocytes, the unity of behavior and of organization inheres primarily in the whole rather than in the elements composing it.

Correlation.—In every normal mass of protoplasm, whatever its growth pattern or degree of differentiation, the many diversified activities are so coordinated that it behaves as a consistent whole, or individual, from the beginning of development onward; without such harmony there obviously could be no organism. How this harmony is maintained has never been fully explained. Recent work on higher plants and animals has shown that diffusible substances play an important role in this connection, and something of the sort may well occur within the limits of single cells. In multicellular tissues the fine protoplasmic strands (*plasmodesms*) connecting neighboring protoplasts in all probability facilitate correlation (Fig. 56). In animals the nervous system functions as a specialized correlating mechanism. It has also been shown that gradients in the rate of metabolism and in electric potential along the various axes of symmetry are correlated with differentiation with respect to these axes. Reversal of the electrical polarity may result in a reversal of morphological pattern. Moreover, there is some evidence that in and about an organ or developing embryo there is a characteristic pattern of potential—a "field"—that exercises some measure of control over what occurs within it. "Differentiation, upon such a view, is to be looked upon as a setting up of new fields, each resulting from changes in size or position during ontogeny or phylogeny." All this suggests that a physicochemical explanation of correlation may be hoped for and that a more satisfactory conception of organic "wholeness" may some day be attained.

Tissues and Organs.—Since the fundamental processes of development—growth, differentiation, and correlation—may occur normally in the several protoplasmic growth patterns, it is often inadequate to define a tissue as a group of cells and their products. Many tissues are just this, but a better definition would be one applicable also to other patterns, including the plasmodial state.

Although we commonly think of an organ as a specialized multicellular structure because of familiar examples, the more comprehensive definition, "any part of an organism performing some definite function," is more nearly adequate if one remembers that a protozoan as well as a metazoan may have distinct regional differentiations associated with special localized functions. On the basis of function, which gives organs their significance, the contractile region within a protozoan cell is as much an organ as the muscle of a frog. The flat, green expansions of certain green algae are functionally "leaves" even though they are coenocytic instead of cellular like the leaves of vascular plants.

These points are perhaps sufficient to emphasize the thought that in our cytological study of animals and plants we shall miss much that is of first importance if we consider cells, their components, and their products only in terms convenient for the description of structure and neglect their relation to the active life of the organism of which they are parts.

Conclusions.—In this chapter we have dealt at some length with the relationship between two units or individualities present in large organisms—the organism as a whole and the cell. Obviously there is a reciprocal action between them when both are present, the part affecting the whole while the whole affects the part. The relative importance of the two has been variously conceived. The proponents of the cell theory stressed the cell as the primary agent of organization, while adherents of the organismal theory insist upon the primacy of the whole, cells when present being important but subsidiary parts. The former regarded multicellular organisms as having arisen phylogenetically as aggregates of unicellular individuals, whereas the latter hold it to be more probable that single unicellular individuals became internally subdivided as they became larger. The probability of an "evolution from Protozoa to sponges and coelenterates by multiplication of nuclei in an already differentiated cytoplasm" has recently been emphasized anew (Kofoid).

This subject can be followed further in other works on biology, but it has been thought well to set forth early in the present book some of the basic facts of structural development insofar as they concern cells as units, together with a suggestion of certain theoretical interpretations. It should then be easier to appreciate the significance to the organism of those cytological details to which we shall soon restrict our attention. The prevalent multicellular state is doubtless the most efficient basis for differentiation in all but very small organisms and has conditioned much evolutionary progress, but we have seen that the essential features of development can occur without it. "The principle of protoplasmic differentiation is more general and fundamental than that of cells as units" (Heidenhain).

CHAPTER III

THE STRUCTURAL COMPONENTS OF PROTOPLASTS

In the previous chapter the fact that the cell is not always a distinct element in tissues was emphasized as one that should aid in clarifying our conceptions of factors responsible for the action of the complex organism as a whole, especially during its ontogeny. Nevertheless in most organisms and tissues the cell does appear clearly as a more or less standardized unit having cytoplasm, nucleus, and membranes. In addition to these there may be other diverse functional and structural differentiations that cause some cells to look very unlike "typical" protoplasts. We shall now extend our description of the protoplast by reviewing in more detail its principal internal features.

Cytoplasm.—The cytoplasm consists ordinarily of an optically clear, somewhat viscous fluid (*hyaloplasm*) in which there may be embedded a multitude of small droplets and granules that give it a visible structure. The fundamental structure necessary to the performance of vital activities is known to lie in the hyaloplasm beyond the limit of visibility with the photomicroscope; this matter will be considered further in the next chapter. The cytoplasmic portion of the protoplast is called the *cytosome*.

The cytosome is often differentiated into fairly distinct regions differing in viscosity. In many cells the more viscous portion, the *plasmagel*, forms a cortical layer of variable thickness just beneath the plasma membrane, while the more fluid portion, the *plasmasol*, lies farther in. The cytoplasm may change rapidly and locally from one state to the other, and it is evident that such alterations play a role in ameboid locomotion and the streaming observed in tissue cells.

In embryonic or meristematic tissues the cytoplasm seems to be less differentiated than the other cell components enclosed within it and more like what we may imagine primitive protoplasm to have been. It is, however, capable of differentiation in many ways. In muscle tissue, for example, it may be almost completely transformed into fine longitudinal myofibrils that function somehow in the act of contraction (Fig. 11). The cytoplasm of nerve cells has delicate neurofibrils probably concerned in the conduction of stimuli (Figs. 12, 13). In the protozoa the cytoplasm, or at least its external hyaline portion (*ectoplasm*), may develop locomotor extensions in the form of undulating membranes, cilia, and flagella of many types. The pseudopodia formed by amebas and myxomycetes

22

consist of both hyaline ectoplasm and granular *endoplasm*. Since most of the visible changes in differentiating cells occur in the cytoplasm, the latter has sometimes been regarded as an *organ of differentiation*, somewhat as the nucleus has been called an *organ of heredity*.

At the outer surface of the cytoplasm, whether it is surrounded by a thick cell wall or not, there is a film of ultramicroscopic thinness, the *plasma membrane*. In case a layer of ectoplasm is present, as in the ameba, the plasma membrane is at its outer boundary. Such a membrane

Fig. 11.—Portions of two human muscle fibers. The myofibrils run lengthwise. Modifications in the associated fibrils at regular intervals are responsible for the transverse striations. (*Courtesy of General Biological Supply House, Inc., Chicago.*)

evidently develops by the accumulation of certain protoplasmic constituents to the exclusion of others and the arrangement of these constituents into a layer having a special type of structure. It seems to resemble in some measure the surface film on a pond or drop of water, where the molecules have been shown to be arranged regularly and closely in a pavement-like layer. The elastic and other physical properties of this external membrane have been studied with the aid of the micromanipulator (page 45). Such studies have shown that when the membrane is torn (if not too greatly) it is quickly renewed by the protoplast.

The physical and chemical properties of the plasma membrane are largely responsible for the physiological behavior of the protoplast, in particular its interaction with its environment. What substances shall enter or leave the protoplast and the rate of their movement are determined not only by the nature of the substances, but also by the character of the membrane. The membrane is semipermeable, *i.e.*, it may allow the solvent but not the solute to pass, and physiologists are attempting to account for this significant property and its fluctuations in terms of physicochemical constitution.

At the boundary between the cytoplasm and each of the other main parts of the protoplast to be described below there is a special membrane of some kind, so that interchanges there, too, are determined by regional

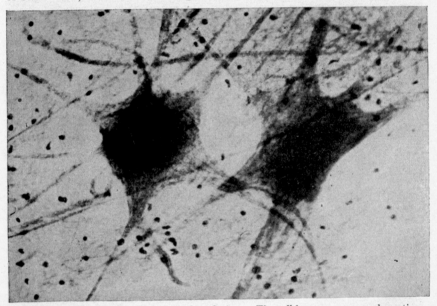

Fig. 12.—Motor nerve cells in spinal cord of ox. The cell has numerous prolongations, the nerve fibers, which are embedded in a tissue known as *neuroglia*. Fine striations in the cytoplasm are *neurofibrils* (compare Fig. 13). (*Courtesy of General Biological Supply House, Inc., Chicago.*)

differentiations involving the cytoplasm. To what extent the special alterations at such an interface involve changes in the materials on either side of it is not well known. There are reasons, both experimental and theoretical, for the view that a membrane formed where two different fluids meet arises by a local modification of both fluids. The membranes within the protoplast, notably that around the nucleus, would in this sense be double structures. Precipitation membranes composed of new components formed by chemical interaction of two fluids probably play a minor role. It should always be borne in mind that the behavior of the protoplast depends not only upon the general composition of its principal parts, but also upon further special modifications in areas where two unlike components meet.

The problem of membranes involves a further special differentiation of the cytoplasm known as *kinoplasm*. This has been studied chiefly in plant cells. It appears typically in the form of strands or channels of fluid streaming with included granules through the unmodified cytoplasm, or *trophoplasm*. It seems to form a more or less continuous system with the plasma membrane, the vacuole membrane, and sheaths of similar material about the plastids and nucleus. Like the membranes, the kinoplasmic strands appear to have a high lipide content. With a few important exceptions, cytologists have neglected the kinoplasm, and it is much in need of further study, especially in view of its apparent relation to the protoplasmic surface membranes.

Nucleus.—The nucleus has claimed a large share of the attention of cytologists ever since its discovery more than a century ago. There are numerous reasons for this. Excepting chloroplasts of most plants, the nucleus is the most conspicuous organ of a protoplast under the microscope, especially in stained preparations. By observing the effects of its removal from certain cells, it has been shown to be necessary for synthetic metabolism in the protoplast. At the time of division it passes through an amazingly complicated but very orderly series of changes that never fail to fascinate the observer. Cytogenetic studies have shown that the mode of ontogenetic development and, hence, the particular characters exhibited by the organism are related to the constitution of the nucleus and, furthermore, that the inheritance or noninheritance of certain parental characters is due to the behavior of the chief nuclear components, the chromosomes, during the reproductive stages of the life cycle. Preoccupation with nuclear behavior has doubtless been too great at times, but fortunately there have been other workers who have stressed the importance of membranes, plastids, and other components of the cytosome, so that altogether a fairly well balanced conception of the protoplast's activity is being built up.

It cannot yet be said that nuclei are present in all animals and plants. In some minute organisms, particularly certain bacteria, is a central body whose reaction as thymonucleoprotein and regular behavior in cell division strongly suggest its nuclear nature. In some stages of the cell cycle this material may be scattered throughout the cell in a finely granular or a diffused form. Under like conditions other bacteria appear homogeneous. In most organisms it is not so difficult to characterize the nucleus, for in spite of many variations, some of them rather extreme, the same general type of fundamental structure seems to be present in practically all groups.

The nucleus, when not undergoing division, is said to be in the *metabolic* or *energic* stage because many of its most important functions are exercised at this time. Unfortunately it has long been called the "resting stage," an obviously inappropriate term. At this stage the nucleus is bounded by a membrane. The permeability of this membrane is known to differ in certain respects from that of the plasma membrane: the two are not formed between the same pair of substances. Although various substances must be interchanged through the membrane, the cytolysis following its tearing by a needle shows that it separates substances capable of strong interaction.

Within the membrane is a mass of clear nuclear sap, or *karyolymph*, in which the remaining nuclear constituents are embedded. The most important of these constituents is evidently a substance in the form of numerous crooked threads, the *chromonemata* (= color threads). These

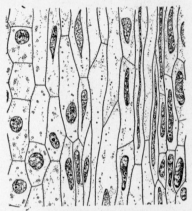

Fig. 13.—Nerve cell from earthworm, showing the fine neurofibrils within the cytoplasm. (*After J. Kowalski.*)

Fig. 14.—Nuclei in young floral axis of *Maianthemum*. In the narrow cells of the developing vascular bundle (right) the nuclei become greatly elongated. Young plastids are present in the cytoplasm.

are so named because they contain a substance (*chromatin*) which is strongly stainable with certain dyes and can thus be made to stand out plainly in the clear, unstained karyolymph. In living nuclei they are only faintly seen or even may be invisible because their refractive index in ordinary light is so nearly like that of the karyolymph, but suitable methods reveal their presence (Fig. 15). Their visibility may vary with alterations in the degree of hydration during the nuclear cycle. They frequently appear, especially in fixed material, to be connected by fine strands (*anastomoses*), forming thus a network (*reticulum*). The extent to which anastomoses are normal structures is uncertain. The chromonemata are of special interest because they represent the chromosomes at this stage. In stages of nuclear division an additional stainable substance (*matrix*) is combined with the chromonemata, giving the chromosomes the compact form characteristic of those stages (Chap. VII).

In some nuclei there are several dense, highly stainable lumps in the midst of the chromonemata (Fig. 16). These are *chromocenters* and seem to represent regions where the chromonemata are more closely packed and have retained more of the matrix. Such regions occur in definite positions in certain chromosomes. When each chromosome has a single one, the number of chromosomes can sometimes be determined by counting the deeply stained spots in the metabolic nucleus. Ordinarily chromosomes can be counted only during nuclear division.

Each typical nucleus has one or more *nucleoli* lying in the karyolymph. These differ chemically from the material of the chromocenters and can

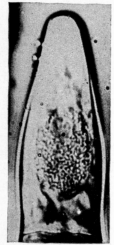

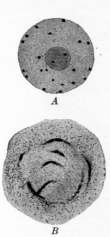

FIG. 15.—Living nucleus in *Tradescantia* stamen hair mounted in paraffin oil. The mottled appearance is due to the numerous contorted chromonemata. (*Photograph by H. Telezynski.*)

FIG. 16.—*A*, nucleus of bean (*Phaseolus*), with chromocenters. (*After E. Kuhn.*) *B*, cell of touch-me-not (*Impatiens*), with nucleus in prophase. Chromocenters are present (see page 87). (*After V. Grégoire.*)

easily be distinguished from them by suitable staining methods. They develop in close union with certain chromosomes in the newly formed nuclei at the close of division; this is why they usually lie against one or more of the chromonemata in the metabolic nucleus. Their number also is related to their connection with chromosomes. These points will be discussed in Chap. VII.

The physical consistency of the nucleus as a whole obviously depends upon the consistencies and relative amounts of its several components—membrane, karyolymph, and chromonemata. In certain animal eggs it behaves under the micromanipulator like a very fluid droplet with a firmer membrane. In cells of several other kinds it seems to be more viscous throughout than the cytoplasm and can be moved about bodily without visible injury. The relative specific gravities of the nuclear components and other portions of the protoplast can be determined by the use of the centrifuge (Fig. 30). In an electrical field, free nuclei or cells very rich in nuclear material tend to pass toward the anode, showing that they carry a negative charge, whereas cytoplasm or cells with little chromatin tend to go in the opposite direction. In the nucleus it is the chromatin that carries the negative charge, the karyolymph and usually the nucleolus being positive.

The nucleus, like the rest of the protoplast, consists of chemical substances of several classes, among which proteins, lipides, and water play the major roles. Of special importance is the chemical nature of the chromatic threads and the chromosomes of which they are the principal constituents, for it is largely upon their composition that the peculiar powers of the nucleus in determining the course of development and the

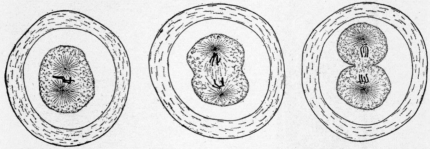

Fig. 17.—Three stages in mitosis in embryo of *Ascaris*, showing centrioles and asters.

phenomena of heredity seem to depend. Analyses have shown that the chromatin is a nucleoprotein composed of nucleic acid and certain basic proteins. Further discussion of the chemical nature of nuclei will follow in the next chapter (page 51).

The Centrosome.—In the cytoplasm of most animal cells and of certain lower plant cells a centrosome is commonly present. It is not found in seed plants. Typically it consists of a minute, deeply staining granule, the *centriole*, or often a pair of these, surrounded by a mass of less stainable substance, the *centrosphere*. In some cells only a centriole is visible, while in others nothing but centrosphere substance seems to be present. The aspect of the centrosome varies widely in cells of different kinds and in different stages of nuclear division, its division also commonly occurring during this process (Fig. 48). It also plays a conspicuous role during the development of certain motile cells, notably male gametes, where it is concerned in the formation of the motor apparatus. Further discussion of centrosomes is therefore deferred to chapters dealing with these topics.

Plastids.—Plastids are protoplasmic bodies characteristic of the vegetable kingdom. They are present in nearly all plant cells and play an important role in metabolism. Plastids confront the biologist with problems of three kinds: cytological, biochemical, and phylogenetic. Cytologists have already learned much about plastids, but some of the most important points regarding their structure, visible alterations, and

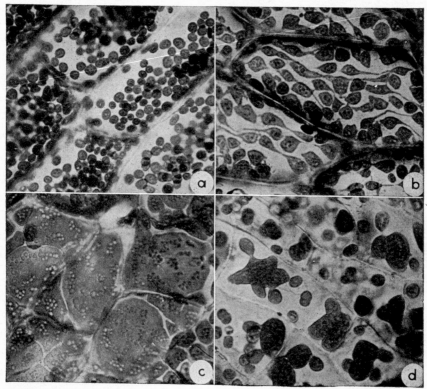

Fig. 18.—Chloroplasts in gametophytes of fern (*Polypodium*). *a*, normal gametophyte. *b, c, d*, persistent modifications (chain-like, plate-like, and budding types) induced in chloroplasts by X-ray treatment of spores. (*After L. Knudson.*)

relation to other cytoplasmic differentiations remain obscure. Biochemists are gradually approaching a better understanding of the exact chemical changes that take place in plastids during the all important process of photosynthesis. They are also studying the significant relation of certain plastid pigments to vitamins. Biologists in general would like to know more about the historical origin of plastids and their role in the divergent evolution of organisms with different types of nutrition.

The familiar green *chloroplasts* (Figs. 18, 19) occupy a peculiarly strategic position in the living world, for within them carbon dioxide and water react in such a manner as to yield a sugar. The energy for the reaction is obtained from visible light. The green pigment chlorophyll absorbs this energy and transfers it to the reacting substances, and oxygen is liberated as a by-product. This process of photosynthesis is the primary source of the world's organic food supply. The reaction resulting in the production of a gram molecule of hexose may be represented in a convenient though misleadingly simple manner as follows: $6CO_2 + 6H_2O + 673$ kg. cal. $= C_6H_{12}O_6 + 6O_2$. The energy of sunlight, after being thus captured and stored, is released to the organism through the process of respiration, which may be represented as follows: $C_6H_{12}O_6 + 6O_2 = 6CO_2 + 6H_2O + 673$ kg. cal.

Chlorophyll is not the only pigment in the chloroplast. Chlorophyll itself exists in two slightly different forms designated as *a* and *b*. Present

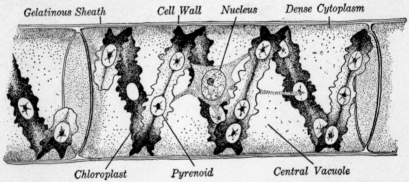

FIG. 19.—A cell of a green alga (*Spriogyra*). (*From Smith, Overton et al., A Textbook of General Botany, 4th ed., New York, The Macmillan Company.*)

with these are the yellow carotenoid pigments xanthophyll and carotene, whose color is evident after the chlorophyll disintegrates in drying autumn leaves. Chemical analysis of tobacco leaves has revealed the following amounts of these pigments in milligrams per square meter of leaf surface: chlorophyll *a*, 29.30; chlorophyll *b*, 10.38; xanthophyll, 10.63; carotene, 3.52. Four of the many known carotenoids show a pronounced vitamin A activity, although their value to the plant is obscure. There is also evidence that vitamin C (ascorbic acid) is present in the chloroplast.

In the algae other pigments accompany the chlorophyll. Familiar examples are fucoxanthin, a carotenoid, in the brown algae and phycoerythrin, a chromoprotein, in the red algae. Other carotenoids such as riboviolascin occur in the purple bacteria. Bearing directly upon the problem of the early stages of organic evolution is the striking chemical resemblance of the complex chlorophyll molecule to that of the red hemin in animal hemaglobin. The place of the magnesium atom in chlorophyll is occupied by iron in hemin, thereby rendering hemoglobin an efficient oxygen carrier.

Plastids with no color are known as *leucoplasts*. Ordinarily they are small and occur in considerable numbers in meristematic plant cells and in parts not exposed to light. Under appropriate conditions some of them enlarge and develop into green chloroplasts or plastids of other colors. Under other conditions, notably in roots and other storage organs, they remain colorless but become active in the conversion of soluble carbohydrates into granules of storage starch; such leucoplasts are therefore known as *amyloplasts* (Figs. 20, 31). Hence the carbohydrate appearing as starch in a potato tuber has been through two plastids. It was first elaborated in chloroplasts in the leaf as a soluble sugar; if not removed at once, it was converted by enzymes into visible starch granules. Later this starch was reconverted to sugar and transported to the tuber, where, within the amyloplasts, it was again transformed into granules of starch. In some plants, *e.g.*, the yellow-green algae, diatoms, and the onion plant, the visible products of synthetic activity are fats.

FIG. 20.—Cells of pea root tip. The elongate leucoplasts contain starch grains. Note their arrangement near poles of dividing nuclei. (*After R. H. Bowen.*)

Of the greatest interest is the recent announcement that the cellulose of plant cell walls is elaborated in minute colorless plastids in higher plants and in chloroplasts in an alga. We shall revert to this important subject in Chap. VI.

Plastids of higher plants are often called *chromoplasts* when they show some color other than green; in literal terms, however, a chloroplast is also a chromoplast, or chromatophore. The ordinary tomato fruit is red because lycopene, related to carotene, appears in the chloroplasts during ripening. Nasturtiums owe their yellow color, though not their red, to their chromoplasts. Such special pigments may develop in leucoplasts or in chloroplasts. The red, light-sensitive eyespots of certain flagellate and algal cells seem to be plastid-like differentiations. Other eyespots have a different origin.

Structure of the Chloroplast.—The fact that a chloroplast swells in distilled water or a hypotonic solution and the manner in which its boundary often appears to separate from the green substance under such conditions indicate the presence of a limiting membrane with osmotic properties. The ground substance (*stroma*) of the chloroplast appears as colorless cytoplasm. By grinding and centrifugation it is possible to separate the plastids from other cell components and to show that 50 per cent of the protein in tobacco leaves is in the plastids. The chlorophyll appears to be confined to numerous small platelets, or *grana*, embedded in the stroma. These grana are sometimes few and large enough to be easily seen, but under some physiological conditions they are so small, numerous, and closely packed that the chloroplast appears very finely granular or even homogeneous. Even in these latter cases the stroma, free of grana, may be observed in pseudopodium-like extensions or in torn specimens. The fibrous appearance often exhibited by chloroplasts is probably due to a linear arrangement of the grana and to variations in the submicroscopic structure of the stroma itself.

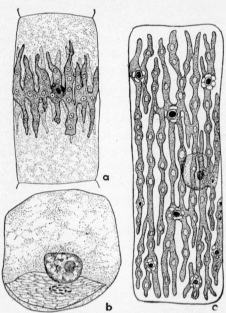

Fig. 21.—Chloroplasts with pyrenoids. *a*, in a green alga (*Draparnaldia*). *b*, in a liverwort (*Anthoceros*); pyrenoid consists of numerous small bodies. *c*, in a green alga (*Oedogonium*); starch granules are near pyrenoids and elsewhere in the plastid. (*c, after F. Schmitz.*)

Chemical tests show that the granum, after the extraction of its chlorophyll, consists mainly of protein and lipide. Attempts have been made to ascertain the exact form of association between these materials and the chlorophyll with the aid of polarized light and fluorescence in ultraviolet light. The results, taken together with observations on the chemical and physical behavior of proteins and lipides, have led to a current hypothesis of chloroplast structure. On this hypothesis the chlorophyll forms a series of monomolecular films on the surfaces of numerous protein layers lying more or less parallel throughout the granum. The chlorophyll molecules have their hydrophile ends associated with the protein and their lipophile ends with lipide molecules.

The arrangement is such that between each two protein layers there are two films of chlorophyll molecules, a double layer of lipide molecules, a few xanthophyll molecules, and water. The distance between two of the protein layers is about 0.005μ. To what extent this represents the true structure no one can say at present, but hypotheses, right or wrong, are valuable as long as they are subject to experimental test.

In some algae the chloroplast contains one or more peculiar bodies known as *pyrenoids* (Fig. 21). These appear like small masses of protein in the midst of the stroma and evidently play some definite role in the elaboration or deposition of carbohydrates, for starch grains develop in their immediate vicinity and commonly form a dense mass about each of them. Such behavior strongly suggests localized enzymatic activity. In the liverwort *Anthoceros* and the pteridophyte *Selaginella* there are compound pyrenoids, the parts of which give the appearance of transformation into starch granules. There are no known pyrenoids in seed plants.

Development and Multiplication of Plastids.—When the meristematic tissues in a young, actively growing bud of a seed plant are examined, it is found that the plastids there do not have their mature characters, but appear rather as very small globules or rodlets; these are plastid primordia, or *proplastids*. As the young stem tip and leaves grow and the cells multiply, the proplastids also grow and multiply by division. This is apparently their only mode of multiplication, for there is as yet no conclusive evidence that they ever arise anew in the cytoplasm. Sooner or later, when the leaf tissues become further differentiated, the enlarged proplastids become transformed into chloroplasts. Division may occur even after they are fully differentiated. In root meristems the story is essentially the same, except that leucoplasts rather than chloroplasts are formed.

The division of the young plastids during the development of most tissues is not definitely correlated in time with that of the nuclei and cells. However in some plants, such as the liverwort *Anthoceros* and various algae having only one plastid per cell, the plastid divides regularly just before or during the division of the other cell elements, thus preserving the one-plastid condition. It should be added that many plastids undergo striking alterations in shape and that these should not be interpreted too hastily as stages of division.

The bud tissues described above are derived from embryonic cells and ultimately from the fertilized egg. This raises the question of the continuity of plastids as individuals, multiplying only by division, through successive life cycles. In the angiosperms, proplastids appear to be present at all stages in the formation of spores and gametes, the plastids thus being continuous from one generation to the next. The inheritance of certain characters involving plastids suggests, however, that in some but not all of these plants the male gamete contributes no functional cytoplasm or plastids to the offspring, inheritance of such characters being purely maternal in such cases. It seems probable that in ferns and bryophytes, too, there is such a continuity of plastids. In these groups it is plain that the motile male gamete loses most if not all of its cytoplasm with any contained plastids before it unites with the egg. In *Anthoceros*, mentioned in the preceding paragraph, the single plastid characterizes all the cells in the life cycle with the exception of the male gamete. Again in certain algae (*Spirogyra*, *Zygnema*), whose gametes have essentially the structure of vegetative cells, the plastids can be observed as distinct individuals through all the reproductive phases (Figs. 117, 118).

In the absence of adequate evidence to the contrary, observations such as the foregoing speak for the probable validity of the theory, long held by many cytologists, that plastids are permanent protoplasmic organs always derived from their predecessors by division. An element of doubt still remains, however, for in certain instances it is reported that the proplastids grade off to the lower limit of visibility, suggesting the possible presence of newly formed ones as yet too small to be seen. Furthermore, it is difficult to distinguish with certainty minute proplastids from other equally small bodies in the cytoplasm. Origin anew might be suspected in view of other cytoplasmic specializations during development. The observation that in certain algal cells the chlorophyll is diffused throughout the cytoplasm recalls the speculation that plastids as organs arose historically when an important function performed throughout the cytoplasm became localized along with corresponding structural alterations in the regions concerned. At present, however, there are not sufficient grounds for stating that anything of this kind occurs in the development of plastids by each individual plant.

This section on plastids may be concluded with the reminder that it is chloroplasts that make available to organisms the remarkable properties of carbon with its capacity for forming the complex compounds required as building materials and sources of energy. It is no wonder that a famous botanist once said that he always felt like taking off his hat to the chloroplast.

Chondriosomes.—The presence of small bodies known as chondriosomes, or mitochondria, is all but universal in the cytoplasm of animals and plants (Fig. 22). They appear in living cells as minute granules, vesicles, rodlets, threads, and strings of beads, and they often vary in abundance and form in different phases of cellular activity. They are reported to arise anew in the cytoplasm, and they can be seen to divide; in special cases only (*e.g.*, certain animal spermatocytes) does the division coincide with that of the cell. In many types of tissue they tend gradually to disappear as differentiation approaches completion. Special techniques are required for their study in fixed preparations. They can be well fixed with fluids containing formalin and potassium dichromate, but both they and the proplastids are dissolved by some of the more highly acid fluids, especially those containing acetic acid, commonly used for the preservation of nuclei.

There is a very large body of literature on the subject of chondriosomes, but they are still an enigma to the cytologist. Naturally many suggestions have been made regarding their significance. For the most part these fall under two general heads: (1) the view that they are reserve products or by-products of some form of cytoplasmic activity common to nearly all organisms, these products being utilized as energy sources or in other ways; (2) the view that they are organs or organ-like bodies playing a definite role in the elaboration of metabolic products or in differentiation.

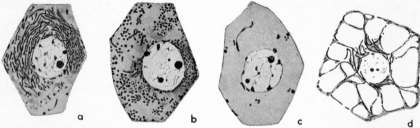

Fig. 22.—Chondriosomes in liver cells of fishes. *a* normal cell from *Fundulus* kept at temperature of 21°C.; *b*, cell from *Fundulus* kept at temperature (37.5 to 40°C.) inducing heat rigor; *c*, cell from *Fundulus* in extreme heat rigor induced at 45 to 50°C.; *d*, normal cell from goldfish. (*After R. C. MacCardle.*)

The first of these views was suggested by the decrease in abundance and frequent disappearance of the chondriosomes as tissues mature and by their apparent use in the elaboration of secretion products in certain gland cells. The second view was suggested by what was interpreted as the direct transformation of chondriosomes into various intracellular specializations, such as myofibrils and neurofibrils, the chondriosome being looked upon as a sort of organ of differentiation. Organ-like roles in connection with enzyme activity, secretion, respiration, and adsorption catalysis have also been regarded as possibilities. Of particular interest was the observation that the chondriosomes bear a striking resemblance to young plastids in form, chemical composition and specific gravity; in fact, many cytologists have inclined to the view that plastids arise in plant cells by the transformation of chondriosomes of a certain type.

The problem of chondriosome-proplastid relationship has been a particularly vexing one for a number of years. Recent work on the shapes, color reactions, and pigmentation of these bodies has emphasized anew their apparent distinctness (Figs. 23, 24), whereas some observers are

unable to accept this view.   If this problem could be definitely solved
with the discovery of the exact reasons why some of the minute bodies
develop into plastids while others in the same cell or in other organisms do
not, we should be nearer to a solution of the more general problem of the
real significance of chondriosomes in protoplasmic activity.   Researches
to date have at least served to foster a more critical interpretation of the
effects of fixation.

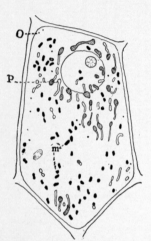

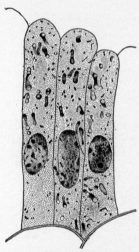

Fig. 23.—Cell from inner side of bean
pod after treatment with Janus green B.
m, mitochondria; *O*, oil globules; *P*, poly-
morphic plastids, colorless and partially
impregnated with chlorophyll (shaded).
(*After H. Sorokin.*)

Fig. 24.—Cells from young shoot of rye.
In the cytoplasm are small granular
mitochondria, large, deeply staining plastid
primordia, and plastids containing starch.
(*After J. A. O'Brien, Jr.*)

Vacuoles.—Vacuoles are liquid-filled cavities in the cytoplasm or, very
rarely, in other portions of the protoplast (Figs. 25, 26).   They are characteristic chiefly of plants, where they are conspicuously developed in cells
of nearly all kinds.   They are also prominent in protozoan cells, while
smaller globules staining with neutral red in the tissues of higher animals
seem to be of the same general nature.   By virtue of their osmotic properties, plant vacuoles function in the maintenance of turgor, which is of
importance to metabolic activity and contributes to the support of
herbaceous bodies.   Furthermore, they serve as repositories for certain
classes of reserve products and by-products.   To what extent such
secretory activity involves reactions within the vacuoles rather than in the
cytoplasm near by is not well known.   The vacuoles in animal tissues play
problematic roles.   The rhythmic filling and discharge of contractile
vacuoles in lower animals and plants appears to be an excretory process,
and it is further thought probable that it aids in the regulation of hydro-

static pressure. The movement of the gametes in *Spirogyra* is dependent in part upon the activity of such vacuoles.

In the meristematic cells of plants the vacuoles are usually much smaller and more numerous than in differentiated cells. As the cells

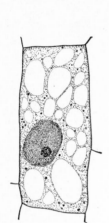

Fig. 25.—Cell from onion root, showing vacuoles.

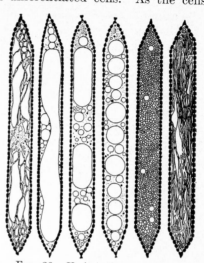

Fig. 26.—Various forms assumed by vacuoles in fusiform cambium cells of locust tree. (*After I. W. Bailey.*)

derived from the meristem enlarge, multiply, and differentiate, their vacuoles increase in size, undergo internal chemical changes, and gradually unite, thus forming one or more vacuoles of large size (Fig. 27). Often vacuoles in living cells can be seen to become fragmented as a

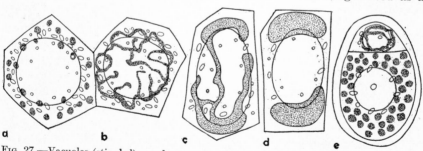

Fig. 27.—Vacuoles (stippled). *a-d,* successive stages in bud of a conifer (*Abies*); *e,* pollen grain of a conifer (*Cephalotaxus*). (*After P. Dangeard.*)

result of protoplasmic streaming; also at the time of cell division they may be passively divided.

The origin of the small vacuoles in the meristem has been variously conceived. It was at one time thought that the cytoplasm contained individualized bodies (tonoplasts) derived only from previous ones by division throughout the life cycle and that with the accumulation of cell sap in the tonoplasts these extended to form the membranes of vacuoles. The vacuole membrane is still called the *tonoplast*. It is now more generally believed that vacuoles arise by a hydration and an accumulation of certain cytoplasmic colloids, the membrane being formed by the cytoplasm at the interface. It is being found very difficult, however, to demonstrate that vacuoles do arise anew in such a manner.

The tonoplast resembles the plasma membrane in physical consistency and to some degree in its semipermeability. It appears, however, to be more resistant to injury and may manifest semipermeability after the cell is killed. Its permeability to certain substances may be remarkably low, the concentration of acids in the vacuoles of some cells being greater than enough to kill the cell if they were applied to it externally. This is notably true of food vacuoles of protozoa during digestion. The results of permeability studies are thought to indicate that the tonoplast contains more lipide than the plasma membrane.

The *cell sap* in plant vacuoles of the common type is a slightly viscous fluid composed of water and substances of many kinds in molecular or colloidal solution. Salts, sugars, organic acids (oxalic, malic, citric, etc.), glucosides, alkaloids, amides, proteins, enzymes, tannins, and other compounds can be identified in different cases. Some cells secrete visible globules of protein, gums, resins, and other materials in such amounts that the sap has a milky appearance. In extreme cases such cells form extensive systems of latex tubes ramifying through the other tissues of the plant; familiar examples are the dandelion and the rubber tree. Globules of rubber are elaborated in the cytoplasm and secreted into the sap in *Ficus*. Crystals of various compositions also may occur in the cell sap.

The reactions of cell sap to chemical tests and in staining procedures may vary widely in different plants and at different stages of development in a given tissue. This is due both to differences in pH and to the presence or absence of certain particular compounds. In meristematic tissues the cell sap ordinarily has a slightly alkaline or a neutral (pH 7) reaction, but as the vacuoles enlarge in the differentiating cells it soon becomes decidedly acid, the pH falling to 5 or even lower. Phenolic compounds such as tannin also have a profound effect upon stainability, the same cell sometimes showing vacuoles of two colors correlated with differences in tannin content. Of several vital stains commonly used for vacuoles, the best is neutral red. It quickly accumulates in the vacuoles of living cells, leaving the cytoplasm and nucleus colorless, and it remains there until death occurs.

Many vacuoles contain natural pigments in their sap. The most prevalent of these are the anthocyanins, which are commonly reddish in very acid saps and blue or purple in more alkaline mediums. Such pigments are mostly responsible for these colors in flowers and fruits. Yellow flavone pigments rarely are evident in the sap of petals (*e.g.*, snapdragons), although they may be made to appear in some white flowers upon hydrolysis of the glucosides of which they are constituents. It is rather the plastid pigments that give so many plants their yellow colors.

Golgi Material.—The Golgi material, named after its discoverer, appears in the cytoplasm of nearly all animal cells prepared with certain special techniques designed to deposit silver or osmium as a dark precipitate. Under such conditions the ma-

terial appears in the form of separate small bodies or as a more or less continuous system of strands, these forms being fairly constant in certain types of cell. Only rarely can it be distinguished from the cytoplasm in living cells. Its composition is not well known, but lipides are evidently present. Its tendency to show blackened and nonblackened portions in silver-impregnated material suggests the occurrence of two main constituents which may not, however, have such an arrangement in the living cell. Its behavior in centrifuged cells indicates its physical distinctness from the chondriosomes and also that its viscosity in different cells varies with respect to that of the cytoplasm. At the time of cell division it is distributed passively and more or less equally to the daughter cells (Fig. 28).

The function of the Golgi material is most evident in gland cells (Fig. 29). During secretory activity in these cells, it becomes more plentiful and droplets of the secretion product make their appearance in contact with it. The droplets accumulate near the surface of the cell and are eventually excreted. It is not yet clear whether this should be interpreted as a synthesis or a condensation of the secretion globules by the Golgi material, or whether the globules themselves, which stain with neutral red, are active vacuoles in which the

Fig. 28.—Metaphase of first division in spermatocytes of a bug (*Euschistus*) prepared by different methods to show filamentous chondriosomes (above) and rounded Golgi bodies (below). Chromosomes at center. (*After R. H. Bowen.*)

secretion is produced from materials in the cytoplasm near by. On the latter theory the Golgi networks seen in silver preparations are interpreted as an alteration of dense chondriosome-containing cytoplasm between the vacuoles in this region of the cell. The role of the Golgi material in nonglandular cells is problematical, though secretory or other elaborative activity on a smaller scale is suggested.

Attempts to "homologize" the Golgi material with some constituent of plant cells have not met with definite success. When meristematic plant cells are treated with the special methods mentioned above, the aspects presented by vacuoles in their various stages of development may be strikingly like those of the Golgi material in animal cells.   That both are involved in secretory activity is also suggestive.   It is true that plastids, too, when similarly treated, often show a strong resemblance to the Golgi material.   In the sperm-forming cells of mosses there is not only a likeness in form and stainability, but a mass of material arising from the plastid performs the same peculiar function as does a product of the Golgi material in animal spermatogenesis (page 121).   This would seem to be a stronger argument for homology.   A third constituent of

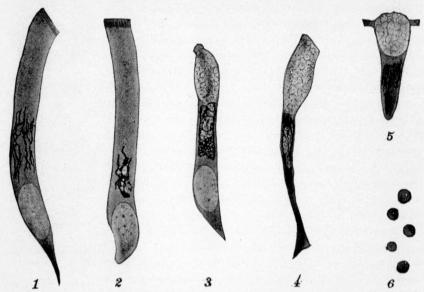

Fig. 29.—The relation of the Golgi apparatus to secretion.   1–5, formation of secretory droplets in goblet cell in intestine; 6, secretory globules with attached bits of Golgi material from pancreas.   (*After R. H. Bowen.*)

plant cells, the so-called *osmiophilic platelets*, has been brought into the controversy.

An interesting light on this question has come from bean root cells subjected to very high centrifugal forces—400,000 times gravity for 15 to 20 minutes.   In cells thus treated the cell constituents become arranged in order of their relative specific gravity as shown in Fig. 30.   It is to be noted that the plastids and chondriosomes are relatively heavy, whereas the osmiophilic platelets are relatively light, just as the Golgi material is shown to be in animal cells similarly treated.

Animals and plants have been going their separate ways in evolutionary specialization for a very long time, the differences in nutrition and cytological structure having become great enough to enjoin caution in the drawing of homologies.   We shall nevertheless continue to be impressed in later chapters by similarities rather than by differences in the fundamental cytological features of the two organic kingdoms.

Ergastic Matter.—Accumulations of nonprotoplasmic materials in or on the protoplast are called *ergastic substances* (*ergon* = work). They are for the most part products of the protoplasm's metabolic work. They may represent reserve materials later used as sources of energy in further work, or the useless by-products of such activity, or supporting structures that render bodies of certain types possible. Such ergastic matter may occur in any part of the protoplast, although it is rarely observed in nuclei. The cell sap, described in a previous section, may be regarded as a mass of ergastic materials in an aqueous medium.

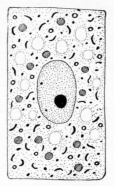
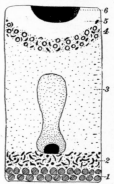

The most conspicuous ergastic substances in plants are carbohydrates, starch and cellulose being the representatives of this group most often observed in tissues. The starch elaborated in the chloroplast appears as visible granules, and when deposited by amyloplasts in storage organs the granules may become very large. Researches on the structure of such granules have shown them to consist of numerous concentric layers which have been deposited successively about a hilum, the point at which deposition began (Fig. 31). Unequal deposition on the various sides results in a granule of eccentric form and structure. Compound grains with more than one hilum are plentiful in some tissues.

The layering in the starch granule has been correlated with periodic activity of the plastid caused by the alternation of day and night. Each layer consists of $C_6H_{10}O_5$ units arranged in a regular "space lattice": the granule is a spherocrystal. When such granules are examined in polarized light between crossed Nicol prisms, they present a characteristic and beautiful appearance, each of them being a bright body traversed by a dark cross with its arms meeting at the hilum (Fig. 32). It is sometimes possible to identify small granules in this way when other tests fail.

FIG. 30.—Normal and centrifuged cells of bean root. In the centrifuged cell (below) the centrifugal end is directed downward. In order of relative and decreasing specific gravity the nonnuclear components are (1) starch granules and plastids (when present), (2) chondriosomes and proplastids, (3) cytoplasm, (4) osmiophilic platelets, (5) cell sap. (6) lipide material. (*After H. W. Beams and R. L. King.*)

Cellulose is the chief material in plant cell walls. Like starch, it consists of $C_6H_{10}O_5$ units (anhydrous glucose residues) arranged in the form of a space lattice, the layers here being relatively flat. Associated with it are other materials; these will be discussed in Chap. VI. Cellulose and hemicelluloses frequently serve as reserve products, notably in the endosperm of certain seeds.

Fig. 31.—Cell from stem of an angiosperm (*Pellionia*) with large starch granules. Most of the plastid substance forms a thick cap at one end of the granule.

Fig. 32.—Potato-starch granules photographed through a polarizing microscope with crossed Nicol prisms.

Glycogen is an important reserve carbohydrate formed in animal cells; it occurs also in blue-green algae and various fungi. Mucilages and gums are further examples of ergastic carbohydrates.

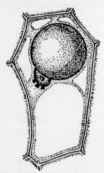

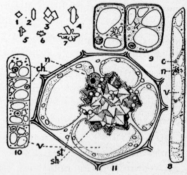

Fig. 33.—Large oil droplet in cell of young root of heliotrope (*Valeriana*). (*After A. Meyer.*)

Fig. 34.—Development of crystal aggregate ("druse") in castor bean plant. 1–5, single crystals and aggregates; 6, 7, dendritic growth; 8–10, developing crystals within cell; 11, druse in mature parenchyma cell at petiole base. (*After F. M. Scott.*)

Proteins as ergastic products occur in crystalline and noncrystalline masses. Perhaps the most familiar protein reserves in plants are the aleurone granules of certain seeds, notably those of cereals, legumes, walnuts, and the castor bean. Such granules may have amorphous protein only, or both amorphous and crystalline components; other substances may be present also. Protein reserves are well known in the yolk of animal eggs where they commonly occur in association with fatty yolk globules.

Plants infected with some viruses show characteristic intracellular bodies not present in normal tissues. These are amorphous in some cases, while certain other viruses result in the formation of both amorphous and crystalline inclusions. Insoluble complexes resembling these can be produced artificially by combining purified viruses with proteins of certain kinds, which suggests that such bodies in infected tissues may be similar combinations of the virus with normal or abnormal materials of the host plant. This single example may serve as a reminder of the mutual assistance rendered by cytology and pathology.

Fats and oils occur as reserves in the form of globules in the cytoplasm of many plant and animal cells, particularly in seeds, spores, and eggs. Minute lipide globules are of common occurrence in the cytoplasm of active cells. Very large oil globules are sometimes encountered (Fig. 33). Waxes are ergastic products of importance in many plants.

Inorganic crystals form another class of ergastic substances (Fig. 34). These occur in great variety in plant tissues, the needle-shaped "raphides" composed of calcium oxalate being very frequently encountered in cytological work on living tissues.

Ergastic substances, then, are of many kinds. The same chemical compound may occur at any one moment as a relatively inert mass in the protoplast; at another moment it may be in solution and participating actively in the work of the protoplasm. Ergastic matter is therefore to be characterized by its relative inactivity rather than its composition. This is in harmony with the view adopted in the following chapter, *viz.*, that protoplasm is an organized living system of substances that by themselves are not living.

CHAPTER IV

PROTOPLASM

Few scientific achievements rank in importance with the discovery that the phenomena of life occur in a colorless, somewhat viscous fluid-like material having certain properties common to all organisms. Every plant and animal type, and probably every individual, has its own characteristic type of protoplasm, but the fundamental features of this substance are strikingly the same everywhere. This highly significant fact was given eloquent expression by Thomas Huxley (1868) in his classic essay on "The Physical Basis of Life," which ranks as a masterpiece of popular scientific exposition.

Physical Characters of Protoplasm.—By direct observation with the aid of the ordinary microscope, protoplasm is revealed as a clear fluid, called *hyaloplasm*, in which there usually are distributed globules, granules, and various special differentiations. Many activities, such as the characteristic streaming in vacuolate plant cells and the responses to certain experimental treatments, may be studied in this way, but the investigator must employ additional special techniques. Among these aids are dark-field illumination, which reveals the presence of very minute particles; ultraviolet photography, which yields images showing fine structural detail; fluorescence in ultraviolet light, which gives evidence of composition; polarized light, by which it is possible to learn much concerning ultramicroscopic structure and chemical composition; the high-speed centrifuge, which yields data on specific gravity and viscosity; the micromanipulator, with which it is possible to operate on living cells under high magnifications; and the electron microscope.

The results of such investigations have been numerous and of exceptional value. For example, it has been possible to measure with considerable accuracy the viscosity of protoplasm in different cells, in localized regions of the same cell, and in the same region at different stages of functional activity. The values obtained range from only two or three times that of water in the granule-free hyaloplasm of certain eggs to hundreds of times this value in some other types of protoplasm. Commonly the viscosity of protoplasm in active cells is about that of glycerin or light machine oil. Exceedingly high values sometimes reported are probably due to secondary differentiations in the protoplast. The average viscosity tends to be lower in plants than in animals.

44

Although nerve cells and epithelial cells show a relatively high viscosity, there appear to be less viscous channels within them.

The viscosity of protoplasm may be experimentally decreased by hydrostatic pressure or by stirring; it may be increased by anesthetics, heat, electric currents, ultraviolet light, and X rays. These changes are reversible, but extreme treatments may result in irreversible coagulation or complete cytolysis. Experiments of this nature have demonstrated the dependence of certain protoplasmic processes, notably cell cleavage and the fascinating phenomenon of streaming with its various results, upon orderly alterations in viscosity. One method of measuring viscosity is that of observing the rate of movement of nickel particles placed within the protoplasm and then subjected to centrifugal or electromagnetic force.

Elasticity, a characteristic of special importance in view of the hints it affords regarding the ultramicroscopic structure of protoplasm, can be demonstrated with the micromanipulator and by observing the tendency of introduced nickel particles displaced by the electromagnet to return to their original position when the current is cut off. Red blood cells and certain nuclei have been stretched between two micromanipulator needles until they were, respectively, 4 and 25 times their original diameter (Fig. 4), and upon release they returned to nearly their normal shape. Such behavior may be due in part to the bounding membranes, but the nickel-particle technique shows clearly that protoplasm itself, and not merely its membranes, is elastic as well as ductile.

Fig. 35.—Surface layer of starfish egg being drawn out with needle on micromanipulator. (*After R. Chambers.*)

Refined mechanical aids have made it possible to learn a great deal about the physical nature of the external membranes of cells. Echinoderm eggs, because of their large size and other desirable characters, have been used for this and many other types of cytological study. After the removal of certain external coats, the protoplasmic surface film of the egg lies exposed. The physical characteristics of this film can be demonstrated by drawing it out in the form of a slender strand from the egg surface and then allowing it to return to its original position (Fig. 35). If not broken the material coalesces perfectly with the egg, while small bits if broken away round up into droplets. This and a variety of other treatments have shown that the surface membrane is elastic and water-immiscible, though permeable; it shrinks without wrinkling, extends without increase of surface tension, easily engulfs droplets of paraffin oil, and undergoes rapid renewal from within when not too greatly torn.

Streaming movements of various kinds appear to be of general occurrence in protoplasm. They have been studied chiefly in amebas, plasmodia of slime molds, dividing animal eggs, and the highly vacuolate cells of plants. The movement may involve the entire protoplast, the cytoplasm streaming as one mass and carrying the various inclusions with it, or only localized portions may be concerned, the other regions showing no visible change. No complete explanation of this fascinating phenomenon has yet been given. With the aid of the motion-picture camera it has been found that the streaming observed in the slime mold results from a rhythmic contraction and relaxation of the protoplasm, and the force involved has been measured. Contraction and relaxation in protoplasm are now attributed mainly to a folding and unfolding of linear protein molecules (see page 48). The energy necessary to protoplasmic streaming is evidently derived from respiration, but the manner in which this energy is utilized in producing the movements is unknown.

Protoplasm as a Colloidal System.—The physical properties of protoplasm are largely dependent upon the fact that it is a complex colloidal system. Matter is in the colloidal state when it has the form of numerous small particles, the resulting properties being most characteristically displayed when the particles are between about 0.1 and 0.001μ in at least one dimension. This is below the reach of the ordinary microscope. Such particles are molecular aggregates except perhaps in the case of extremely large molecules. In a colloidal system at least two *phases* are essential: a medium which constitutes the continuous phase and a second substance dispersed as particles within it. The phases may be liquid, solid, or gaseous, and they may have any chemical composition so long as they are dissimilar enough to remain physically distinct. The chemical constituents of a given phase are called *components*. The important feature of all colloidal systems, which vary greatly in minute structure, is that the phases lie in contact with each other over a surface of enormous extent, even in a minute cell. This fact means much when it is remembered that many reactions are promoted by forces acting at surfaces.

It is, of course, the fluid colloidal systems that are of particular significance in biology. Such a system is known as a *sol* if it flows readily and as a *gel* if it does not. It may be made to pass from one state to the other, often by relatively small alterations in temperature, electrical charge, or the degree of hydration. Thus a sol may become a gel (gelation, pectization), and the gel may again become a sol (solation, peptization). Irreversible coagulation may also occur. In a fluid colloidal system most of the continuous phase is free and easily removable, but some of it may constitute a denser solvation layer at the surface of the other phase and strongly resist forces tending to remove it. When the layer consists of water, the colloidal particle is said to be hydrated.

That protoplasm is a colloidal system is indicated by many of its characteristics. Like other colloids it differs from true solutions in its manner of flow, in the relation of its viscosity to stress, and in behavior involving surface tension, adsorption, and permeability. Its physical consistency varies widely during certain processes such as cell division and is strongly affected by stimuli of various kinds. It even exceeds some other colloidal systems in its resistance to separation of phases by centrifugal forces: after being centrifuged for 1 hour at 400,000 times gravity, *Ascaris* eggs recovered and divided, and cleavage actually occurred during centrifugation at 100,000 times gravity.

It is not known at present what type or types of colloidal structure are characteristic or essential in protoplasm. Although protoplasm frequently shows within the visible range a structure like that of an emulsion, it is uncertain how far such a structure continues into the submicroscopic range. As a matter of fact there are rather definite indications that the structure is not primarily of the emulsoid type: protoplasm is elastic, emulsions are not; protoplasm has a limited, though high, imbibition limit, whereas emulsions do not; protoplasm coagulates, emulsions do not (coagulation of milk involves the protein, casein, not the fat forming the visible emulsion); across the plasma membrane is a continuous water path, and if the other phase or phases were discontinuous the membrane would disintegrate in water. Such considerations point to the existence of some sort of structural framework not capable of indefinite dispersion like an emulsion.

The view that protoplasm has an important fibrous element in its structure along with nonfibrous constituents has recently gained strong support. The "fibrillar theory" of many years ago was based largely upon what was directly seen in living and fixed cells. Our modern interpretation has come not only from investigations of protoplasm with a variety of new techniques, but also from physical and chemical studies on inorganic colloidal systems, on certain products of biological activity, and especially on the proteins. The "fibers" that now concern us are mainly something far smaller than the workers of half a century ago had in mind.

Especially instructive are the results of researches on the structure of inorganic systems, notably those formed by vanadium pentoxide, zinc oxide, and silicon hydroxide in water. In polarized light between crossed nicols, these substances when flowing in narrow channels show double refraction of a type that indicates the presence of minute linear elements lying parallel; moreover, such an arrangement is sometimes assumed spontaneously without flow. The linear elements here are evidently chains of elongate molecules: in the silica gel, for example, the $Si(OH)_4$ molecules join end-to-end, losing H_2O at each junction, to form long chains. When such long molecules or molecular chains have a random arrangement, the system is isotropic. When they lie closely parallel and are free to move upon each other, they are in the paracrystalline, or "liquid-crystal," state, and if they lie in a medium of different refractive index, the system exhibits double refraction. In the gel state, characterized by considerable firmness and elasticity, the chains evidently tend to associate in a sort of network or to unite closely here and there into bundles, or micelles. Such elastic gels may quickly liquefy when jarred or stirred owing to a property known as *thixotropy*.

In such phenomena the cytologist finds welcome clues to the submicroscopic structure of protoplasm. For example, double refraction can be detected in muscle cells, plastids, chromosomes, and mitotic spindles; furthermore, ice crystals formed within these structures tend to

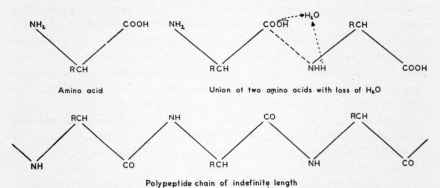

Amino acid   Union of two amino acids with loss of H_2O

Polypeptide chain of indefinite length

Fig. 36.—The constitution of the polypeptide chain. The symbol R stands for side chains of several kinds: NH_2, $COOH$, SH, OH, etc. (*Adapted from Frey-Wyssling.*)

be oriented accordingly. Gelled regions in protoplasm frequently pass into the sol state when stirred with the micromanipulator needle. Protoplasm is elastic. A certain myxomycete plasmodium can pass through pores 1μ in diameter slowly and by itself, but it is destroyed if pressed through gauze with openings 200μ in diameter. All such observations, together with the visible fibrous differentiations more directly observable, point to the conclusion that protoplasm has a fibrous constituent in its fundamental structure.

It is now thought probable that the submicroscopic fibrous constituent of protoplasmic structure consists primarily of proteins. Researches on proteins show that their molecules consist of amino acids arranged in the form of long polypeptide chains (Fig. 36). Such a chain may be extended as a "fibrous molecule" which could, with a molecular weight of 35,000, reach a length of 0.1μ. The results of studies with X rays and polarized light show that molecules in this extended form, singly or in bundles (micelles), are present in tissues with mechanical functions (muscles, tendons) and in certain products of protoplasmic activity (hair, silk). The molecules in silk, which is inelastic, are fully extended, whereas those in wool, which is elastic, are wavy or folded. In other proteins the chain may be very closely folded, forming a "globular molecule." With a molecular weight of 36,000 such a molecule would have a diameter of about 0.005μ. Such molecules constitute the so-called *mobile proteins*, while the fibrous molecules form the *structure proteins*. It has been possible to separate the two kinds in cells: about an eighth of the proteins in an echinoderm egg and about two-thirds of those in kidney cells are of the structural type. There is controversy over the question of the degree of distinctness and the relative importance of the two types in determining the physical characters of protoplasm, but the extremely suggestive nature of the above findings is evident.

Chemical Nature of Protoplasm.—The immense difficulty of ascertaining the chemical composition of protoplasm with any degree of accuracy scarcely needs to be pointed out. With protoplasm are always associated some of its products; relative amounts of the constituents vary in different tissues and at different phases of activity; the high sensitivity to reagents and the alterations occurring at death greatly complicate the problem of analysis. It is nevertheless possible to form a general idea of its composition, and with further improvements in method our knowledge of it will doubtless gain in definiteness. In general it is found that protoplasm in the active state consists of more than 75 per cent water and less than 25 per cent materials representing the dry weight. The dry matter is roughly 90 per cent organic (proteins, fats, carbohydrates) and 10 per cent inorganic.

Water, one of the commonest substances in nature, is of the utmost importance to organisms. Without water or something like it—and there is nothing like it—life as we know it is inconceivable. Water acts as a solvent and conveyor of reacting materials, is a medium of reaction, and participates in reactions through hydrolysis and dehydration. Because of its unique properties it very largely determines the character of the colloidal system of which it is a part as well as the types of reaction that occur. In inactive protoplasm, such as that in dry spores, the percentage of water may fall to a very low value. The protoplast contains free water and water bound at the surface of the colloidal particles. The bound water is difficult to remove by heat, and it also resists the effects of very low temperatures, remaining unfrozen after the free water has crystallized. It is probably this crystallization of free water that kills protoplasm at low temperatures: spores that have been deprived of their free water may survive the temperature of liquid air. It has recently been found that undehydrated cells may not be killed by intense cold if the temperature is lowered very rapidly through the freezing range: the water then vitrifies instead of crystallizing, and the cells survive and resume activity after the temperature is raised very rapidly through the range where crystallization would otherwise occur. This has an interesting bearing on the problem of storing living material at low temperatures.

The *inorganic salts* in protoplasm are fairly numerous though small in amount. They occur in part in the free water and in part as ions bound by the organic constituents. They incorporate many of the 40 or more essential elements, some of which are present in extremely small amounts and can be detected only by extremely sensitive methods. The amounts present often do not indicate the amounts necessary, but in some instances their ratio of concentration is very significant. For example, sodium lowers viscosity and increases the permeability of membranes, whereas calcium, necessary to membrane formation, has the opposite effects; in combination the two are antagonistic. The ratio of calcium to sodium salts is about the same in sea water, blood, and balanced protein-lipide emulsions, a fact that surely has interesting theoretical implications for the student of evolution.

Among the *carbohydrates* the pentoses, hexoses, and their condensation products (polysaccharides) are of special importance in the constitution and activity of protoplasts. The pentoses, $C_5H_{10}O_5$, are one of the main components of nuclear chromatin (page 51), while various pentosans, $(C_5H_{10}O_5)_n$, are the principal constituents of many plant mucilages and gums and are components of pectins. Among stored foods are hexoses, $C_6H_{12}O_6$, including glucose, levulose, mannose, and galactose, as well as hexosans, $(C_6H_{10}O_5)_n$, notably starch in plants and glycogen in animals. Cellulose, a hexosan, is the main constituent of most plant cell walls. Carbohydrates other than the pentoses do not enter directly into the actual constitution of protoplasm but serve as sources of energy and building materials.

Fats and oils occur in great variety in protoplasts. Although it is often impossible to tell in what degree a given kind is a true constituent or only a product of protoplasm, there can be no doubt that some of them, notably the phospholipides, are among the fundamental constituents. The fragrant essential oils of plants are not fats but belong to other chemical classes. Although of great commercial importance, their value to the plant is questionable.

True fats, which contain only carbon, hydrogen, and oxygen, are salt-like combinations (esters) of fatty acids and glycerol (the glycerides) or of fatty acids and other alcohols (the sterols and most waxes). The fats are of importance as reserve food and together with sterols and waxes function in retarding loss of water at surface membranes. Ergosterol, a sterol found in plants, becomes the antirachitic vitamin D upon irradiation with ultraviolet light. Vitamins A and E are commonly found in tissues high in fat. Variable amounts of free fat occur in cells, but much of the fatty material exists in some form of combination with the proteins.

The compound fats are combinations of fatty acids, nitrogen-containing bases, and either phosphorus or carbohydrates. Such fat-like compounds containing nitrogen with or without phosphorus are called *lipides*. The phospholipides are of special interest, for they appear to perform a major role in the formation and activity of protoplasmic surface membranes, thus sharing largely in determining permeability and water-immiscibility. Lecithin, a prominent member of this class, is abundant in all cells. It occurs in a finely divided state in the cytoplasm, and by virtue of its possession of hydrophile and lipophile groups it probably functions in maintaining the colloidal state.

The *proteins*, which with lipides and water represent the main constituents of protoplasm, are elaborate compounds containing carbon, hydrogen, oxygen, nitrogen, often sulphur, and sometimes phosphorus. They are built up from amino acids with NH_2 substituted for H in the group attached to the COOH group. The protein casein has about 20 amino acids in its molecule. Every kind of organism evidently differs in some measure from every other in its proteins, a fact that is of importance with respect to such matters as immunity, allergy, and the differentiation of species.

The simple natural proteins, which yield only amino acids when hydrolyzed by enzymes or acids, are present in great variety in protoplasts. Albumins and globulins are important constituents of cytoplasm and are often present in large quantities in eggs and seeds. The enzyme urease is a globulin, and other enzymes also are proteins. Other simple proteins characterize the cereals (*e.g.*, glutenin, oryzein, zein, gliadin, hordein) and animal tissues (*e.g.*, keratin, elastin, gelatin, collagen). The histones are relatively simple, while the simplest and most basic of all natural proteins are the protamines. The best known protamine (salmin) from fish sperm has only four amino acids, and its formula is $C_{81}H_{115}N_{45}O_{18}$.

The conjugated proteins in nature are simple proteins in combination with other organic groups; they yield amino acids and nonproteins when hydrolyzed. As examples may be mentioned the glycoproteins in mucus and "tissue cements," the chromoproteins in certain plant and animal pigments, the lecithoproteins probably present in all cytoplasm and its membranes, and the nucleoproteins found in various parts of the protoplast and of special importance in nuclei.

Special attention should be given to the proteins of nuclei. As pointed out previously (page 28), the material composing the chromonemata, which are significant constituents of the chromosomes, is mainly a nucleoprotein made up of proteins and nucleic acid. This highly stainable material has been called *nuclein* or, more commonly, *chromatin*. The proteins concerned are relatively simple ones such as protamines (in fish sperm) or, more commonly in animals, the somewhat more complex and less basic histones. In plants the nuclear proteins are less well known, but they appear to resemble histones in composition. Of great significance is the previously cited fact that each type of organism studied seems to have its own peculiar kind of protein. So far as nuclear materials are concerned, differences between species appear to reside largely in the protein portion of the nucleoprotein molecule and probably to a lesser degree in the nucleic acid portion responsible for the chromatin's high stainability with basic dyes. Nucleic acid is composed of chemical groups of three main types: (1) phosphoric acid groups, (2) pentose carbohydrate groups (sometimes hexoses?), and (3) purine and pyrimidine bases. Nucleic acid, like the proteins with which it is associated, has the remarkable ability to form long chains. Of extraordinary significance is the recent discovery that the tobacco mosaic virus, which like other viruses has the power of increasing its substance when in a protoplasmic medium, is a nucleoprotein.

The karyolymph consists mainly of proteins less highly polymerized than those of the chromosomes. The nucleolus has at least two main constituents: (1) a protein that does not stain with iron-hematoxylin and (2) a stainable sulphuric ester of a polysaccharide. At certain stages a form of nucleic acid can be detected in the nucleolus and in some cases in the cytoplasm. The small amount of mineral matter in nuclei lies in the chromatic elements rather than in the karyolymph, to judge from the location of ash in incinerated tissues. The enormous chemical complexity of the nucleus is evident when one considers that in a sperm cell of ordinary size the nuclear portion has a dry weight of scarcely a billionth of a milligram; yet this minute mass of material, which constitutes about 3 per cent of the weight of the living sperm head, carries the physical basis of the paternal hereditary contribution to the next generation.

The Staining of Protoplasm.—The staining reactions of protoplasm depend upon its chemical composition, its colloidal state, and certain characteristics of the dye solutions. It is mainly the proteins that take up the stains, but certain products of other kinds, such as minute fat droplets, may be so abundant and stainable as to obscure the effects of the stains on the protoplasm itself. The dyes employed, aside from valuable natural ones like hematoxylin and carmine, are for the most part coal-tar products. These dyes are commonly employed as salts and fall into two main classes: basic dye solutions carry the color in the cations, whereas acid dye solutions carry it in the anions. Familiar examples of the former group are safranine (red), crystal violet (blue or violet), and methyl green; members of the latter group are eosin (red), methyl blue, and fast green.

The successful staining of living protoplasm with "vital" dyes, which are nontoxic in dilute solution, requires considerable skill. Some of these dyes are indicators of the degree of acidity or alkalinity, since they alter their color in passing through characteristic regions of the pH scale. In this way it has been found in cells of various kinds that the living nucleus is slightly alkaline, with a pH of about 7.5 to 7.6, whereas the cytoplasm is usually at about 6.7 to 6.9, or slightly acid. Injury causes the acidity to increase, the pH of the cytoplasm falling to 5.2 to 5.5. The cell may later recover, but not if the hydrogen-ion concentration is maintained too long at this level. When an ameba is placed in a dilute solution of methyl red, it becomes pale yellow throughout, showing that the pH in all parts is well above 5.2. If a slight amount of acid is then injected into the cytoplasm near the nucleus, a local reddening of the cytoplasm and then of the nucleus indicates a lowering of the pH to some point below 5.2. Both regions soon recover their yellow color, showing that the protoplasm contains or produces buffering substances tending to maintain its normal reaction in the vicinity of pH 7, the neutral point.

Living nuclei can be stained with dilute solutions of weakly basic dyes, which enter cells freely, or by acid ones when injected. Protozoa may live with nuclei and chromosomes stained with neutral red, and certain stages of mitosis in plants can occur with chromosomes colored by Hoffmann's violet or malachite green. Cytoplasm ordinarily does not take the stains markedly, much of the color observed being rather in vacuoles and inclusions. Lipide-soluble dyes appear to stain the cytoplasm itself in some degree.

The fixation of tissues with special fluids designed to render their components firm and more resistant to reagents employed in sectioning techniques also has effects on staining. The staining may be greatly improved by previous fixation, but one must always be on guard against interpreting fixation artefacts as natural appearances. After fixation the nucleus acts as an acid and stains markedly with basic coal-tar dyes. This is because the nucleic acid, although combined with other substances in such a way as to render the living nucleus actively alkaline, nevertheless gives the nucleus a strong potential acidity. Hence when fixed tissues are placed in properly prepared solutions of basic dyes, the negative bonds of the phosphoric acid groups in the nucleic acid unite with the colored cations of the solution. The cytoplasm, on the contrary, commonly acts as a base in fixed tissues and unites with the colored anions in solutions of acid coal-tar dyes. It is by manipulating a pair of dyes differing in both color and reacting power that double-staining effects are achieved.

The proteins react as they do in such procedures largely because they are amphoteric, *i.e.*, they have the properties of both bases and acids because of the uncombined NH_2 and $COOH$ groups in the amino acids of which they are composed. The reaction of a given cell protein depends upon the relation existing between its isoelectric point and the pH of the medium: it acts as an acid and stains with a basic dye if its isoelectric point is below the pH of the solution. When the relation of these two factors is reversed, the protein acts as a base and takes the acid dye. Hence when it is desired to stain the nucleus with one dye and the cytoplasm with another, success may depend upon adjustments of the pH of the solutions with respect to the somewhat different isoelectric points of the two regions. Exact values are difficult to determine because of the chemical complexity of the protoplasmic system and the further complications introduced by other variable factors.

One of the most useful staining techniques now used in cytology is the Feulgen reaction, which consists in the restoration of color to decolorized basic fuchsin by aldehyde groups in the pentose component of thymonucleic acid. It is thus rather highly specific for chromatin and can be used to distinguish chromosomes from other bodies. Ribonucleic acid, occurring in nucleoli and cytoplasm, usually gives a negative Feulgen test, but it can be detected through the absorption of ultraviolet light which it shows in common with thymonucleic acid of the chromatin.

Conclusions.—The matters discussed in this chapter all have a more or less direct bearing on the work of the cytologist, who is aware that his own understanding of every cytological object and process will be deepened by what the physicist and chemist can help him to learn about protoplasm. Complete comprehension of protoplasmic activity is a goal that cannot be approached rapidly and perhaps can never be reached, yet it is helpful to have in mind a provisional picture of protoplasm as a physicochemical system.

Protoplasm is an extraordinarily complex mixture of materials of many kinds, each of which has some share in determining the nature of its activities. It may be thought of as a vast array of ions, molecules, and molecular aggregates, some of them large enough to be visible, forming a colloidal system of numerous phases. Certain proteins, because of their linear molecules and chain-forming ability, seem to constitute a sort of loose submicroscopic framework to which some of the lipides, phospholipides, and other materials are attached. Lecithin, with its hydrophile and lipophile groups, acts as a link between proteins and fats. Water molecules in great numbers, together with inorganic ions and molecules, occur in the interstices of the framework. The whole mass is capable of streaming because the unions between the various substances in the framework are readily broken and reestablished in new ways. Local variations of this structure occur in the membranes, plastids, nuclei, and other microscopically visible specializations within the protoplast.

Protoplasm is therefore more than a mere mixture: it is a delicately balanced *organized system* of substances combined in certain proportions and patterns and interacting harmoniously in a consistent manner through long and varied life cycles. Life is the resultant of all these amazingly well-correlated activities: it is a property not of this or that component, but of the system as a whole. The subject of this chapter is one that should interest not merely the cytologist, but every person interested in his relation to the rest of nature, for protoplasm is the physical basis of his being as well as of every other living thing.

CHAPTER V

THE DIVISION OF THE PROTOPLAST

The division of one protoplast into two can be seen with little difficulty under a microscope, yet the process is one that investigators armed with many techniques have only begun to understand. The significance of much that is seen occurring is evident, but precisely how the various changes are accomplished remains to be discovered. Ordinarily the division of a free cell or a tissue cell results in two cells that have the same structure and capacities as the cell that produced them. In the development of the body (*soma*) of a large organism, a long series of such divisions occurs, the many resulting cells eventually becoming unlike in appearance as the soma differentiates. When a reproductive cell—a spore or an egg —is produced, it has all the capacities essential to the development of a complete individual. We are therefore faced with the problem of determining how the highly complex organization of the protoplast can be duplicated when division occurs and, further, just what it is in this organization that enables a spore or an egg to become an adult organism manifesting both general and particular characters of the previous generation. It is the first of these questions that now concerns us.

For the study of somatic cell division in plants, one may employ large cells that can be kept living in aqueous mediums or paraffin oil while being examined with the microscope. The cells of certain filamentous algae (*Zygnema, Sphacelaria*), the marginal cells of very young leaves (*Tradescantia*), and the hairs on certain stamens (*Tradescantia*) and grass stigmas (*Arrhenatherum*) have been used very successfully in this way. Young root tips have long been favorite material for somatic-division studies in higher plants, for the regular arrangement of the cells and the large number of divisions visible in one stained section render them almost perfect objects for the purpose (Fig. 37). In animals the dividing eggs of echinoderms and fishes are particularly good (Fig. 38). In later stages of somatic development the embryonic membranes of mammals and the tail fins of tadpoles yield excellent division figures (Fig. 157). The somatic type of division is also well displayed by spermatogonia (but not by spermatocytes).

It should be realized that details of the division process vary widely in different organisms and tissues. In this chapter we shall confine attention to typical examples.

SOMATIC CELL DIVISION IN PLANTS

Cell division includes both the division of the nucleus by a process known as *mitosis*, or *karyokinesis*, and the division of the cytosome, or

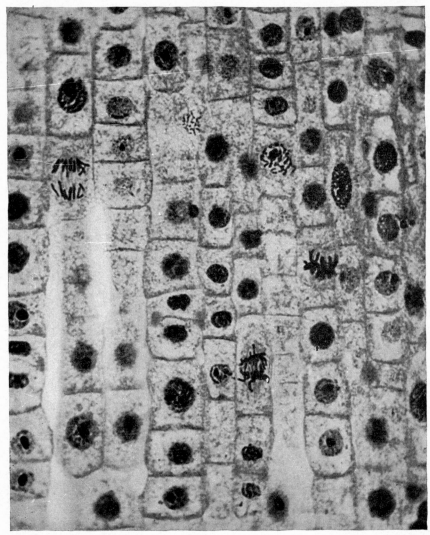

FIG. 37.—Portion of longitudinal section of root tip of onion. Prophase, metaphase, anaphase, and telophase stages of mitosis are visible. (*Courtesy of G. H. Conant.*)

cytokinesis. Mitosis often occurs without cytokinesis, as in coenocytes, and sometimes cytokinesis takes place without nuclear division. Mitosis and cell division are therefore not synonymous terms.

Comparatively little is well known concerning the particular factors responsible for the onset of cell division.   Since the mitotic changes are so conspicuous and precede cytokinesis, it is often assumed that cell division begins with the nucleus, all other changes being a consequence of

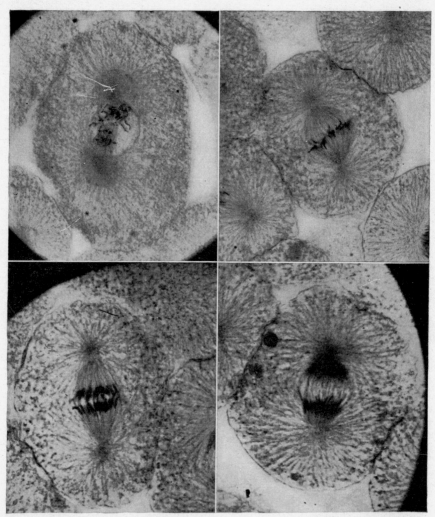

F<small>IG.</small> 38.—Mitosis in embryonic cells of whitefish: prophase, metaphase, and two stages of anaphase.   (*Courtesy of General Biological Supply House, Inc., Chicago.*)

its behavior.   In certain meristematic cells with large vacuoles it has been shown, however, that the cytoplasm forms a sort of diaphragm, or *phragmosome,* across the cell at the plane of future cytokinesis before the nucleus, about to divide, becomes oriented with respect to this plane

(Fig. 39). This indicates that the plane of cell division is determined by factors acting at an early stage throughout the cell and not by the nucleus alone.

Mitosis.—Mitosis is a process in which each of the chromosomes, the principal constituents of the nucleus, undergoes a longitudinal doubling, the halves of all the chromosomes then separating into two similar groups which reconstitute two new nuclei (daughter nuclei). Only rarely or under very exceptional circumstances does a nucleus, without respect to the chromosomes as individuals, divide by simple constriction (*amitosis*); mitosis is the almost universal method of nuclear division.

In the root tip of a plant with large chromosomes the course of mitosis is essentially as follows (Fig. 40). The nucleus in the metabolic stage

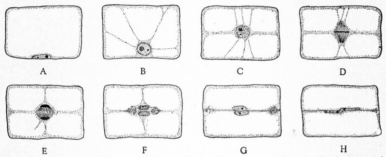

FIG. 39.—Division of vacuolate pith cell, showing the cytoplasmic diaphragm (phragmosome) present before mitosis. Semidiagrammatic. (*After E. W. Sinnott and R. Bloch.*)

preceding a division contains numerous chromonemata which, because of their number, length, and coiled or contorted condition, can seldom be traced far as individuals. The *prophase* comprises all the changes that transform the chromosomes from this metabolic condition, in which their chromonemata have little or no matrix about them and are all uniformly dispersed in the nucleus, into the compact separate individuals seen at the mid-point of mitosis. In the early part of the prophase the mass of chromonemata becomes less uniform, so that the threads belonging to different chromosomes stand apart more clearly as individuals, though their length at this stage usually precludes following them from end to end. They are more or less spirally coiled, and close examination shows them to be longitudinally double; hence at this stage each chromosome is actually represented by two chromonemata running closely parallel. The two longitudinal halves of a chromosome at this stage or at any other are known as *chromatids*. As the prophase advances to its middle stage, the chromonemata tend to relax their coils and thicken somewhat, so that the doubleness appears more plainly. In the later prophase the second chromosomal constituent, the *matrix*, accumulates about each chromo-

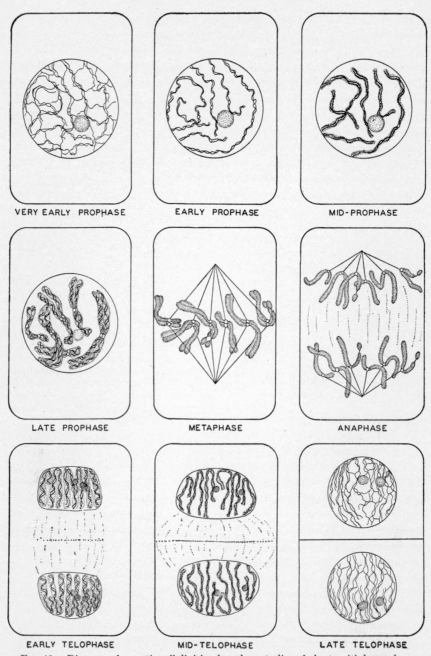

VERY EARLY PROPHASE   EARLY PROPHASE   MID-PROPHASE

LATE PROPHASE   METAPHASE   ANAPHASE

EARLY TELOPHASE   MID-TELOPHASE   LATE TELOPHASE

FIG. 40.—Diagram of somatic cell division based on studies of plants with large chromosomes. The relation of one chromosome pair to the nucleolus is indicated. Three stages of cytokinesis by cell-plate development are shown in the last row. Further explanation in text.

nema which again becomes more closely coiled; thus the chromosome soon becomes a thicker, smoother, double body comprising two chromatids, each composed of chromonema and matrix. In ordinary preparations the deeply stained matrix renders the chromonema invisible, but suitable methods reveal it. In some cases there is visible evidence that the chromonema in each chromatid is in turn longitudinally double, the whole chromosome by the end of the prophase therefore having four *half-chromatids*. The nucleolus commonly disappears late in the prophase as the matrix becomes abundant and stainable.

The nucleus next passes rapidly through a stage known as the *prometaphase* into the *metaphase*. This involves a complicated series of changes in which the karyolymph, probably with the cooperation of some cytoplasmic substance, becomes transformed into the *achromatic figure*, or

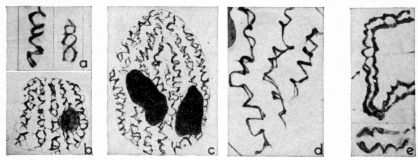

Fig. 41.—Stages in mitosis in root tips. *a*, anaphase; *b*, telophase; *c, d*, early prophase; *e*, late prophase. (*After L. W. Sharp.*)

spindle. That this change consists primarily in a definite rearrangement of materials, presumably protein chains, into positions parallel with the longitudinal axis of the spindle, and a differentiation into two components, one relatively firm and the other more fluid, is indicated by several lines of evidence: the spindle, unlike the material previously present, is anisotropic; it offers axial resistance to swelling or shrinking agents; it splits longitudinally in shrunken cells; Brownian movement of occasional particles in the more fluid regions is greatest parallel to the longitudinal axis; fixation usually gives the spindle a longitudinally striated or fibrillar aspect.

The spindle in root tips commonly begins its development at two opposed poles of the nucleus, apparently outside the nuclear membrane shrinking inward in these regions (Fig. 42). Sometimes it develops more or less simultaneously throughout the nucleus with no membrane shrinkage. In either case the membrane eventually disappears, leaving the chromosomes, which have meanwhile moved toward the equatorial plane of the nucleus, in the midst of the spindle. The double chromosomes, normally constant in number in a given kind of plant, quickly become arranged in such a way that a certain specialized portion of each of them occupies a position in the equatorial plane. This portion consists of the spindle-attachment regions, or *kinetochores*, of the two chromatids. The two kinetochores face opposite spindle poles, while other portions of the chromosome may lie in any position. When this stage is reached, the nucleus is in the *metaphase* of division.

As the kinetochores take up their positions at the equator, a new element appears in the mitotic figure. At the kinetochore of every chromatid there appears a small mass of material which gradually extends poleward through the spindle substance as a so-called *tractile fiber*. Whether this represents a local modification of the spindle substance, a fluid extruded

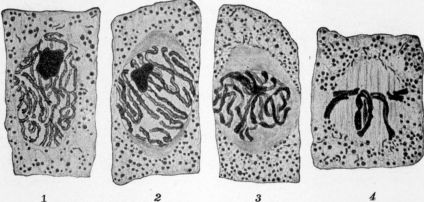

1   **2**   **3**   **4**

Fig. 42.—Spindle development in root tip of hyacinth. Explanation in text. (*After W. Robyns.*)

from the chromatid, or an actual pseudopodium-like extension of the chromatid is not yet agreed upon by cytologists. The fact that it sometimes contains a Feulgen-positive material strongly suggests its chromosomal origin. That it actually exerts a tractile force is seriously doubted.

In the *anaphase* the two chromatids of each chromosome separate and pass toward opposite poles, the kinetochores moving ahead along the course of the tractile fibers. After each chromatid becomes free from the other and goes its independent way, it should be referred to as a chromosome, the two half-chromatids being advanced accordingly to the rank of chromatid. In the anaphase, as in the metaphase, the general morphology of the chomosomes is usually well displayed, for they tend to lie well separated from one another and show the location of their kinetochores clearly (Fig. 43). Long chromosomes may present a very confusing appearance during the earlier portion of the anaphase, for even though the kinetochores pass poleward regularly, the other portions which have been lying in various positions are drawn into many odd shapes. By the close of the anaphase the tractile fibers have disappeared, and the chromosomes at each pole form a close group. Between the two groups lies the spindle through which they have recently passed. The mechanism of their anaphasic movement will be discussed in a later section.

The *telophase* is the stage during which the two groups of chromosomes, after completing their anaphasic movement, reorganize as the two new nuclei. Some of the alterations undergone by the chromosomes in the prophase are now reversed: the matrix loses its stainability or disappears, leaving the chromonemata visible, while the latter associate more closely with their neighbors and form a uniform threadwork

Fig. 43.—Chromosomes at late prophase, metaphase (polar view), and anaphase of mitosis in microspore of *Trillium*. The spindle is not well shown in smear preparations of this kind. (*After H. E. Warmke.*)

dispersed throughout the enlarging nucleus. The presence of two chromonemata in each anaphase chromosome may account for the fact that in the completed telophase nucleus there often appear to be more chromonemata than the known number of chromosomes.

While the chromosomes are undergoing their transformation, other telophasic changes take place. Nucleoli appear among the chromonemata as the matrix disappears, and it is known that they arise at definite points on certain chromosomes. If there are two or more nucleoli, they may fuse or remain separate, depending upon their relative positions. The nuclear membrane arises about the group of chromosomes as the telophase begins. The karolymph appears and increases in amount as the nucleus enlarges, but its origin and its relation to the disappearing matrix are not understood.

The extent to which the telophasic alterations are carried varies with the type of tissue and rate of division. In older regions of a root tip where divisions occur slowly, a metabolic stage characterized by finely dispersed chromonemata is developed, whereas in regions where mitoses occur in very rapid succession, a prophase may begin before the preceding telophase has advanced so far. The stage between two mitoses occurring in rapid succession is called the *interphase*.

The division cycle of the chromonemata in somatic mitosis may be summarized as follows for a single chromosome. In the metabolic stage the chromosome is represented by two chromonemata which rank as chromatids. In the early prophase these appear as a double spiral thread. As the prophase advances the two become less closely associated, and by the time the metaphase is reached each of them has divided into two half-chromatids, making four chromonemata in the whole metaphase chromosome. In the anaphase the two chromatids move apart toward opposite poles. Each is now an independent daughter chromosome, and its two chromonemata are now chromatids. These chromonemata represent the chromosome through the telophase and the ensuing metabolic stage. Thus a chromonema becomes visibly

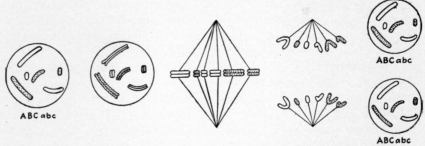

ABCabc

ABCabc

ABCabc

Fig. 44.—Diagram illustrating the equational character of somatic mitosis.

double slightly over one mitotic cycle in advance of the time at which the halves are to separate. There are reasons for believing that the threads are doubled submicroscopically before any doubleness is seen and, further, that the chromosomes, particularly large ones, may even be more highly compound in terms of visible chromonemata than indicated in these paragraphs. The foregoing will serve as a convenient provisional disposition of the matter until some alternative interpretation has become better established. Chromosome structure will be discussed further in Chap. VII.

Finally, the significance of the mitotic form of nuclear division may be emphasized. At the close of a typical mitosis there are two nuclei that are quantitatively and qualitatively similar to each other and to the nucleus from which they arose. The qualitative aspect is of special significance. The nucleus is not merely a homogeneous mass of some protein or other substance, but an intricately organized system of materials of many kinds with definite chemical and spatial relations. The chromonemata contain a series of special constituents essential to normal development, and in mitosis these constituents, after being doubled, are equally apportioned to the two daughter nuclei (Fig. 44). As a result, the organization and capacities characteristic of the original nucleus are exactly reproduced in the two new ones: *somatic mitosis is equational*. From this it follows that the essential organization present in the nucleus of a fertilized egg is reproduced in all the nuclei of the adult soma, for all these result from a succession of equational mitoses. A simple quantitative mass division of the nucleus without respect to its differentiated components would disrupt the system, and normal development could not continue. In the chapter on meiosis we shall encounter a form of nonequational division, but it is an orderly process of such nature that a complete outfit of materials is still maintained.

Cytokinesis.—The division of the cytoplasmic portion of the protoplast is variously correlated in time with mitosis. In some tissues no cytokinesis follows, in others it follows after all signs of recent mitosis have disappeared, whereas in the root meristem and other somatic tissues of higher plants it commonly begins immediately, even before mitosis has been completed. In this last case mitosis and cytokinesis appear like two parts of one process, for the region of the cell in which cytokinesis commences is still occupied by the remains of the mitotic spindle. As a result, cytokinesis in these tissues is of a type characterized by the development of a *cell plate*. Cytokinesis in many other plant cells and in animals is accomplished by constriction or furrowing.

Studies on living cells, notably those of stamen hairs, show that cytokinesis by cell-plate formation begins as follows. The spindle becomes less prominent near the two early telophase nuclei and widens at the equator into a barrel-shaped figure, the *phragmoplast*. Some chemical change within it is indicated by the fact that it now stains like the cytoplasm with chrysoidine, a vital dye, whereas during metaphase and anaphase it did not. Meanwhile, even before widening begins in some instances, small droplets appear near the equator and gradually unite to form a continuous cell plate across the phragmoplast (Figs. 45, 46). In some cells the cell plate appears as a continuous film from the start. In fixed material the developing cell plate commonly appears at first like a series of granules or spindle-fiber swellings at the equator. The phragmoplast continues to fade away near the nuclei and to widen at the equator, while the cell plate extends at its margins until the lateral walls of the cell are reached. The remains of the phragmoplast then disappear.

That the young cell plate is composed of fluid is shown by the fact that upon plasmolysis the two new cells easily round up from each other, leaving fluid but no definite membrane between them. Very soon, however, the cell plate undergoes both physical and chemical alterations, and if the two cells are then separated by plasmolysis a firm membrane remains in the intervening fluid. Strictly speaking, cytokinesis, the division of the cytosome, has occurred as soon as the halves of the original protoplast are capable of rounding up as two independent protoplasts, for to do this each of them must have completed its plasma membrane on the side next to the cell plate. The cell plate, with certain modifications, remains as the intercellular substance, or middle lamella, upon

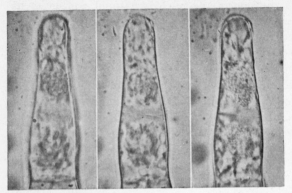

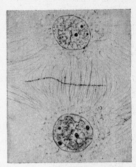

Fig. 45.—Formation of cell plate in *Tradescantia* stamen hair. (*After W. A. Becker.*)

Fig. 46.—Phragmoplast with cell plate in iris endosperm. (*After V. Jungers.*)

which the cellulose wall layers are deposited, thus completing the partition which separates the new protoplasts in plant tissues of this kind. The development and nature of the cell wall will be described in the next chapter (page 75).

SOMATIC CELL DIVISION IN ANIMALS

Somatic division in animals differs in many cases from that in most plants in two conspicuous features: (1) the achromatic figure is often much more elaborate, having a pair of asters at the spindle poles and commonly a centrosome at the focus of each aster; (2) cytokinesis is accomplished by a furrow which progresses inward from the periphery of the cell, rather than by a cell plate originating in the middle and extending to the periphery.

Mitosis.—Chromosome behavior during mitosis in animals is essentially like that in plants. The same series of principal phases is passed through, and the main significant result is the same: the division of the nucleus is equational, the original nucleus and the two daughter nuclei all being alike in chromosomal composition and functional capacity. In recent years chromonemata have been studied less in animals than in plants. Animal and plant mitoses may differ in minor ways, but it seems likely that the two kingdoms will not be found to disagree widely in any very fundamental feature of chromosome behavior.

The achromatic figure develops in typical cases as follows (Fig. 48). Lying in the cytoplasm near the nucleus is a *centriole*. As the prophasic alterations within the nucleus begin, the centriole divides if not already double, and the daughter centrioles move slowly apart. About each

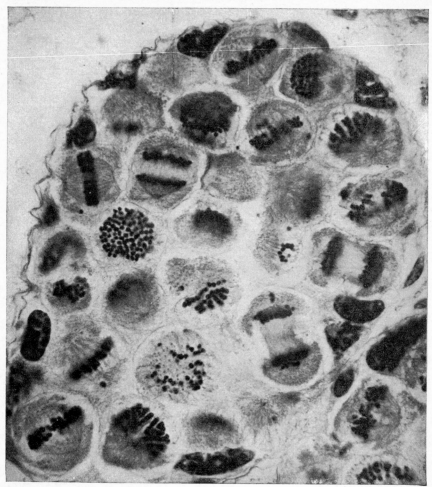

Fig. 47.—Section of spermary of crayfish (*Potamobius*), showing numerous stages of mitosis. (*Courtesy of General Biological Supply House, Inc., Chicago.*)

of them there appears in the cytoplasm a system of radiations known as an *aster*. Between the two may be seen a bundle of lines called the *central spindle*, all three parts together constituting an *amphiaster*. The centrosomes continue to diverge, the asters increasing in prominence, until they reach opposite sides of the nucleus. By the time they reach these positions, and often before this, the nuclear materials complete their prophasic changes and the nuclear membrane disappears, all the elements concerned—amphiaster, karyolymph, chromosomes—establishing the metaphase figure. In many cases each centriole is now clearly double, having divided nearly one nuclear cycle in advance of the pro-

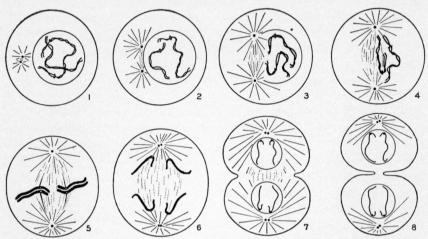

Fig. 48.—Diagram of astral mitosis and cytokinesis in an animal cell.

phase in which its halves are to separate. Such astral figures are also found in certain fungi and algae (Fig. 49).

The asters, in the possession of which the mitotic figure differs so conspicuously from that in higher plants, are evidently developed by the formation and gradual extension of centripetally moving streams, or "astral rays," in the cytoplasm about the centrosomes. The regions

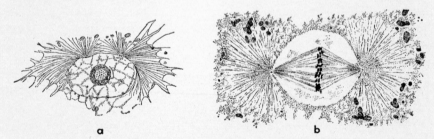

Fig. 49.—Astral mitosis in brown algae. *a*, centrioles with asters moving apart along nuclear membrane in apical cell of *Stypocaulon*. *b*, metaphase in oögonium of *Fucus;* the spindle is intranuclear. (*a, after W. T. Swingle; b, after S. Yamanouchi.*)

between the streams are gelled, so that the whole aster, in spite of its fluid streams, has a relatively firm consistency and can be moved about in the more fluid cytoplasm with a micro-needle. When one of the minute oil-like droplets occasionally seen in the sand-dollar egg is pushed from the fluid portion of the cytoplasm into the periphery of the aster, it is carried inward toward the center. The centripetal movement of fluid along the rays is somehow compensated by a gradual outward movement of other materials. There is evidence that the fluid rays contain oriented "structure proteins." The precise origin of the spindle portion of the achromatic figure is more difficult to determine. Both the karyolymph and some cytoplasmic component between the diverging centrosomes evidently develop an orientation revealed by the appearance of "fibers" on fixation, but the manner in which they share in the development of the spindle is not yet clear.

In the anaphase and telophase the chromosomes behave as already described for plants, the chromosomes moving to the poles where they reorganize the two daughter nuclei. The equator which they have left ordinarily shows no conspicuous change, though a little refractive and stainable material may often accumulate there. The asters, near which the daughter nuclei lie, remain conspicuous until after cytokinesis, a process in which they appear to play a major role.

Cytokinesis.—Typical cytokinesis in animals, like that in higher plants, involves the achromatic figure, but it does so in a very different manner. It involves also a special series of changes at the cell membrane, these acting with the internal forces to produce the cleavage furrow which divides the cytosome.

The large eggs of echinoderms, amphibians, and certain other animals are particularly well suited to studies of the factors responsible for cell cleavage. With the completion of the achromatic figure, the echinoderm egg becomes noticeably elongated, and this is correlated with an enlargement of the two elastic, semisolid asters. It is also found that the cortical plasmagel becomes firmer in consistency just before the furrow appears and remains so during its inward growth. That this gelation of the protoplasm is a major factor in producing the furrow is indicated by the results of treatments causing a return to the sol state. Thus if the asters in a cleaving egg are liquefied by stirring with a micro-needle, the furrow developing between them disappears. Similarly, when the rigidity of the cortical plasmagel is reduced by hydrostatic pressure, the furrow ceases to grow inward or even recedes, depending upon the degree of solation; furthermore, when the pressure is removed, gelation occurs once more and the inward growth of the furrow is resumed. It is believed by some investigators that the gelation produces its cleaving effect by exerting a contractile tension in the equatorial plane of the cell, since gelation in certain other colloidal systems is known to produce such forces.

These changes within the cell are correlated with alterations at its surface. By observing the movements of small particles adhering to the surface membrane of an egg beginning its cleavage, it can be established that a wave of local stretching, or increase in area, begins at the polar regions and progresses toward the site of the furrow. This stretching continues as the furrow develops, the surface actually moving inward along the walls of the furrow and becoming the membranes of the daughter cells. In at least one instance it has been reported that this ingrowth stops short of the middle of the egg, the membranes in the central area being formed anew in association with a granular substance accumulated there. The physicochemical problem of accounting for these changes in terms of alterations in viscosity, surface tension, and other factors has long occupied the attention of biologists, and it is believed that substantial progress is being made toward its solution.

Highly interesting contributions to the eventual solution of this problem have been afforded by nucleate and nonnucleate egg fragments obtained from normal eggs by shaking, centrifugation, or constriction with a hair noose. When nonnucleate fragments of *Arbacia* eggs were treated with parthenogenetic agents (hypertonic sea water, ultraviolet light), asters appeared and cytokinesis frequently followed. In some cases numerous successive divisions occurred, giving nonnucleate blastulae, one of which had as many as 500 cells and lived a month or more. In an amphibian (*Triton*), similar phenomena were observed. A fragment with a nucleus and accessory asters formed a blastula containing nuclei and asters in some cells but only asters in others. Such accessory asters may be retentions from previous mitoses, or they may be *cytasters*, which have long been known to form anew in cells under experimental treatment. Such facts indicate a degree of independence between the nuclear cycle and the astral cycle, the two being well correlated in normal cells, although either is capable of continuing alone for a limited time.

Cytokinesis by furrowing in tissue cells presents an even more difficult problem than that in free cells. The activities of any one of the cells are determined in part by its neighbors, yet it seems likely that the principal forces at work in cleaving eggs are paralleled in tissue cells. Asters may be less prominent in the latter, but such cells can still have localized regions of high viscosity, and the furrows in the two cases are often strikingly similar. There is also the further problem of accounting for the furrows that cleave large multinucleate plasmodia into cells with single nuclei.

Between the limiting membranes of adjacent cells of a tissue is a layer of material known as *intercellular substance*. This is primarily a secretion of the protoplasm and varies greatly in amount in different tissues. Its physicochemical complexity is indicated by the variety of fibrous and other modifications that may appear within it, and these may have a large share in determining the functional value of some tissues, such as certain connective tissues and cartilage.

FURTHER ASPECTS OF CELL DIVISION

Causes of Anaphasic Chromosome Movement.—To anyone who follows the nucleus through all the visible changes comprising one mitotic cycle, it is plain that the problem of explaining this cycle in terms of physics and chemistry is one of extraordinary complexity. It has nevertheless been hoped that an understanding of at least one phase of the process, anaphasic chromosome movement, might soon be reached. A full account of attempts to solve this part of the problem would occupy many pages, but the conclusion would be a brief one, *viz.*, that no satis·factory solution has yet been found. At the same time it should be helpful to enumerate some of the principal observations and hypotheses that promise to contribute to an eventual explanation.

The early theory that spindle fibers attached to the chromosomes simply contract and drag the chromosomes apart has not fared well in the light of subsequent work. Recently, however, an oscillatory independent movement of the several chromosomes at metaphase observed in living cells has brought the suggestion that localized alterations in viscosity (gel-sol changes) in the immediate neighborhood of the chromosomes play a role in their later movement, for gelation, as stated in the previous section, is known to be accompanied by contraction in many nonliving colloidal systems.

Appearances near the kinetochores, in particular the formation of "tractile fibers" and small projections on the chromosomes where movement begins, strongly suggest a slow streaming of the viscous materials; moreover, the aster when present is known to have streams flowing toward the poles. Despite these appearances it has not yet been possible to demonstrate that diffusion streams in the spindle substance are a major factor in chromosome movement, and if this were demonstrated the streaming would still have to be explained.

Elongation of the spindle, which is sometimes observed and can be experimentally modified, has been cited as a factor in chromosome movement. In one prominent hypothesis the initial separation of the chromatids was attributed to an action of the tractile fiber mechanism, subsequent movement poleward being due to spindle elongation in the region between the two lots of chromatids attached to it. This interpretation, too, has met obstacles: elongation may not occur; experimental alterations of spindle viscosity may not produce the expected effects on movement; chromosomes in some organisms, notably in hybrids, may not all move poleward even though they occupy the equatorial plane together at metaphase.

Forces of electrical repulsion and attraction have long been looked upon as factors of special importance. As investigations continue it becomes increasingly probable that repulsions of some sort do play a role, though forces of attraction are more difficult to demonstrate. If the chromosomes, which carry a negative charge, lie in a spindle with positive poles, the combination of forces could result in movement. The same result could follow if between all parts there were repulsions and these varied in relative intensity during the nuclear cycle. Attraction of centrioles for chromosomes is sometimes strongly suggested in the prophase when they move along together on opposite sides of the nuclear membrane, but its importance here or in anaphase is still uncertain.

Anaphasic movement evidently depends not only upon the spindle mechanism, but also upon changes going on in the chromosomes themselves. This is indicated by special cases, including hybrids, in which metaphasic arrangement and anaphasic movement occur only after chromosome doubleness, particularly at the kinetochore, has developed to a certain stage, even though the spindle is active earlier. It has also been thought that a special sheath-like differentiation at the chromosome surface undergoes local and progressive viscosity changes in such a way as to result in endwise movement. In spermatocytes of certain fungus flies (*Sciara*) the achromatic figure is monopolar, and 10 single chromosomes lie scattered within it. Of the 10, 6 regularly go toward the single pole and 4 away from it, although all have spindle attachments facing the pole. Furthermore, the 4 which pass away from the pole and are eventually extruded from the cell are always the same 4 out of the set of 5 originally contributed by the male parent. This indicates clearly that the reactions of a chromosome in the spindle are determined in part by specific constitutional features of the chromosome itself.

All the foregoing considerations lead to the conclusion that the behavior of chromosomes at anaphase and other phases of mitosis is brought about by a nicely correlated combination of forces, even though it is not yet possible to name them all or to estimate their relative importance. To a certain extent we know well *what* occurs: the equational separation of certain key materials of the nucleus. We also know *why* this occurs, in the sense that we can state its biological significance with respect to ontogeny and heredity. *How* it occurs we know least of all. Cytologists, now that they may take advantage of new developments in physical chemistry, are ever more confident that an adequate explanation of chromosome movement can some day be reached.

Time Occupied by Cell Division.—The amount of time required for a somatic division to be carried through and the rapidity with which divisions succeed one another are found to vary in different tissues and organisms. They also vary with temperature. Mitosis in the *Tradescantia* stamen hair occupies about 30 minutes at 45°C., 75 minutes at 25°, and 135 minutes at 10°. In dividing stigma hair cells of *Arrhenatherum* at 19°, the prophase occupies 36 to 45 minutes, the metaphase 7 to 10, the anaphase 15 to 20, and the telophase 20 to 35; total, not including interphase, 78 to 110 minutes.　In the brown alga, *Sphacelaria*, growing at nearly the same temperature, the process requires less than half as much time.　Mesenchyme cells of the chick growing in tissue cultures at 39°C. pass through prophase in 5 to 50 minutes, usually more than 30; metaphase, 1 to 15, usually 2 to 10; anaphase, 1 to 5, usually 2 to 3; telophase and cytokinesis, 32 to 133; total, 70 to 180 minutes.　Choroidal cells from chick embryos and cartilage cells from adult fowls carry through their division in about half this time under like conditions.　In fibroblasts from a 1-day mouse in a 2-day tissue culture, about 10 minutes elapse between the initiation of the equatorial furrow during anaphase and the completion of cytokinesis.　In the development of the male gametophyte and gametes from microspores of the water fern *Marsilea*, there are nine successive cell divisions and then a transformation of certain cells into spermatozoids.　All this has been observed to occur in as short a time as 10 to 12 hours; hence the divisions and the intervals between them must be of short duration.

The Shape of Cells in Tissues.—Obviously the shape of a tissue cell must be related to its internal differentiation and to the more general conditions pervading the tissue or organ of which it is a part.　It is nevertheless a matter of considerable interest to determine what shapes tissue cells assume when conditions are as simple and uniform as possible.

Investigations in this field have shown that in a flat epithelium or epidermis the cells in surface view tend strongly to be hexagonal in outline. If a flat plasmodium with its nuclei scattered at random in one layer were divided into uninucleate cells by walls with minimal surface area, a hexagonal pattern would result.　Such a pattern is seen in the cucumber epidermis.　When one of the hexagonal cells divides, the new wall forms stable three-rayed intersections with two opposite walls of the hexagon, the daughter cells being pentagons, and two of the adjacent cells becoming heptagons (Fig. 50).　With subsequent divisions, chiefly of the larger cells with more than six sides, the number of sides per cell varies still further in the tissue, but the general average remains not far from six.

A similar play of forces at cytokinesis in a uniform three-dimensional plasmodium would result in the formation of a mass of cells each having 14 sides and trihedral intersections, tetrahedral angles being unstable and rare.　If the space were uniformly divided into polyhedral cells with equal volume, minimal surface area, edges of equal length, and no intercellular spaces, each cell would have the form of an orthic tetrakaidecahedron, which has 8 hexagonal and 6 quadrilateral faces.　Cells in uniform tissue masses such as pith approach this 14-sided form.　Further divisions disturb the regularity of the pattern more than they do in an epithelium, since the divisions may occur in so many different planes, but through mutual adjustments of the plastic walls the average number of sides continues to be close to 14 so long as the cells are of uniform size. Cells at the surface of the mass have a smaller average number of sides. The development of intercellular spaces in such tissues brings further modifications of cell shape.

Light on the problem of cell shape has also been sought through experiments in which many balls of lead or putty were compressed in cylinders. Although the resulting mass of polyhedrons did not originate as a tissue does, it was found that when the balls were of uniform size they came out of the press with an average of 14 sides, with the exception of the peripheral ones which had an average of 10.75. After mixtures

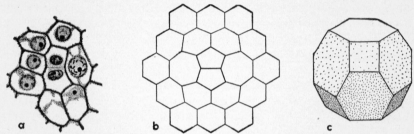

FIG. 50.—*a*, transverse section of epidermal cells of cucumber. *b*, diagram of cell division in a simple epithelium. *c*, model of an orthic tetrakaidecahedron. Explanation in text. (*After F. T. Lewis.*)

of large and small balls were compressed, the average number of sides was more than 14 for the large ones and less than 14 for the small ones, the average number for all taken together being close to 14. A method has also been developed for making wax casts of cells for the study of their shapes.

This is but a brief glimpse of another field of cytological research that should lead to a better understanding of the role of cells in growing and differentiating tissues. One way in which a cell affects the behavior of its neighbors is suggested by certain geometrical features mentioned above: the division of a given cell adds one side to each of two others; cells with more than the average number of sides grow larger and divide sooner than those with fewer sides. Hence cell division is not merely a multiplication of units; it is also a factor in correlating the activities of the cells. In Chap. II we stressed the point that the behavior of regions in a growing mass depends in part upon their positions in the whole. We now see that cell partitions within a tissue affect the activities of the units they separate not only by virtue of their constitution and consequent effect upon the diffusion of materials, but also through the geometrical form they impose upon the cells by tending to develop in accordance with the laws of minimal surface area.

CHAPTER VI

THE CELL WALLS OF PLANTS

The tissue cells of plants, like those of animals, are separated by intercellular substance. In both cases each cell has a delicate plasma membrane, but in plants each has in addition a relatively firm wall between the membrane and the intercellular substance. Such cell walls vary greatly in degree of development and structural complexity. Their chief constituent is cellulose, and with this other materials are usually associated. Surely nobody needs to be reminded of the importance of cellulose as supporting material in large plants or of the varied roles played by this substance in our modern life.

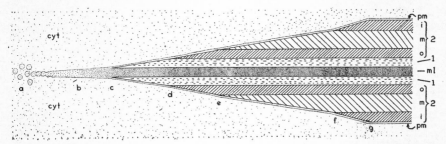

Fig. 51.—Diagrammatic representation of successive stages (left to right) in formation of plant cell wall with secondary thickening. *a*, origin of cell plate; *b*, cell plate transforming into middle lamella, or intercellular substance (*ml*); *c*, beginning of deposition of primary wall layers (1, 1); *d*, *e*, *f*, beginning of deposition of outer, middle, and inner portions (*o*, *m*, *i*) of secondary wall layers (2, 2); *g*, completion of wall thickening; *pm*, plasma membrane; *cyt*, cytoplasm. (*Based on researches of W. A. Becker, I. W. Bailey, T. Kerr, and others.*)

Development of the Wall.—In a section of plant tissue under a microscope of moderate power the partition between any two cells appears as a triple structure (Fig. 54, *a*). In a meristematic tissue, such as that in the root tip or the cambium, the three layers are very thin and semifluid, but all are present: each cell has its own cellulose wall lying against an intervening layer of noncellulosic intercellular substance. The outer wall of an epidermal cell is, of course, single. We shall now recall the development of this condition as described in the foregoing chapter (page 65) and then proceed with an account of the further changes that transform the early walls into the elaborate structures seen in such mature tissues as wood. The successive stages in the entire process are represented diagrammatically in Fig. 51.

Through the equator of the cell between the recently formed daughter nuclei there is formed a continuous fluid film, the *cell plate*, which extends until it reaches the lateral walls. Physical and chemical changes, including the deposition of pectin, transform this into a somewhat firmer layer of intercellular substance, the *middle lamella*. The protoplasts then deposit upon each side of the middle lamella a thin *primary wall* of cellulose. This is the stage observed in the meristem. The primary wall undergoes some thickening, but it remains very plastic during the further growth and divisions of the cells. In some tissues no further layers are added, the primary layers, with certain chemical transformations, becoming the walls of the mature tissue cells.

In other tissues, notably woody ones, additional wall layers are added, a *secondary wall* of cellulose being deposited upon each primary wall (Fig. 54, *b*). Each secondary wall is composed characteristically of

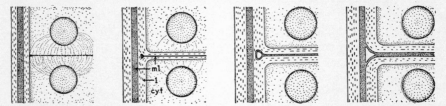

Fig. 52.—Four stages in the establishment of the connection between the middle lamella of a newly formed wall with that of the lateral wall of the divided cell. *ml*, middle lamella; 1, primary wall layer; *cyt*, cytoplasm. (*After P. Martens.*)

three layers, of which the middle one is commonly the thickest. At this stage the plasma membranes of the two protoplasts are separated by a partition in which there can be distinguished as many as nine layers: the two secondary walls each composed of three layers, the two primary walls, and the middle lamella. This elaborate structure is not necessarily uniform over the entire extent of the wall, however. Here and there are small areas in which no secondary layers are deposited, leaving *pits* in which only a delicate membrane separates the two protoplasts. This membrane may be pierced by fine pores, and in some cases it has a central thickening, the *torus*. The secondary layer may overarch the margin of the membrane, forming the *bordered pit* characteristic of certain vascular cells of gymnosperms (Fig. 53). Another form of localized deposition is seen in the spiral and ring-like thickenings formed by protoxylem cells before their elongation has been completed.

The manner in which the several layers of the newly formed partition become continuous with those of the lateral walls of the original meristematic cell is illustrated in Fig. 52. As the extending cell plate, or young middle lamella, meets the lateral partition, there is developed at its edge a swelling with a minute cavity. This gradually extends through the lateral primary wall until it unites with the lateral middle lamella, the small cavity in its margin enlarging as an intercellular space in the midst of the intercellular substance. Deposition of cellulose meanwhile continues on all sides of the two protoplasts, including the new middle lamella, so that each new cell has its own continuous primary wall. It is only after cell divisions have ceased that thick secondary wall layers are added.

Although cellulose and pectin are the chief constituents of cell walls, other materials are commonly associated with them in mature tissues. Some of these, notably lignin and suberin, as well as the main constituents themselves, vary greatly in relative amount in the various layers of the wall and in the walls of different tissues. They have pronounced effects upon reactions to stains. Lignified cellulose, which contains a pentosan (*e.g.*, xylan) and an organic substance with an aromatic nucleus, stains vigorously with safranine or crystal violet, whereas unlignified cellulose walls do not. One should not, however, rely too strongly upon staining reactions as criteria of chemical composition. Suberin, formed in special abundance in corky tissues, is an aggregate of various anhydrides and glycerides of certain organic acids. Cutin is similar in composition and occurs mainly as an external coating on epidermal cells. Other organic compounds, such as tannins, oils, and resins,

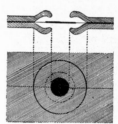

Fig. 53.—Diagram of bordered pit in wall of conifer wood. (*After I. W. Bailey.*)

are also deposited in old cell walls and are largely responsible for the characters of heartwood in trees. Mineral matter, including certain salts of silicon and calcium, may also occur in wood, and the location of ash in incinerated tissues indicates that such matter is restricted largely to the primary wall layers. Among certain algae and fungi, chitin and keratin occur as wall constituents.

Minute Structure of the Cell Wall.—The results of chemical studies and physical researches with X rays on the cellulose wall have shown that it has a crystalline structure, *i.e.*, it is composed mainly of units arranged in a regular three-dimensional pattern. The primary unit is the anhydrous glucose residue, $C_6H_{10}O_5$. Such residues are united by primary valencies into long cellulose chains, and these are linked laterally by secondary forces to form a regular space lattice. The intermolecular cohesive forces result in the formation of larger groupings, or *micelles*. The presence and the nature of amorphous materials between the groups of cellulose chains are debated points.

As a result of the regular parallel arrangement of the submicroscopic chains in the primary and secondary cellulose wall layers, these layers are anisotropic in contrast to the isotropic intercellular substance. This

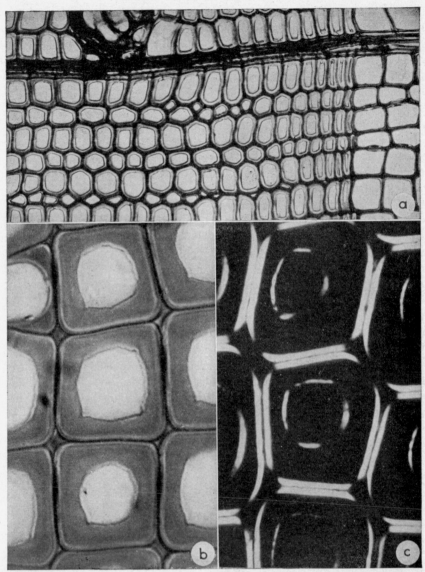

Fig. 54.—Thickened cell walls in secondary xylem of plants. *a*, wood of spruce (*Picea*).
b, transverse section of wood of *Trochodendron;* the primary walls are deeply stained, the
secondary walls and the intercellular substance are not. *c*, transverse section of wood of
Trochodendron photographed with polarized light through crossed nicols; outer and inner portions of secondary wall bright, middle lamella and thick middle portion of secondary wall
dark. (*a, courtesy of U. S. Forest Products Laboratory; b, c, after T. Kerr and I. W. Bailey.*)

can be seen, for example, in a transverse section of wood viewed between crossed nicols on the polarizing microscope: here the two thin layers of the secondary wall appear bright, while the thick layer between them appears dark (Fig. 54, *c*).   In a longitudinal section the thin layers are dark and the thick one bright.   This shows that the cellulose chains, although highly variable in orientation, tend to lie more nearly parallel to the cell's longitudinal axis in the thick layer and more nearly at right angles to it in the thin ones.   The intercellular substance is dark when viewed at any angle. . In the cotton fiber the thin primary wall has two systems of chains following spiral courses in opposite directions in a matrix of pectic and waxy material.   The secondary wall is much the same, except that the chains form smaller angles with the longitudinal axis and show more reversals of direction.

Under some circumstances, as when the cell walls are swollen or dried, coarse fibers become visible in the wall substance.   This involves a rupturing of the system of cellulose chains and may not indicate accurately the arrangement that the chains had in the untreated wall.   When properly handled, the fresh untreated secondary walls of some cells show microscopically visible striations revealing the true orientation of the chains.   The orientation may also be shown by the arrangements assumed by iodine crystals induced to form within the wall substance and by the shape of cavities resulting from enzymatic activity when fungus hyphae invade thick secondary walls.

The relative arrangement of cellulose and lignin in the secondary wall is strikingly shown in the fiber tracheids of certain tropical dicotyledons. When the tracheid is swollen, delignified with cuprammonium hydroxide, and stained with Congo red, the transverse section has the appearance shown in Fig. 55.   Comparison with longitudinal sections shows the radiating dark lines to represent a system of longitudinally arranged, branching plates having a high proportion of cellulose and a low proportion of lignin, the lighter lines between them being regions in which cellulose is less and lignin more abundant.   When a fiber tracheid is decellulosed with sulphuric acid and stained with iron alum-hematoxylin, a similar pattern appears, but here the dark regions are those containing a high proportion of lignin and a low proportion of cellulose.   Both substances are continuous throughout the wall, but their relative abundance varies along different radii.

Concentric zones appearing in the secondary wall are due in different cases to at least three causes: variations in the cellulose pattern, variations in the intensity of lignification, and the alternation of cellulosic and noncellulosic layers.   In the cotton fiber the numerous concentric zones have been correlated with the daily metabolic cycle, a compact anisotropic layer being formed each day and a looser, relatively isotropic layer each night.

Fig. 55.—Minute structure of secondary cell wall of *Siparuna*. Above, delignified fiber tracheid, showing radiating pattern in the remaining cellulose. Below, fiber tracheid after removal of cellulose, showing radiating pattern of lignin. (*After I. W. Bailey and T. Kerr.*)

Plasmodesms.—The cell walls in plant tissues do not completely separate the protoplasts. It appears to be generally true that the latter are connected by numerous delicate protoplasmic strands known as *plasmodesms* passing through fine channels in the walls. Where they are relatively coarse and not too numerous, they may show plainly in sections (Fig. 56), but in many tissues, particularly in meristems, their extreme delicacy and the destructive effects of technics involving dehydration make their demonstration very difficult. For the same reasons their mode of origin has not yet been clearly established.

That plasmodesms are actually protoplasmic strands has sometimes been questioned, an alternative view being that they are merely peculiar

Fig. 56.—Section of endosperm of persimmon (*Diospyros*), showing plasmodesms connecting the cells through the enormously thickened walls. (*Courtesy of General Biological Supply House, Inc., Chicago.*)

structural features of the wall. Among the evidences cited in favor of their protoplasmic nature are the following: they occur only in walls separating two protoplasts; when protoplasts are plasmolyzed, they often remain connected with the wall by numerous fine strands; by plasmolysis the plasmodesms may be withdrawn from their channels; their staining reactions are like those of protoplasm; they give a positive test for oxydase; in germinating seeds the digestion of the endosperm walls proceeds along the plasmodesms; after hardening the plasmodesms in formalin the endosperm walls have been dissolved with sulphuric acid, leaving them as connections between the undissolved protoplasts; the tobacco mosaic virus passes readily through walls having plasmodesms, but not into the guard cells of stomates, where plasmodesms are apparently absent. The transfer of materials from cell to cell by way of the very slender plasmodesms has not been directly observed, although mass movement of protoplasm has been seen occurring through larger pores having a diameter of 1.5 to 2μ in the green alga *Codium*. In the red algae, peculiar cell connections have been described, but actual protoplasmic continuity here is still subject to doubt.

It is probable that the functional significance of plasmodesms is to be found in the conduction of stimuli promoting correlation and in the transfer of certain materials important in metabolism. The same interpretation is warranted for the intercellular bridges in animal tissues. By virtue of such protoplasmic continuity a tissue or a complex organism would seem to be better able to function consistently as an individual than it would if only nonprotoplasmic materials separated its protoplasts. At the same time it is to be remembered that certain correlating factors, *e.g.*, electrical gradients and the diffusion of dissolved substances, can exist in systems that are partly or even wholly nonprotoplasmic.

The Formation of Cellulose by the Protoplast.—This topic is at present a highly controversial one, but it is included here because of its prominence in cytology today and its great biological interest. For many years the prevailing view has been that cellulose first becomes visible at the surface of the protoplast, where it is deposited as successive layers having the crystalline structure described in foregoing pages.

According to an opposing view, which has come into prominence during the past decade, cellulose first appears in the cytoplasm in the form of minute ellipsoidal bodies having a size of about 0.5 by 1.5μ. These form chain-like aggregates and are built into the wall along with a colloidal material that cements them together. Moreover, the wall can be broken down into such ellipsoidal bodies by the use of hydrochloric acid and centrifuged out of the mixture.

In recent papers on the ellipsoidal particles it is claimed that they are produced by plastids. In the green alga *Halicystis* ring-like masses of carbohydrate are formed just beneath the membranes of disc-shaped chloroplasts. These break up into "mercerized" cellulose particles of uniform size which are liberated into the cytoplasm when the plastid membranes disintegrate. They are then built into the developing wall in successive layers. In the cotton fiber there are small disc-shaped colorless plastids in which cellulose particles appear in a similar manner. In the green cells of the leaves and stem of the cotton plant, both starch-forming chloroplasts and cellulose-forming leucoplasts function simultaneously.

The conflicting evidences and interpretations involved in the controversy centering about the ellipsoidal bodies cannot be reviewed here, but the subject is one that cytologists will continue to follow with the greatest interest. The theory of the origin of cellulose in plastids is especially intriguing in view of the fact that starch, which resembles cellulose so closely in chemical composition, is elaborated in such cell organs. A completely satisfying answer to the question of whether these two materials, which are about the only solid substances deposited in large amounts by plant protoplasts, have similar or dissimilar cytological origins would indeed be a major and welcome achievement.

CHAPTER VII

THE CHROMOSOMES

It is not difficult to account for the fact that the chromosomes have long held a major share of the attention of cytologists. They are individualized protoplasmic units present in definite numbers and multiplying regularly and only by division. Because of the precision with which they are distributed at mitosis, every nucleus of the developed plant or animal body has a descendant of every chromosome present when development was initiated. Furthermore, when reproduction occurs the chromosomes are passed on to the next generation through the spores or gametes. Their physicochemical composition is such that they have specific and profound effects upon the course of development and hence upon the organism's characters. As a consequence of all this, they play a major role in heredity.

Some of the above points were brought out in the chapter on cell division. It was also shown there that the chromosome has two main structural constituents: the chromonemata, present throughout the entire nuclear cycle, and the matrix, which is conspicuous only during certain phases of mitosis. The chromosome, although it is a persistent individual reproducing by division in every mitotic cycle, passes in each cycle through a series of structural changes that alter its appearance profoundly. At metaphase and anaphase it is clearly evident as a distinct individual, whereas in the metabolic stage, when its chief functions are being performed, it is rarely possible to determine its limits.

In this chapter we shall consider in greater detail the form and the structure of chromosomes, chiefly in somatic tissues, and discuss the constitution of the chromosome complement, or outfit of chromosomes making up a given nucleus.

Somatic Chromosomes.—The general morphology of somatic chromosomes is best displayed at the metaphase and anaphase of mitosis. If special technical methods are used, much can also be learned about their structure at these stages, but so far the most reliable information of this kind has come from chromosomes passing through meiosis. Chromosomes may differ greatly in size in different organisms, in unlike tissues, and in some degree in plants grown in different nutrient solutions. Fixation often affects their size. Nearly all chromosomes at anaphase lie between 1 and 20μ in length. It is easy to understand why investiga-

84

tors have preferred larger ones, like those of amphibians and liliaceous plants, for studies of chromosomal constitution. Special mention will be made of the giant salivary-gland chromosomes of certain insect tissues later in the chapter.

The form and the structure of a typical somatic anaphase chromosome are represented in Fig. 57. It is an elongate body consisting of matrix and two spiral chromonemata recently formed by division. The two may be so closely associated that they seem to be one, or they may appear as clearly separate threads more or less twisted about one another. They represent the chromatids which will separate in the anaphase of

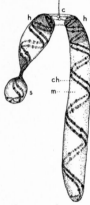

FIG. 57.—A typical somatic chromosome at anaphase of mitosis. Semi-diagrammatic. *c*, kinetochore; *ch*, chromonema; *h*, heterochromatic region; *m*, matrix; *s*, satellite; *no*, nucleolus organizer.

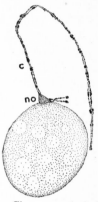

FIG. 58.—Chromosome 6 in meiotic prophase in maize, showing its nucleolus organizer (*no*) in contact with the large nucleolus; short region to right of it is the satellite. *c*, kinetochore.

the next mitotic cycle. Along the chromonemata are small lumps, the *chromomeres*. These are rarely evident in preparations of anaphase chromosomes even when the matrix has been rendered transparent, but during the prophase, when the threads have less chromatic material, they frequently show clearly. They are best studied in meiotic prophases (Figs. 58, 64, *b*; 78).

An important feature of the chromosome is the specialized region at which its reactions with the spindle mechanism seem to be largely centered. This region is called the *kinetochore*. (Other terms in the literature are *centromere, primary constriction*, and *kinomere*.) The kinetochore commonly appears as a relatively achromatic region. In certain large chromosomes it can be seen to be traversed by two slender strands which evidently represent the chromonemata. In the double metaphase chromosome there are accordingly four (Fig. 59). In some instances a minute body, the *kinosome*, has been made out at the middle of each strand. The portions of the chromosome on either side of the kineto-chore are known as *arms*. These are equal or unequal in length depending upon the kinetochore's position, which is constant for a given chromosome. Telokinetic chromosomes, *i.e.*, those with terminal kinetochores, have been reported in animals, but they seem to be very rare in plants. A number of supposedly telokinetic chromosomes have been shown to have a minute second arm. The present tendency is to regard the telokinetic condition, at least in plants, as an abnormality that does not long persist. In metaphase and especially in anaphase the chromosome tends to be bent at the kinetochore.

Chromosomes may have more or less prominent "secondary constrictions" in one or both of their arms. Special methods may reveal more of these than appear after ordinary treatments. Commonly one chromosome of each of the *genomes*, or basic outfits composing a nucleus, has in one arm an especially prominent secondary constriction with which there is associated a particular function, the organization of the nucleolus. The small segment of the chromosome distal to this constriction is called a *satellite*. In the anaphase the exact extent of the *nucleolus organizer*, or specialized region directly concerned in the development of the nucleolus, is not evident, for the chromosome is very compact and no nucleolus is present. Its features appear much more clearly in certain plants during the meiotic prophase, when the chromosome is extended and devoid of matrix (Figs. 58; 64, *a*). During the telophase, as the matrix loses its stainability and disappears, the nucleolus makes its appearance in connection with the chromonemata at or near the constriction. Hence the number and the position of the nucleoli in the resulting metabolic nucleus are dependent upon the number and location of the nucleolus-forming chromosomes in the telophase. It is known that the material for the nucleoli is derived from all the chromosomes present, but in some manner it is collected or organized as a nucleolus only at the nucleolus organizer. In the ensuing prophase the nucleolus commonly disappears, partially or completely, as the matrix accumulates and becomes highly stainable.

Another important feature of chromosomal constitution is *heteropyknosis*. This term, which means "difference in density," refers to the condition present when all or a definite part of a chromosome remains denser and more highly chromatic than the other chromosomes or parts through the nuclear cycle. In the anaphase the stained chromosome may exhibit this feature weakly or not at all, but during the telophase the *heterochromatic* part retains its compactness and stainability while the *euchromatic* parts undergo the usual telophasic transformation (Figs. 60; 64, *d*). Most commonly it is the regions near the kinetochore that are heteropyknotic. In some plants this makes it possible to estimate the number of chromosomes in a metabolic nucleus by counting such heterochromatic masses (*chromocenters*) (Fig. 16). Other such regions may occur elsewhere in the chromosome, the nucleolus organizer frequently having this character. Structurally, such portions seem to be regions in which the chromonemata are more closely coiled, and by treatment with NH_4Cl it has been found possible to relax the coils.

The significance of heteropyknosis is not yet fully evident. Recent researches on the giant chromosomes in the salivary glands of the fruit fly (*Drosophila*) indicate some connection between heterochromatic regions and the nucleic acid cycle. It is thought to have a role in the synthesis of the thymonucleic acid in the nucleus and also to affect the ribonucleic acid content of the cytoplasm of the egg. Since the nucleolus also contains ribonucleic acid compounds, it, too, appears to be involved

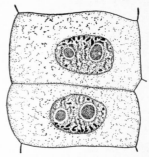

FIG. 59.—Portion of somatic chromosome of *Trillium* at metaphase, showing structure of kinetochore. Description in text. (*After L. W. Sharp.*)

FIG. 60.—Two cells recently formed by division of one in root tip of onion. Chromocenters at opposite poles of the pair of nuclei.

in this chemical cycle. This is strongly emphasized by the origin of the nucleolus in direct connection with the nucleolus organizer, which is typically heterochromatic, and by the reciprocal relationship existing between the chromosomal and nucleolar cycles: the nucleolus appears as the telophase chromosomes lose or alter their stainability, and it disappears as the prophase chromosomes regain it. This cyclic change has always puzzled cytologists, and now it seems that a solution of the puzzle is being found.

In the chapter on cell division, reference was made to an uncertainty regarding the number of chromonemata actually present in a chromosome. Some observers do not admit the presence of more than one at anaphase and telophase, many hold that there are two, and some believe that there are four, each possibly having its own individual matrix. Since visual observation involves the interpretation of structures so near the limit of visibility, more refined techniques have been brought to bear upon the problem. The most promising of these has been irradiation with X rays, which are capable of causing breaks in the chromonemata. The procedure is as follows. Cells are irradiated at whatever stage it is desired to ascertain the chromonema number, *e.g.*, during the telophase or the metabolic stage. They are afterwards allowed to grow until the nuclei have had time to reach the anaphase of the succeeding mitosis. The anaphase figures are then examined for broken chromosomes or chromatids, and from the types of abnormality observed inferences are drawn regarding the number of chromonemata present at the time the breakage was induced.

The possible types of breakage and their effects upon the appearance of the anaphase chromosomes are shown diagrammatically in Fig. 61. If the chromosome has only *one* chromonema and it is broken by the X ray, both of the separating chromatids at anaphase should lack a portion, since they were formed by splitting of a thread already broken. This is a so-called *chromosome break*. The part lost may lie near by. If there are *two* chromonemata at the time of breakage, a variety of results may appear at anaphase: (1) a normal chromatid may be seen separating from a deficient one, with a single fragment lying near by; this indicates the break of but one of the two chromonemata—a *chromatid break*. (2) Two deficient chromatids may be seen separating, with a double fragment near by; this looks like the result of a chromosome break, but it could be due to the breakage of two associated chromatids by the same X-ray "hit." It is known that two threads may thus be broken even when they are more than 0.1μ apart. (3) A chromatic "bridge" may appear at anaphase as a result of a reunion of the broken ends of the two associated chromatids, giving a chromosome with two kinetochores which may pass toward opposite poles. If there are *four* chromonemata at the time of breakage and only one of them is broken, a chromatid with two equal longitudinal halves may be seen separating from one with unequal halves. This is a *half-chromatid break*.

The results obtained with this method thus far by different workers are equivocal. Some find evidence for the presence of two chromonemata at somatic telophase and a division of these into four either in the late metabolic stage or very early in the prophase. Others conclude that there is but one chromonema in the telophase, this becoming doubled late in the metabolic stage. To what extent such discrepancies are due to differences in the type or condition of the materials used, or to variations in the procedures, remains to be determined. An interesting piece of evidence is the appearance of two satellites and sometimes two nucleoli side by side on a telophase chromosome.

It has been suggested that the process of doubling may involve a succession of reactions extending over a considerable period of time and that various phases of the process may be affected by different agencies

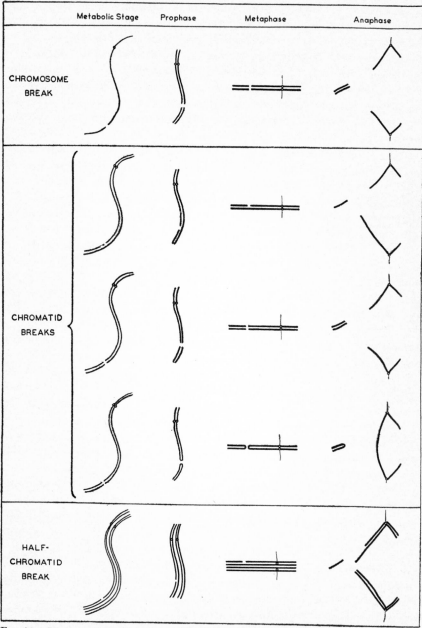

Fig. 61.—Diagram illustrating the method of investigating the number of chromonemata in a chromosome by means of X rays. Explanation in text.

and conditions. Furthermore, it is not known to what degree the threads may be longitudinally compound below the range in which X rays can affect their parts individually. It may therefore be helpful to distinguish provisionally three levels of doubling: (1) *elementary doubling*, in which the ultimate longitudinal constituents (protein chains?) of the chromosome become duplicated or multiplied, probably through the formation of new ones close to the old ones by a process analogous to crystallization or polymerization; (2) *effective doubling*, in which the thread somehow reaches a stage at which a given agency such as X rays may affect one longitudinal fraction and not another; (3) *visible doubling*, in which a thread appearing single under the microscope becomes double by a process that looks like a real splitting.

Studies on chromosome structure are complicated by the fact that the chromonemata are spirally coiled in some degree at all stages of

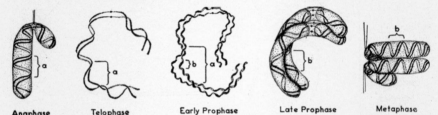

| Anaphase | Telophase | Early Prophase | Late Prophase | Metaphase |

Fig. 62.—Diagram of the chromonema coiling cycle through mitosis. While the gyres (*a*) of one series are relaxing and disappearing, a new series (*b*) is developed; thus two coiling cycles overlap in the mitotic cycle. Further explanation in text. (*Based on mitosis in Trillium microspore as described by A. H. Sparrow.*)

the somatic nuclear cycle. During this cycle the changes undergone appear to be somewhat as follows (Figs. 62, 63). In anaphase the two spirally coiled chromonemata recently formed by division in the prophase (page 61) lie mostly close together and twisted about each other. In the enlarging telophase nucleus they tend to separate somewhat and relax their coils, although the number of spiral turns, or gyres, remains about the same as it was in anaphase. In the following early prophase these gyres begin to disappear, but before the uncoiling is completed each of the constituent chromonemata (chromatids) begins independently to form numerous new gyres. In the advancing prophase these new gyres become fewer and larger while the chromatids gradually untwist. By the end of the prophase the chromatids have lost their twists and old gyres (relic coils) and have developed individual matrices. At this time the chromonemata, with their new gyres now closer together, reveal the doubleness which becomes effective in the next mitotic cycle. The metaphase chromosome thus consists of two chromatids which have become nearly or completely untwisted and in each of which there are two chromonemata in the form of a double-stranded spiral like that of the preceding anaphase.

Meiotic Chromosomes.—The next chapter is to be devoted to chromosome behavior during meiosis, the process by which a reduction

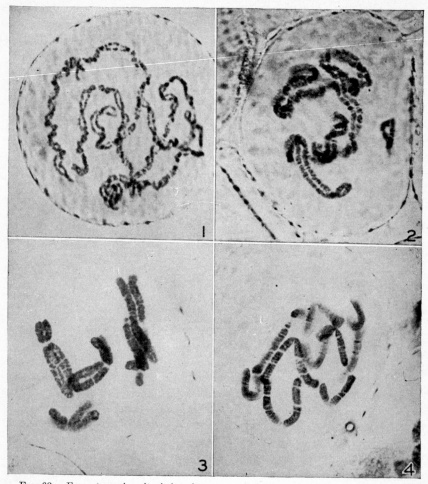

FIG. 63.—Four stages in mitosis in microspores of *Trillium grandiflorum*. 1, prophase: twists and relic coils (large gyres) from previous cycle still present; small gyres developing in each chromatid. 2, later prophase: new gyres in chromatids now larger and fewer. 3, metaphase. 4, anaphase. See text and Fig. 62. From temporary acetocarmine smears. (*After A. H. Sparrow.*)

in the number of chromosomes is accomplished at a certain point in the life cycle. In the present section we shall merely review a few facts that will serve to complete our description of fundamental chromosome structure.

Meiotic chromosomes are especially favorable for the study of chromonemata, first of all because in higher plants they occur in cells (microsporocytes) that lie more or less free from each other in the anther. These cells can therefore be pressed out on a slide in large numbers for study in the living condition or for special treatments. In the prophase of the first of the two nuclear divisions in the microsporocyte they are usually longer and straighter than at any other period in the life cycle; moreover, they contain very little stainable material except in the chromomeres. Hence in some plants, e.g., maize, the more minute structural features of different chromosomes can be clearly seen and

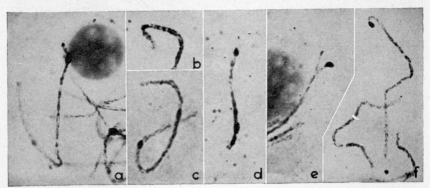

Fig. 64.—Chromosomes (synapsed pairs) of maize at mid-prophase in microsporocytes. a, chromosome 6 attached to nucleolus by its nucleolus organizer (compare Fig. 58). b, portion of chromosome 8, showing chromomeres. c, chromosome 7 with heterochromatic region next to kinetochore at right, knob at left. d, B-type chromosome seen in certain strains; euchromatic region above, and heterochromatic region below. e, portion of chromosome 9 in a strain heterozygous for knob size. f, chromosome 9 with terminal knob. (After B. McClintock.)

closely compared (Figs. 58, 79). One result of such studies on plant microsporocytes and animal spermatocytes has been to show that the various chromomeres tend to appear in regular and constant patterns in particular chromosomes. In maize and its relatives large chromatic knobs also occupy definite positions. This characteristic longitudinal differentiation of the chromosome suggests a corresponding functional differentiation, and this conception is borne out by the results of cyto-genetical studies.

In the meiotic prophase other structural features, such as kinetochores, heterochromatic regions, and nucleolus organizers, also stand out clearly (Fig. 64). The nucleolus organizer in maize appears as a swollen heterochromatic region immediately proximal to the secondary constriction in the shorter arm of chromosome 6. In the meiotic prophase the nucleolus formed at the preceding telophase is still present in contact with it. That the heterochromatic region rather than the constriction itself acts as the organizer is shown by the fact that in abnormal cells which have lost the satellite, the constriction, and part of the organizer the remaining portion of the organizer forms a nucleolus.

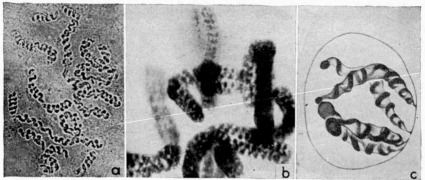

FIG. 65.—Spiral chromonemata in chromosomes. *a,* chromonemata in microsporocyte of *Tradescantia* after removal of chromosome matrix with hot water. (*After T. Sakamura.*) *b,* chromosomes in microsporocyte of *Trillium,* showing the major coils and in certain regions (at top, faintly) the minor coils. (*Photograph by A. W. S. Hunter. After C. L. Huskins.*) *c,* nucleus of a protozoan (*Spirotrichonympha*)*;* each of the four chromosomes is attached to the nuclear membrane by a fiber. Compare Fig. 66. (*After L. R. Cleveland.*)

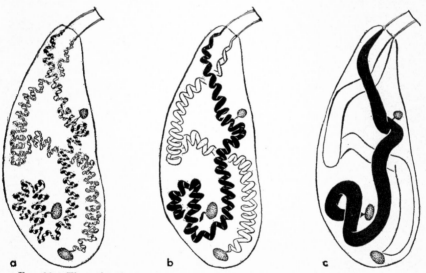

FIG. 66.—Three drawings of a telophase nucleus of a protozoan (*Holomastigotoides*). *a* shows the major and minor coils of the chromonemata; *b* shows only the major coils; *c* shows the larger supercoils which result from the elongation of the chromosomes. Compare Fig. 65, *c.* (*Courtesy of L. R. Cleveland.*)

In some plants, *e.g., Trillium* and *Tradescantia,* the meiotic chromosomes at metaphase and anaphase are extremely large. Their coiled chromonemata appear with admirable clarity in good preparations (Fig. 65), and they can easily be watched while being subjected to various experimental treatments. Thus by treatment with warm water the matrix can be dissolved away, leaving the chromonemata intact on the slide (Fig. 65, *a*). In some plants it has been found that the chromonemata in meiotic chromosomes are doubly coiled, *i.e.*, they not only form the large "major" spiral so easily seen but have in addition a minute "minor" spiral running throughout their length (Fig. 65, *b*).

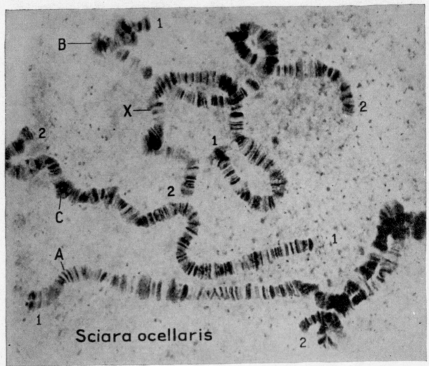

FIG. 67.—The salivary-gland chromosomes of a fungus gnat (*Sciara*). Each of the four consists of two homologous members of the diploid somatic complement in intimate lateral union; note the doubleness at end 1 of chromosome A. From an iron-acetocarmine smear preparation. Magnification, 575 ×. (*Photograph by O. O. Heard. After C. W. Metz.*)

The same condition has been found in certain somatic chromosomes (Figs. 65, *c*; 66).

Salivary-gland Chromosomes.—That the chromosome possesses a definite longitudinal differentiation in structure and functional effect is most convincingly shown by the amazing chromosomes in the salivary glands and certain other larval tissues of the two-winged flies (Diptera). These chromosomes were first observed in 1881, but it is only during the past 10 years that they have become well enough known to be of service to the cytologist and cytogeneticist. It was a stroke of good fortune to find them in the Diptera. Many years of cytogenetical research had made the fruit fly, *Drosophila melanogaster*, the most important animal in that field, yet further progress in the correlation of the genetical phenomena with chromosome behavior seemed to be blocked along some lines by the small size of the fly's chromosomes. All this is now changed. The giant salivary-gland chromosomes have characters that render them almost ideal for the purpose, and as a result the science of cytogenetics has received a great stimulus. They are also furnishing valuable new information regarding the fundamental structure and composition of chromosomes. It is fortunate that the cells containing

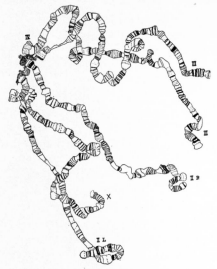

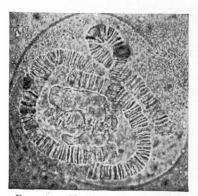

Fig. 68.—Arrangement of salivary chromosomes in the nucleus of *Drosophila melanogaster*. The arms of the chromosomes extend from the chromocenter formed by their heterochromatic portions. (*After T. S. Painter.*)

Fig. 69.—Nucleus of living cell in salivary gland of a fly (*Chironomus*), showing giant chromosomes. (*After H. Bauer.*)

them are so located that the skilled investigator can prepare them for study by simple and rapid methods.

The first striking character of salivary-gland chromosomes is their great size (Fig. 67). They are usually between 70 and 110 times as long as the chromosomes in the oögonial cells. When moderately stretched for the study of certain structural details they may be 150 times the length of the oögonial chromosomes, the longest chromosomes of the complement then reaching a length of about half a millimeter. In some flies all the chromosomes lie well separated in the nucleus. In others, including *Drosophila melanogaster*, the heterochromatic portions about their kinetochores are all grouped into a single mass known as the *chromocenter* (Fig. 68).

No less striking is the visible structure of the salivary chromosomes, and it is largely this feature which is responsible for their great value in cytogenetics. Even in the living and unstained nucleus it can be seen that they have conspicuous transverse bands (Fig. 69). The longest chromosome in *Drosophila melanogaster* has more than 2000 of these bands. In fixed material prepared with the acetocarmine and Feulgen techniques the bands stain vigorously, leaving the interband regions weakly stained or colorless. The differentiation with the latter technique is particularly sharp, showing that the thymonucleic acid is restricted almost entirely to the bands. Ultraviolet-absorption studies lead to the same conclusion.

Each band appears to be composed of one or more discs of chromatic granules extending across the cylindrical body of the chromosome. These granules have been called chromomeres, although their variation in size and number, even in a given band, indicates that here this term does not designate units all of the same rank. One general interpretation placed upon the whole chromosome is that it consists of a large number—dozens or even many hundreds—of chromonemata that have multiplied as the nucleus grew without any mitoses to separate them, their chromomeres remaining closely associated or united laterally as the discs. Studies of the earlier stages in the development of salivary-gland nuclei lend some support to this view. If, however, the chromonemata in the fully developed salivary chromosome, which may have a thousand or more times the volume it had before enlargement, are comparable to the original chromonema, they must be present in very great numbers; moreover, if an ordinary chromonema were extended to the length of the salivary chromosome without the addition of new material, it would be of submicroscopic thickness. The longitudinal fibrils seen connecting the discs in stretched chromosomes probably do not, therefore, represent individual chromonemata. Some workers regard them as large bundles of chromonemata, while others interpret them as distortions of an alveolar structure pervading the chromosome (Fig. 70). The finer structure of the salivary chromosome is at present a very controversial subject, although it is agreed that the transverse bands are natural features having the cytogenetic usefulness indicated below.

Of the greatest importance is the fact that the bands form a pattern that is constant for a given chromosome. On the basis of differences in size, spacing, and other characteristics of the bands it is possible for the investigator to distinguish particular regions of the various chromosomes. Data of this kind have been recorded in pictorial "chromosome maps." The usefulness of band patterns to the cytogeneticist should be obvious. In later chapters it will be shown how variations in genetical characters and even differences between races and species may be correlated with differences in band pattern, so that it becomes possible to assign contributing causes of certain characters to particular chromosomal regions. Thus the salivary-gland chromosome map becomes to the specialist a sort of biological spectrum indicating the organism's genetical constitution, much as an absorption or a bright-line spectrum reveals the chemical composition of an inorganic body.

Chromosome Complements.—Any group of chromosomes composing a nucleus, whatever their number or kind, is a chromosome *complement*. The simplest typical complement is one made up of several members differing variously in form and function but acting together as a complete and harmonious system; such a complement is a *genome*, or *set*. Since

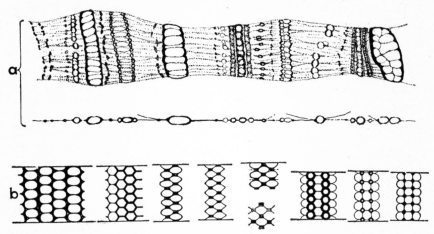

Fig. 70.—Drawings and diagrams illustrating (*a*) the theory that the salivary-gland chromosome consists of many reduplicated chromonemata with their chromomeres and (*b*) the theory that it has an alveolar structure with chromatic matter variously distributed within it. (*a, after T. S. Painter and A. Griffen; b, after C. W. Metz.*)

only one chromosome of each kind is present, the nucleus (or tissue, or organism) with such a complement is said to be *monoploid*.

A nucleus may contain one to many genomes. In typical cases, sexually reproducing organisms exhibit an alternation of two chromosome numbers in the course of the life cycle. Two gametes, each monoploid, unite to form a zygote which has every kind of chromosome in duplicate and is therefore *diploid*. In higher animals and plants this diploid condition is maintained by equational mitoses throughout the development of the body. When the animal produces gametes, the diploid number is reduced by the process of meiosis to the monoploid number, each gamete having a single complete genome which may include members from both of the original genomes. In the plant this reduction in number occurs when spores are produced. The monoploid number is then maintained through the development of the gametophyte and the gametes it produces. In plants having such an alternation of gameto-phytic and sporophytic generations in the life cycle, therefore, this alternation is typically, though not invariably, correlated with an alternation of monoploidy and diploidy in the nuclei.

In subsequent chapters we shall describe in detail the cytological features of such typical cycles and review other cycles of quite different types. We shall also deal with cases in which the nuclei show an alternation not of one and two genomes, but rather of two and four, or three and six, or four and eight. Such a condition, which is known as *polyploidy*, is largely responsible for the high chromosome numbers observed in many organisms, especially among plants. Because of the frequent occurrence

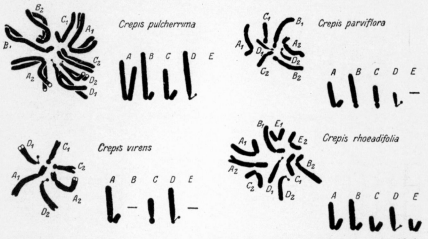

Fig. 71.—Genomes and diploid complements in *Crepis*. *Pulcherrima* should be *pulchra* subsp. *typica*; *virens* should be *capillaris*; *rhoeadifolia* should be *foetida* subsp. *rhoeadifolia*. (*After M. Navashin.*)

of polyploidy here and there among organisms, it is advisable to use the general terms *gametic number* and *zygotic number* for the reduced and unreduced chromosome numbers in life cycles.

Nuclei with different numbers of genomes tend to have different numbers of nucleoli. This is because a given genome commonly includes but one chromosome with a nucleolus organizer. As a result, the nuclei in ordinary tissues often show as many nucleoli as there are genomes, although the correlation is disturbed by the tendency of the fluid nucleoli to fuse if they come in contact. The character has, however, in many instances been a useful one in estimating the number of genomes present.

Most known genomes consist of relatively few members: among flowering plants 12, 8, and 7 are the most frequent numbers. *Crepis*, a genus of composites, has been especially valuable in studies involving chromosome complements because of the small number and distinct form of the chromosomes composing its genomes (Fig. 71). *Crepis capillaris* has a genome of only 3 members, all of which differ in their length and in kinetochore location, while one of them has a satellite. In *Datura*, another genus prominent in cytogenetics, there are 12 members (Fig. 72). The genome has 2 members in some fungi, 4 or 5 in some species of *Crepis*, 7 in the garden pea, 8 in the onion, 9 in the cabbage, 10 in maize, 12 in many conifers, 19 in some willows, 2 or more in aphids, 6 in the house fly, 12 in various salamanders, 19 in the cat, 30 in the cow, sheep, and horse, and 24 in man (Fig. 73) and the Rhesus monkey. Somatic nuclei, of course, contain double these numbers.

In a diploid chromosome complement the two members constituting each pair of similar chromosomes are said to be *homologous*. They have

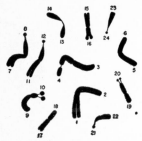

Fig. 72.—The genome of *Datura stramonium* from a monoploid root tip. The ends of the various chromosomes are designated by arbitrary numbers. (*After S. Satina, D. Bergner, and A. F. Blakeslee.*)

Fig. 73.—Diploid complement of 48 chromosomes from human spermatogonium. (*After O. Minouchi and T. Ohta.*)

an ultimate common origin and affect the same group of reactions in the life of the organism. As a general rule the chromosomes of the complement in a somatic cell may occupy any relative position in the nucleus or the mitotic figure without respect to their homologies. In exceptional cases, however, notably in Diptera, there is a strong tendency for the homologues to lie rather near each other. This is well shown in the ganglion cells and spermatogonia of *Drosophila* (Fig. 74). The somatic complement of *D. melanogaster* has 8 members: two large V-shaped pairs, one very minute pair, and one pair of sex chromosomes (*XX* in the female, *XY* in the male). In the salivary glands and certain other larval tissues the pairing becomes very intimate, each giant chromosome being in reality two homologous members in close union. Such a condition, which resembles the *synapsis* normally occurring in the meiotic prophase, is not known to occur elsewhere in somatic nuclei. This phenomenon is exceedingly useful to the cytogeneticist, for it often makes it possible for him to compare very minutely the chromosomes of two strains or species after a cross has been made between them (page 184). It is surely regrettable that other groups of organisms do not have giant chromosomes.

Conclusions.—The chromosome should be thought of as a persistent individual that reproduces only by division and in this sense maintains its individuality throughout successive nuclear and life cycles. In every nuclear cycle it passes through a series of alterations which may obscure its continuity although they do not disprove it. There is no evidence that individualized masses of matrix persist, but all the evidence obtained directly and indirectly (*e.g.*, by X-ray alterations induced during the metabolic stage) indicates that the chromonema with its characteristic longitudinal differentiation in structure and function does persist. The

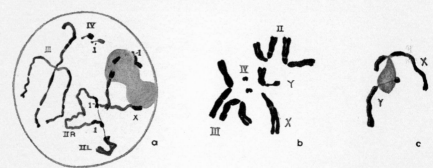

Fig. 74.—Chromosomes of *Drosophila melanogaster*. *a*, prophase in nucleus of giant cell of ganglion of female. Proximal ends of *X*-chromosomes separated from distal portions by nucleolar material; kinetochores marked 1. *b*, chromosomes at metaphase of mitosis in ganglion cell of male. *c*, *X*- and *Y*-chromosomes associated with nucleolus during prophase. (*After B. P. Kaufmann.*)

chromonemata in the metabolic stage are relatively free from enveloping matrix and lie more exposed to the other nuclear materials, which indicates that the chromosomes exert their effects upon cell activities mainly at this time. Their compact arrangement within a matrix appears to be significant in connection with mitotic distribution rather than with metabolism. Later on we shall point out how alterations occur in the organization of the chromonema from time to time, its parts being rearranged or exchanged with those of other chromonemata, but these changes are not such as to invalidate the basic concept of chromosomal individuality and continuity.

The various nuclear materials or ultimate units necessary to the normal life of the organism are nearly everywhere carried in several chromosomes rather than in only one or a very large number. This small group, or genome, is to be regarded as an organized system of interdependent members, and not as a simple collection of materials. Studies on altered chromosomes show that the primary requisite is the presence of the right assortment of units or materials and that their relative positions in some instances affect their action; the number of chromosomes in which they are carried seems to be a matter of minor importance. This is probably one reason for the lack of any general correlation between the numbers of chromosomes composing genomes and the relative complexity of the organisms in which these genomes are found.

CHAPTER VIII

MEIOSIS

In all organisms reproducing sexually the doubling of the gametic chromosome number (*diplosis*) by the union of the nuclei of two gametes is compensated by a halving of the resulting zygotic number (*haplosis*) at some other point in the life cycle. This quantitative alternation is in itself a matter of considerable interest, but the full significance of the changes involved can be appreciated only when one is aware of the peculiar and orderly manner in which the reduction in number is accomplished and of the effect that the alteration may have upon the capacities of the nuclei that result. "Chromosome reduction" means not merely the change from the zygotic to the gametic number, but also, more specifically, the segregation (*disjunction*) of the two chromosomes composing each homologous pair in the zygotic complement.

These changes are brought about by two successive nuclear divisions in the course of which the chromosomes are actually divided only once, and the whole process constitutes *meiosis*. A nucleus undergoing meiosis consequently gives rise to a quartet of nuclei, each of which has the gametic chromosome number. Any cell in which meiosis is initiated may be termed a *meiocyte*. In most animals the meiocytes are the primary spermatocytes, each of which produces a quartet of spermatozoa, and the primary oöcytes, each of which produces an egg and three (or two) polar bodies. In most plants the meiocytes are sporocytes, each of which produces a quartet of spores.

In this chapter we shall give first a preparatory general account of the behavior of the chromosomes with special reference to their distribution to the resulting four nuclei. This will be followed by a detailed account of the changes occurring at each of the rather well-marked stages characteristic of meiosis. For convenience the first and second meiotic divisions will often be referred to simply as *I* and *II*. Only the ordinary diploid-monoploid cycle will be considered here, discussion of chromosome behavior in polyploid plants being deferred to a later chapter.

Distribution of Chromosomes in the Meiotic Divisions.—Meiosis begins in a nucleus with a diploid chromosome complement. The two genomes were brought together at the previous gametic union; hence the two chromosomes composing each homologous pair in the offspring of a cross are derived one from each parent (see, however, page 216). The two homologues influence the same group of reactions and characters in the organism, but their composition varies in such a way that their influence may be either the same or in certain respects different.

The distribution of the chromosomes in the two meiotic divisions is shown diagrammatically in Fig. 75. The remarkable alterations in form undergone by the chromosomes during the successive stages are not represented here; these will be described in the following section. A diploid number of 6 is arbitrarily chosen. The members of the two genomes are distinguished by shading and by large and small letters. Dots in the uppermost nuclei indicate location of kinetochores.

Referring to the first column in the diagram, we see that the six chromosomes are arranged in no particular order in the nucleus. In the prophase of the first meiotic division the two chromosomes of each homologous pair approach each other and become very intimately associated, but they do not actually fuse; this is *synapsis*. The chromosomes are now in the *bivalent* condition. Not long afterward each of the members of the synapsed pair becomes visibly double apparently by splitting; the bivalents now have the form of *tetrads*, the four members of each tetrad being *chromatids*. At the end of prophase *I* the nucleus still has all the chromosomes, but they appear as the monoploid number of tetrads.

In metaphase *I* the tetrads are arranged in the equator of the spindle, and in the anaphase each of them separates into two *dyads*, or pairs of chromatids, which pass to the two poles. In the diagram the arrangement at metaphase is such that sister chromatids (those formed by the recent splitting) pass to the same pole; hence it is the members previously brought together by synapsis which separate here, and this form of separation is called *disjunction*.

Each of the resulting nuclei then undergoes a second meiotic division. Here the two chromatids composing each dyad separate equationally (along the recent split) and pass poleward. Meiosis thus results in a quartet of nuclei in each of which there is one complete genome with three members. The four chromatids of each tetrad now lie in four different nuclei.

Several features of the process thus far described should be carefully noted, for it will be necessary to qualify present statements after other modes of distribution have been considered. (1) As illustrated in column 1, the first division is disjunctional and the second equational for all the chromosomes. (2) In the resulting quartet of nuclei there are genomes of two kinds with respect to the derivation of their members from the two original genomes. (3) The arrangement shown at metaphase *I* is only one of several possible ways in which the chromosomes could be arranged and still have all the separation disjunctional at anaphase. With three

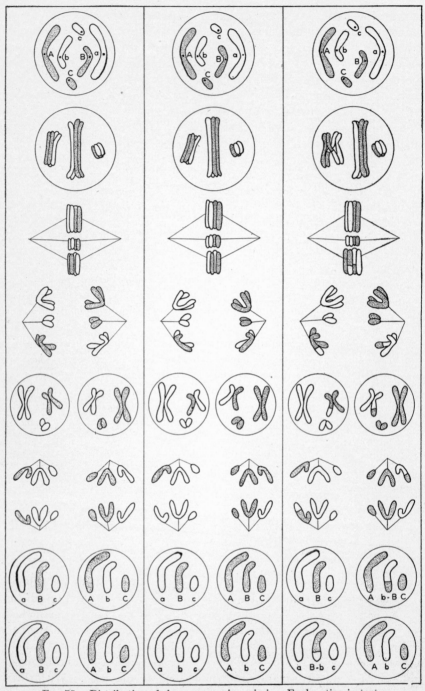

Fig. 75.—Distribution of chromosomes in meiosis. Explanation in text.

chromosome pairs the number of such possible arrangements is four; hence a nucleus at the close of meiosis might have any one of eight possible types of genome: $A\ B\ C,\ a\ b\ c,\ A\ B\ c,\ a\ b\ C,\ A\ b\ c,\ a\ B\ C,\ A\ b\ C,\ a\ B\ c$.   A given quartet would have two of these types.   There are both cytological and genetical evidences that this randomness of orientation at metaphase *I* does prevail.   With more chromosome pairs the number of possible types of genome would of course be greater, the formula for this number being 2^n, where *n* equals the number of pairs.   (4) These various genomes differ qualitatively, and therefore in their effects upon reactions and characters, only to the extent that the chromosomes in the original diploid comple- ment differed from their respective homologues.   If there had been no such differences originally, the genomes in the quartets would all be qualitatively alike in spite of differences in the derivation of their mem- bers; hence meiosis does not always result in nuclei differing in actual constitution.   Ordinarily, however, there are some original differences, so that the genomes eventually resulting from meiotic chromosome dis- tribution do show qualitative differences.

Turning now to the second column of Fig. 75, we see what would result if the tetrads, instead of all separating disjunctionally in division *I*, were to be so oriented at metaphase that separation would be equational for at least one of them (the *Bb* pair in the diagram).   Sister chromatids of such a tetrad would separate equationally to opposite poles, and disjunction would follow at division *II*.   The other tetrads would disjoin at *I*, with equational separation at *II*.   The result would be a quartet of nuclei with four types of genome rather than two.   Equational division of whole tetrads at *I* may indeed occur, but it is now thought that it must at least be very exceptional, the reported cytological evidence for it having received a new interpretation.

The third column of Fig. 75 illustrates the interpretation now generally placed upon cytological and genetical evidence indicating the occurrence of equational separation in division *I*.   In one of the tetrads is shown a *chiasma, i.e.,* a place at which two of the four chromatids actually exchange corresponding portions.   Such *crossing over* is a normal feature of meiosis in most organisms and commonly occurs in all the tetrads; moreover, a single tetrad may have more than one such exchange.   It is only for the sake of simplicity that the diagram shows only one in the whole complement.   Crossing over complicates the process of meiosis, but the complication must be faced because it affords an explanation of certain genetical phenomena to be discussed in later chapters.

If, now, all the tetrads are oriented in the spindle at metaphase *I* so that kinetochores of sister chromatids face the same pole, the proximal portion (near the kinetochores) of the tetrad with the chiasma will separate disjunctionally in *I* and equationally in *II* (prereduction), while the distal portion beyond the chiasma separates equationally in *I* and disjunctionally in *II* (postreduction). The proximal portions of the chromatids eventually lie in the four quartet nuclei precisely as they do in column 1. The distal portions also lie in the four nuclei. The complication introduced by crossing over appears when the relative positions occupied by the two portions are considered.

In the few cases supported by adequate cytological evidence (visibly unlike homologues; data on chiasmata) and genetical evidence (distribution of genetical factors), it appears that the four chromatids behave as described above: the regions near the kinetochores disjoin in *I*, while equational division in *I* occurs only in certain regions determined by crossovers. If these latter regions show visible differences in the two homologues, their postreduction is evident, but it does not follow that the whole tetrad separates in this way. Hence reduction in the strict sense (disjunction) does not take place in all portions of the complement or even in all portions of the same tetrad at the same division. It is only after both meiotic divisions have been carried through that chromosome reduction is complete. It is only then that all disjunction is finished, and only then does each nucleus have the reduced number of completely univalent chromosomes.

The points brought out in this section may now be summarized. *In meiosis each chromosome enters into synapsis with its homologue and also splits longitudinally, giving thus a tetrad composed of four chromatids. The four chromatids of every tetrad are distributed in two divisions to the four nuclei formed at the close of meiosis. Each chromosome (or portion of a chromosome) is disjoined from its homologue (reduction) in one of the divisions and divided equationally in the other. It is probable that disjunction in the first division is the rule for the kinetochores and near-by regions, the second division therefore being equational for these regions. This order can be reversed in other regions when crossovers occur.*

Each of the four nuclei of the resulting quartet contains a single genome composed of members from one or both of the genomes of the original diploid complement. The four nuclei are qualitatively alike or unlike depending upon the amount of difference between homologous chromosomes in the original complement. Every kind of chromosomal unit is present singly instead of in duplicate in each nucleus.

Detailed Account of the Phases of Meiosis.—Most of the significant features peculiar to meiosis are found in the prophase of the first division; when these are understood the subsequent stages present few difficulties. The phases of the entire process will now be described in order (see Fig. 76). It is to be remembered that the details of meiotic chromosome behavior vary a good deal in different organisms and that the purpose of

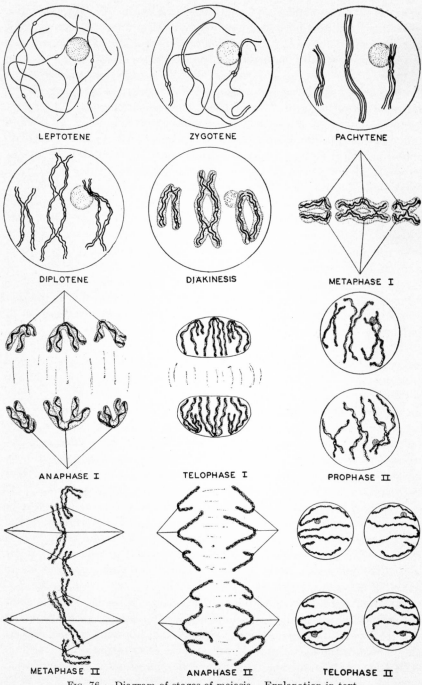

LEPTOTENE   ZYGOTENE   PACHYTENE

DIPLOTENE   DIAKINESIS   METAPHASE I

ANAPHASE I   TELOPHASE I   PROPHASE II

METAPHASE II   ANAPHASE II   TELOPHASE II

FIG. 76.—Diagram of stages of meiosis.   Explanation in text.

this account will be best served by confining attention largely to those features more or less common to all of them.

Leptotene Stage.—The chromonemata, after having presented a rather confused picture since the premeiotic telophase, become more distinct from one another in the early meiotic prophase and appear as very long and slender threads. They are present in the diploid number, and each represents a chromosome. Because of their great attenuation and the scarcity of enveloping matter, their chromomeres show plainly. They commonly appear single, but there is evidence that they are actually double in constitution. In some meiocytes, notably in animals, the threads may all be oriented with one end toward the same side of the nucleus, forming a so-called *bouquet* (Fig. 77).

Zygotene Stage.—The leptotene threads now become very closely associated laterally in pairs, each of them cohering, though not actually

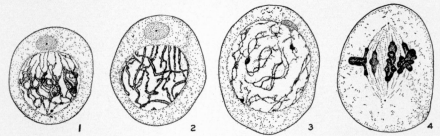

FIG. 77.—Stages in meiosis in spermatocyte of salamander. 1, leptotene threads developing; 2, pachytene stage; 3, diplotene stage; 4, metaphase *I*.

fusing, with its homologue (Fig. 78). This selective pairing, or synapsis, begins at one or more points, often at the ends or the kinetochore, and gradually extends "zipper-like" until it is complete. The extension and the slenderness of the chromonemata, which reach their maximum length at leptotene-zygotene, are believed to bear a causal relation to the synaptic union. In some nuclei, notably in those with threads arranged in a "bouquet," one portion may be occupied by paired threads while the rest shows only threads still unpaired; this is the *amphitene* condition. As the threads pair, they immediately begin to shorten and thicken.

It appears likely that synapsis is facilitated by the arrangement assumed by the chromosomes at the close of the last premeiotic anaphase. All the members of the complement then lie more or less parallel, with their kinetochores directed toward the pole, so that in the resulting telophase nucleus their arrangement is not a haphazard one. Furthermore, in some organisms a loosely paired arrangement of homologues is evident during the premeiotic mitoses or even earlier (page 99).

Pachytene Stage.—After synaptic pairing has been completed, the nucleus is said to be in the pachytene stage, for the threads are then noticeably thicker than in the leptotene (thin-thread) stage. The thick double pachytene threads are present in the monoploid number, and each of them is bivalent, since it consists of two homologous chromosomes in synaptic association (Figs. 77–79). They may be arranged at random or in the bouquet position.

Late in the pachytene stage each of the two chromosomes of each synapsed pair becomes visibly double, presumably because of the enlarge-

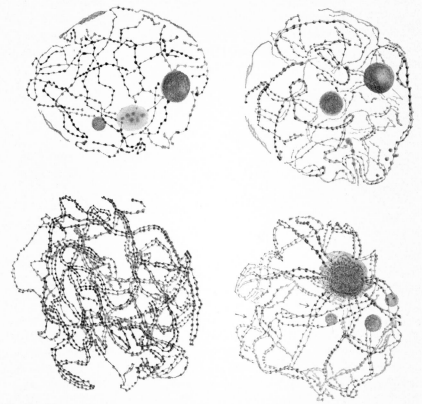

Fig. 78.—Leptotene, zygotene, pachytene, and very early diplotene stages in microsporocytes of *Trillium*. Arrows indicate chiasmata. (*After C. L. Huskins and S. G. Smith.*)

ment of the structures concerned. If the doubleness reported in the premeiotic telophase has persisted, although invisible, this represents its reappearance. The pachytene threads are now quadruple: each is a tetrad of chromatids.

Diplotene Stage.—In each of the tetrads the four chromatids begin to separate, one pair of sister chromatids from the other two, as though the synaptic force holding them together were being replaced by a repulsive force. At one or more points they are prevented from separating by chiasmata, where two of the chromatids have exchanged portions by crossing over (Fig. 81). A tetrad with one chiasma thus has the form of an X, while one with two at or near its ends appears as an O. When there are several, the regions between them form a series of such openings, one of which usually includes a region on both sides of the kinetochore. The number and the location of chiasmata may differ characteristically in different organisms. In general there are more in long chromosomes than in short ones.

During the diplotene stage the tetrads continue the shortening begun in the pachytene stage. This involves a coiling of the chromonemata

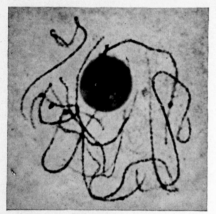

Fig. 79.—Pachytene stage in microsporocyte of maize. Chromosome 6 attached to nucleolus above; chromosome 1 looped over 6; chromosome 3 at upper left. (*After B. McClintock.*)

Fig. 80.—Diplotene stage in spermatocyte of an amphibian (*Desmognathus*). Only 6 of the 14 tetrads in the nucleus are shown. The clearest chiasmata are at the right. (*After F. W. S. Scudder.*)

within the matrix, which begins to be more evident at this time. With such changes the chromosomes pass gradually into the diakinesis stage.

Diakinesis Stage.—This stage is characterized by the presence of compact tetrads lying well spaced out in the nucleus, often near its membrane. This is therefore a favorable stage for counting the chromosomes. They have continued to shorten as their chromonemata have continued to coil, sometimes into both major and minor spirals. The matrix has become abundant, giving them smoother contours. They have the form of X's, V's, O's and other more complex shapes depending upon the number and location of chiasmata. Since the matrix tends to form a common mass about any two closely associated chromonemata, the tetrads often look merely double instead of quadruple. Commonly the one having the nucleolus organizers is in contact with the nucleolus.

In many organisms the tetrads show fewer chiasmata than they did in the diplotene stage. This is due to a process called *terminalization*, in which the four chromatids, after opening out two by two to give the diplotene stage, continue to open into the chiasma on its proximal side while the opening on its distal side closes, the result being a gradual movement of the chiasma along the tetrad, even to its end.

The meiocytes, or cells in which all the foregoing prophasic changes occur, are in most cases relatively large cells with large nuclei. Their size increases through a portion if not all of the prophase. In plant sporocytes the increase is moderate, while in animal spermatocytes it is often greater and involves a temporary "diffusion" of the chromosomes at about the diplotene stage. The animal oöcyte undergoes an enormous increase in size at this stage, developing most of the features that are to characterize the egg which it eventually becomes. The oöcyte nucleus becomes very large during this "growth period," its chromosomes sending out thready processes in all directions and losing their stainability. This suggests a synthetic function comparable to that performed during the metabolic

Fig. 81.—Tetrads in advanced diplotene stage from spermatocytes of grasshopper. They show, respectively, one, two, three, and four chiasmata. (*After F. A. Janssens.*)

stage, when the chromonemata are again in extensive contact with the other substances in the nucleus. Eventually the chromosomes again become compact and stainable and assume the form characteristic of the diakinesis stage.

Metaphase I.—At the close of the diakinesis stage the achromatic figure is developed, and the tetrads become arranged in its equator with their kinetochores facing its two poles. In a lateral view of the metaphase figure they appear about as they did at late diakinesis except for the more clearly evident location of their kinetochores and sometimes their greater compactness. When viewed from the direction of the spindle pole they can easily be counted unless they are very long and crowded. Large chromosomes show their coiled chromonemata particularly well at this stage and at anaphase, many of the best studies on minute structure having been made on such chromosomes. For example, some genera of plants show a "double-coiled" condition in their chromonemata only at this time.

Of special interest is the fact that longitudinal doubleness (the so-called *tertiary split*) may become visible in the chromonema of each chromatid at metaphase and anaphase *I*, the tetrad therefore having eight half-chromatids. In other cases it is first seen during division *II*. Occasionally it has been demonstrated as early as diakinesis or even the diplotene stage. The results of X-ray studies suggest that it is present below the limit of visibility much earlier. In any event it represents the plane of anaphasic separation in the first postmeiotic mitosis. In a plant this would be the first mitosis in the spore, in an animal the first mitosis in the fertilized egg.

Anaphase I.—The tetrads now separate into dyads which begin to move apart toward the opposite poles of the spindle. Often there appears to be considerable resistance in the region of a chiasma to the disjunctive forces, so that the tetrad may elongate and assume an odd shape (Fig. 82). Eventually the two dyads become free. Meanwhile the two chromatids composing each of them commonly widen out from each

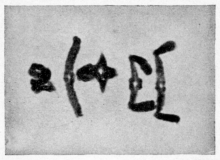

Fig. 82.—Late metaphase *I* in microsporocyte of peony (*Paeonia*), showing the five tetrads about to separate into dyads. In the third the kinetochores are at the points above and below; a chiasma is present in each arm. In the fourth and fifth the kinetochores are at the sharp angles; subterminal chiasmata are present at the equator. (*After K. Sax.*)

other except at the kinetochore (Fig. 84). Thus a dyad with a nearly terminal kinetochore appears as a single V, while one with a median kinetochore is a double V. As already pointed out, genetical evidence indicates that the two chromatids of a dyad, at least in the region of the kinetochore, are as a rule sisters. This interpretation has further cytological support in the chromosomes of an amphibian, which show the kinetochore of the dyad not yet divided at this time, although it has two kinosomes and two tractile fibers. Its division is completed in *II*. In maize also two tractile fibers can be seen extending from each dyad in *I*. At the end of the anaphase the two groups of dyads form compact groups at the poles.

Telophase I and Interkinesis.—The polar groups of chromosomes at the close of anaphase *I* nearly always undergo a certain amount of telophasic transformation similar to that seen in somatic nuclei. In most cases, however, the alteration is not carried far enough to form fine-textured metabolic nuclei, the individual chromosomes often being discernible at least in part up to the beginning of prophase *II*. The abbreviation of *interkinesis,* or stage between divisions *I* and *II,* reaches an extreme in certain animal oöcytes, where the chromosomes at the close of anaphase *I* immediately become arranged in new spindles for division *II*. In ordinary interkinetic nuclei where the chromosomes can still be seen, the two chromatids of each dyad, although more slender than during the anaphase, continue to remain closely associated at the kinetochore and widened out elsewhere; hence they tend to appear as X's with arms varying in length according to kinetochore position.

Cytokinesis does not invariably follow division *I*. In the microsporocytes of many vascular plants and in the meiocytes of certain lower plants the two nuclei lie in a common mass of cytoplasm and undergo division *II*, after which the meiocyte is divided simultaneously into four cells (Fig. 101, *4*). In other plant meiocytes, cytokinesis does occur after

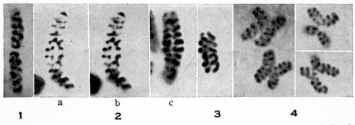

Fig. 83.—Chromosomes in first meiotic division in microsporocytes of *Tradescantia*. 1, bivalent at metaphase about to disjoin; in each half the apparently single thick spiral is actually composed of two chromonemata which represent the chromatids. 2, *a, b, c*, metaphase bivalents; the two spiral chromonemata in each of the dyads, which are about to disjoin upward and downward, are separating from each other laterally (*a* and *b* are two prints from the same negative). 3, one dyad at anaphase; the two chromatid spirals now lie side by side. 4, four dyads at anaphase; in each of them the two chromatids remain closely associated only near the kinetochore. (*After K. Sax and L. M. Humphrey.*)

I (Fig. 84). In animals the primary spermatocyte is divided into two secondary spermatocytes in which division *II* then takes place. The primary oöcyte divides very unequally to form a minute polocyte (polar body) and the secondary oöcyte; division *II* follows in the latter but not always in the former (Fig. 91). Further cytological features of these reproductive stages are to be added in the next three chapters.

Prophase II.—This prophase is much simpler than prophase *I*. When the transformation of the chromosomes in telophase *I* has not been carried very far, prophase *II* consists in little more than their resumption of a more compact form in each of the daughter nuclei of division *I*. The two chromatids of each dyad tend to retain in some degree the divergent position they first assumed in anaphase *I*, so that their association, except at the kinetochore, is usually looser than that observed in somatic prophases.

Metaphase II and Anaphase II.—The dyads in the two nuclei now take up positions with their kinetochores at the equators of newly formed spindles.   In many cases they are longer than they were in metaphase *I*, and this, together with their simpler structure, causes division *II* to resemble a somatic mitosis much more closely than division *I* does.   In

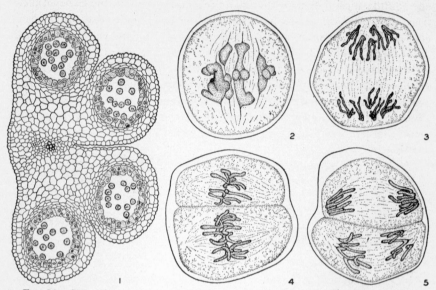

Fig. 84.—Stages in meiosis in angiosperm microsporocytes.   1, transverse section of lily anther with sporocytes.   2, metaphase *I* in May apple.   3–5, anaphase *I*, metaphase *II*, and anaphase *II* in lily.   Chromosome doubleness is obscured by fixation in 4.

the anaphase the chromatids of each dyad move apart to the spindle poles, thus completing the meiotic distribution of the chromosomes.

Telophase II.—The four groups of chromosomes now reorganize as a quartet of nuclei.   Each of them contains one complete genome, this

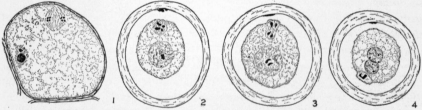

Fig. 85.—Meiosis and syngamy in a threadworm (*Ascaris*).   1, metaphase of first meiotic division in oöcyte; two tetrads present.   The sperm has already entered the egg (at left); the smaller dark body is its nucleus.   2, 3, second meiotic division; first polar body disintegrated above; sperm chromosomes near center of egg.   4, sperm and egg nuclei about to unite; first polar body above and second one below because of rotation of egg. During these stages a perivitelline space develops between the thickened wall and the egg.

genome being composed of one chromatid (now a chromosome) from each of the tetrads present in metaphase *I*.   Each chromosome has the chromonemal doubleness which will become effective in the ensuing postmeiotic division. Cytokinesis follows in typical cases, giving a quartet of uninucleate cells (spores; spermatids soon to become spermatozoa; egg and polocytes).

Problems of Meiosis.—The foregoing account of meiosis will serve as a prerequisite to our later discussion of the mechanism of Mendelian heredity, but it does not fully indicate the prominent position that the process holds in present-day cytological research. Meiosis, like practically every other process in the organism, continues to present numerous problems, the solution of which would shed needed light upon phenomena occurring at various stages of the life cycle. We should therefore consider for a moment a few such questions now engaging the special attention of cytologists.

What initiates meiosis? What are the physiological conditions associated with the change from the ordinary somatic type of nuclear division to the meiotic type, and what relation do these conditions bear to the prior changes that bring on the reproductive phase in the organism? Experimental treatments frequently result in the partial or complete replacement of the meiotic by the somatic type of division in meiocytes, and various suggestions have been made, for example, regarding the apparent effects of a retardation or an acceleration of the prophasic process upon the character of the division. So far, however, the main question has received no satisfactory answer.

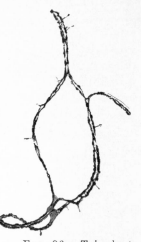

Fig. 86.—Trivalent chromosome in meiotic prophase in maize. Each member shows its two chromatids in regions not in synapsis. The kinetochores of all three members lie in contact. (*From a preparation by B. McClintock.*)

What causes synapsis? The synaptic reaction occurs between apparently single chromosomes having the peculiar constitutional relationship designated as homology, and only under physiological conditions that are essentially normal. It is manifested primarily between corresponding minute portions or units in the two threads, synapsis being normal in all respects only when the various units or portions in the two have the same serial order. Moreover, if three or more homologous chromosomes are present in the meiocyte, only two as a rule synapse closely at any given region, as though the synaptic force were somehow neutralized by the union of two homologous portions (Fig. 86). In the "somatic synapsis" of salivary-gland chromosomes three or more do unite closely. These phenomena remind one of electrical attractions, the agglutination of bacteria, the formation of one-strain groups of myxobacteria at the time of fruiting in mixed cultures, and especially the regular pair-by-pair union of nuclei of two strains in the multinucleate reproductive organs of certain fungi. Here again we have valuable suggestions but no complete explanation of the important feature we wish to understand.

What causes diplotene opening? The fact that the synaptic mates in the tetrad tend to separate soon after each of them becomes visibly double suggests a causal connection between these two events. The hypothesis that single threads attract while double ones repel one another has been prominent in cytology for some time. At present it appears doubtful that singleness in itself is a decisive factor in bringing homologues into proximity, since doubled homologues also move together in some instances. Moreover, it is visible doubling only, and probably not actual doubling, that immediately precedes the opening of the chromatids at diplotene. With regard to repulsions, it seems more likely that they are an important factor, not only in diplotene opening, but also in the spacing of the chromosomes at diakinesis and metaphase and in the widening out of associated chromatids at anaphase I.

Does coiling have a role in meiosis? In meiosis, as in somatic nuclear cycles, coiling makes it possible for long chromonemata to be carried in chromosomes of compact form during their segregation into daughter groups. A special meiotic role of factors influencing coiling is indicated by the complete uncoiling and great attenuation of the chromonemata in the leptotene stage. The hypothesis has been advanced that it is just this condition, brought on by a stronger or more prolonged action of certain physiological factors, that makes complete synapsis possible, the chromonemata at this one stage in the life cycle being in a condition permitting forces acting over short distances between individual pairs of homologous units to bring two long series of such units into close association. The physical causes of coiling are being sought in order to improve our understanding of the chromosomal changes from diplotene onward, notably shortening and chiasma terminalization, and to gain insight into the molecular architecture and growth of the chromonemata.

What is the mechanism of crossing over? That two of the four chromatids actually do exchange corresponding portions, in all probability at a chiasma, has been proved with heteromorphic homologues, *i.e.*, homologous chromosomes differing here and there in certain visible features which make it possible to identify particular regions of the chromosomes before and after the exchange. How the exchange is actually accomplished is still an unsolved problem. It is known that breakage of chromonemata may be induced by such agencies as X rays and that under certain circumstances freshly broken ends tend to unite in new patterns. It is therefore a logical assumption that something of the kind may occur naturally in crossing over, the precision with which corresponding portions are exchanged being a consequence of their orderly arrangement in synapsis.   On the other hand, theories have been propounded to account for crossing over without actual breakage.   The idea is that new threads are developed parallel to the old ones immediately after the chromomeres of each synaptic mate have doubled by division in the pachytene stage, and that when the synaptic mates have a sharp twist at any given point two of the resulting chromatids may contain chromomeres

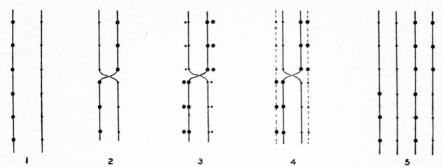

Fig. 87.—Diagram illustrating theory of crossing over involving formation of new strands between newly formed chromomeres.   1, original chromosomes.   2, chromosomes with half-twist.   3, chromomeres doubled.   4, new strands developing; between the third and fourth pairs of chromomeres they result in crossover chromatids.   5, the tetrad of chromatids after crossing over.   (*Based on theory of J. Belling.*)

from different mates on either side of this point because the new chromomeres form the new unions with their nearest neighbors (Fig. 87). Under this theory, crossing over is a concomitant of chromosome division.

Finally, there is the problem of the relation of meiosis to the phenomena of genetics.   So far as major features such as synapsis, disjunction, random assortment, and crossing over are concerned, this problem has been solved, as will be shown in the later chapters of the book.   Numerous other questions, however, remain open, and it is hoped that these will be answered by further refinements in our knowledge of the constitution and behavior of meiotic chromosomes.

CHAPTER IX

CYTOLOGY OF REPRODUCTION IN ANIMALS

One of the major cytological crises in the reproduction of organisms, *viz.*, meiosis, has just been described in some detail. Another major crisis, the fusion of nuclei in the union of gametes, has also received brief mention. It now becomes necessary to relate these processes more closely to life cycles by describing the various other events that precede, accompany, and succeed them in the reproductive phases. This will be done in three chapters. Again we should be reminded that such events occur in numerous variations in different organisms and that our descriptions are designed to include examples that are fairly representative of what occurs in each class of organism considered, even though no single species can be expected to show all the stages precisely as described. We consider first the animals.

The Germ Cells.—The term *germ cells* is applied in the case of animals to those specialized cells whose ultimate descendants are to be female or male gametes (eggs or spermatozoa) and often certain accessory cells, but not somatic cells. When the specialization first becomes recognizable, there may be but one *primordial germ cell*, or several, or a considerable number of them. It is a striking fact that the differentiation of these cells from the somatic cells occurs very early in the ontogeny of the organism. They can be distinguished during larval stages, and in some animals it has been determined that they are set apart from the somatic cells in one of the earliest cleavage divisions of the fertilized egg. In extreme cases, notably certain insects, the cytoplasm of the future germ cells can even be distinguished in one end of the yet undivided egg (Fig. 88). In the case illustrated one of the eight nuclei formed by the third embryonal mitosis enters this specialized cytoplasm, which is then cut off as the primordial germ cell from the larger somatic portion of the young embryo.

The primordial germ cells, whatever their number and time of origin from embryonic tissues, commonly pass through a period of multiplication. After their divisions cease, they migrate to the site of the future ovaries or testes. These organs then develop and incorporate within them the sperm cells, which undergo a new series of divisions. In the ovary these multiplying cells are called *oögonia;* in the testis they are called *spermatogonia.* Hermaphroditic animals may have separate ovaries and testes, or both oögonia and spermatogonia may be present in

118

one organ. Accompanying the germ cells are certain accessory cells, such as the nurse cells in the insect ovary and the Sertoli cells in the mammalian testis. In some cases such special cells represent transformed germ cells, while in others they are derived from other tissues. Up to this stage the nuclear divisions in all the cells—somatic, germ, and accessory—are of the equational type, every nucleus having a diploid chromosome complement like that of the zygote nucleus from which they have all descended.

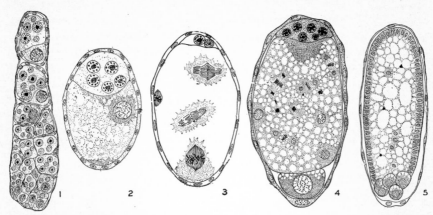

FIG. 88.—Oögenesis and early embryogeny in a fly (*Miastor*). 1, section through ovary. At the top is a nurse chamber with several nuclei; with it is associated a young oöcyte. Earlier stages in the development of this condition are seen below. 2, oöcyte nearly full grown; note "pole plasm" at its lower end. 3, third embryonal mitosis following syngamy, showing three of the four division figures (the small figure is a dividing polar body nucleus). The pole plasm is being provided with a nucleus. 4, pole plasm with its nucleus cut off as the primordial germ cell; nuclei above continuing to divide without cytokinesis. 5, primordial germ cell has divided into eight oögonia (four shown); main portion of embryo undergoing superficial cleavage into cells. (*From R. Hegner: The Germ-cell Cycle in Animals, The Macmillan Company.*)

Spermatogenesis.—After the spermatogonia in the testis have ceased multiplying, there is initiated a series of changes peculiar to this stage of the life cycle. The spermatogonia commonly enlarge somewhat and are then termed *primary spermatocytes*. Each of them then undergoes two successive divisions which are meiotic in character: each spermatocyte divides into two *secondary spermatocytes*, and these immediately divide into four *spermatids*. The chromosomes in these divisions behave according to the scheme described in the previous chapter, the nuclei in the quartet of spermatids each having one genome, or monoploid complement, in place of the diploid complement present in the spermatogonia and the somatic tissues.

In the two spermatocyte divisions the various cytoplasmic inclusions, in particular the Golgi bodies and chondriosomes, are usually distributed rather equally to the four spermatids. This results from a tendency of such inclusions to be grouped near the equator of the cell or about the poles of the mitotic figure, so that cytokinesis separates them into more or less equal groups (Fig. 28).   Only in a few known cases does this involve an actual division of individual chondriosomal bodies.   In some spermatocytes the Golgi bodies form a conspicuous mass, the *idiosome*, about the centrioles, and this breaks up into smaller portions during the divisions.   The centrioles that function in the second meiotic division have usually become doubled by the time the division is completed.   As a result of these events each spermatid consists of cytoplasm, a nucleus with the gametic chromosome number, chondriosomes, one or more Golgi bodies, a pair of centrioles, and frequently other inclusions.

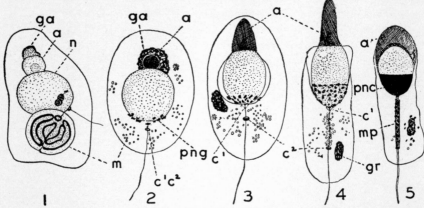

Fig. 89.—Stages in the transformation of the animal spermatid into a spermatozoon. 1, spermatid of an insect (*Brochymena*).   (*Redrawn from R. H. Bowen.*)   2–5, spermatids of the guinea pig; *ga*, Golgi apparatus; *gr*, Golgi remnant; *a*, acrosome; *n*, nucleus; *m*, mitochondria (in *Brochymena* they form a nebenkern); *c¹*, *c²*, centrioles; *png*, postnuclear granules; *pnc*, postnuclear cap; *mp*, middle piece.   (*From J. B. Gatenby and H. W. Beams, based on studies by Gatenby, Vejdovsky, and Meves.*)

The transformation of the spermatid into a *spermatozoon*, or sperm, is known as *spermiogenesis*.   This process involves a very remarkable series of changes which have been found to occur, with minor variations, in animals of many types.   Each of the spermatid components behaves in a characteristic manner (Fig. 89).   From one of the two centrioles a slender filament grows out and pierces the cell membrane; this is the axial filament of the future tail of the spermatozoon.   As the filament continues to grow, the centrioles become modified and connected with the nucleus in various ways.

The chondriosomes in mammalian spermatids become grouped in a region near the posterior pole of the nucleus, where they form a compact sheath about the proximal portion of the axial filament.   In insect spermatids the chondriosomes usually unite into a single large mass, the *nebenkern*, which soon divides and elongates as two long strands wound about the axial filament in the lengthening spermatid.

The Golgi material commonly forms a single large body, the *acroblast*, situated near the posterior pole of the nucleus. Most often the acroblast appears like a heavily staining cup holding a less stainable material. Soon it begins to move along the nucleus to the anterior pole of the cell and then continues its migration back along the other side, following a path previously taken by the centrioles. At some stage of this migration a small droplet of matter appears to exude from the acroblast. The droplet enlarges and organizes as the *acrosome*, a specialized structure at the tip of the spermatozoon, and a portion of it often differentiates as a pointed *perforatorium*. What remains of the acroblast, now known as the *Golgi remnant*, moves backward along the developing tail and is eventually lost from the cell in a mass of protoplasm sloughed off at the close of spermiogenesis. In species having no acroblast the acrosomal material appears to come from numerous small Golgi bodies.

Conspicuous modifications of the spermatid nucleus ordinarily appear after most of the changes described above have been carried out. Its chromatic matter gradually becomes concentrated, often against the nuclear membrane in the anterior region, while its achromatic component decreases in amount. Eventually the nucleus becomes a dense and apparently homogeneous body closely united anteriorly with the acrosome and posteriorly with one or both of the centrioles, from which the axial filament extends. The cytoplasm lengthens out along with the axial filament and chondriosomal filament sheaths.

The mature spermatozoon, or male gamete, consists typically of two main parts; the *head*, comprising the nucleus, the acrosome, a surface membrane, probably cytoplasmic in origin, and occasionally other elements; and the *tail*, which is made up of the axial filament, the filament sheaths, and a small amount of residual cytoplasm. In many cases, notably mammalian

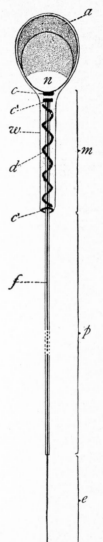

Fig. 90.—Diagram of typical mammalian spermatozoon. *a*, acrosome; *n*, nucleus; *c, c'*, centrioles and their derivatives; *w*, cell membrane; *d*, chondriosomal matter; *f*, axial filament of tail; *m*, middle piece; *p*, principal piece of tail; *e*, end piece of tail. (*After R. H. Bowen.*)

sperms, the basal portion of the tail is more or less distinctly differentiated as a middle piece containing the centrioles and chondriosomal elements in a sheath of undifferentiated cytoplasm (Fig. 90). Posterior to this is a principal piece, with a thin sheath but no undifferentiated cytoplasm, and an end piece, which represents the naked end of the axial filament.

The spermatozoa of many animals reveal in their external form little or no evidence of the above differentiations, but taper so gradually toward one or both ends that no subdivision into parts is possible on such a basis. Furthermore, some animals, *e.g.*, certain crustaceans and spiders, have spermatozoa with no tails. Except for the lack of development of a motor apparatus, the changes within the spermatid in such instances are fundamentally similar to those in spermiogenesis of the ordinary type.

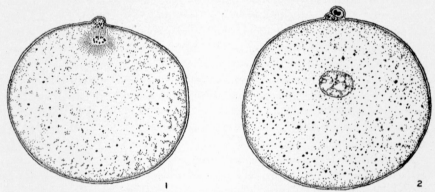

Fig. 91.—Maturing egg of a worm (*Cerebratulus*). 1, anaphase of first meiotic division with first polar body budding off. 2, polar bodies completed; egg nucleus near center.

Oögenesis.—In the ovary the oögonia enlarge somewhat and become *primary oöcytes*. It is in these cells that meiosis is initiated. Enlargement continues, especially during the remarkable "growth period" which comes at about the time the chromosomes are in the late pachytene and the diplotene stages of the first meiotic prophase (page 111). During the growth period the oöcyte becomes supplied with nutritive materials (yolk) and develops other features characterizing the egg. In some animals, groups of nurse cells or a surrounding layer of cells, the follicular epithelium, have a part in these activities.

At the close of the growth period the chromosomes assume the compact form characteristic of diakinesis and lie scattered in the enormous oöcyte nucleus (the germinal vesicle). The relatively small first-division spindle assumes a position perpendicular to the cell membrane, and at anaphase and telophase the *first polocyte*, or polar body, is budded off with one of the daughter nuclei (Figs. 91, 85). The nucleus remaining in the secondary oöcyte undergoes the second meiotic division, usually at once, forming a *second polocyte* with one of the daughter nuclei. The other daughter nucleus of this division remains in the now mature *ovum*, or egg. The first polocyte may or may not divide to complete the quartet of cells expected after meiosis. At the close of these meiotic divisions, or maturation divisions, as they are frequently called, the nucleus of the ovum has the gametic number of chromosomes.

The mature ovum, or female gamete, is bounded by a delicate *vitelline membrane* and sometimes by additional jelly-like layers. In some animals a thick layer of nutritive albumen is deposited about the ovum, and around this may later be added further structures, such as the shell membrane and calcareous shell of the bird's egg. The egg of a bird at the time it is laid is therefore more than an egg. The ovum proper has been enormously distended by great amounts of yolk material, its surface membrane lying at the outer boundary of this yolk. Most of its protoplasm has taken the form of a flattened yolk-free mass, the *germinal disc*, lying just beneath the membrane at one side (this side lies uppermost in an egg at rest in an incubator). It is surrounded by "white" and a shell which form no part of the egg proper. If the egg is a fertile one, fertilization was accomplished before these modifications and additions appeared, and the development of the resulting embryo has already advanced to the blastoderm stage (page 128). This development is resumed when the egg is incubated.

Syngamy.—The term *syngamy* denotes the sexual union of two gametes, regardless of their relative structure and behavior and the nature of the consequences. When one gamete is large and apparently passive while the other is small and active, the process is referred to as the *fertilization* of one gamete, the egg, by the other, the sperm, since the arrested development of the egg is thereupon resumed. The induction of development by experimental agencies is accordingly called artificial fertilization, or artificial parthenogenesis. Although syngamy and fertilization are often used as interchangeable terms, it should always be remembered that normal gametic union in any case is a mutual reaction and that it is the fusion product that proceeds with development.

Syngamy in most animals includes typically the entrance of the sperm into the egg, a structural transformation of the sperm often accompanied by related structural changes in the egg, a union of the gametic nuclei, and certain physiological alterations in the egg, some of which are initiated even before the sperm's entrance has been completed. In some animals the rhythmic movements of the tail which bring the sperm to the egg continue after the two gametes have come into contact and suggest a boring action instrumental in gametic union. In other cases, however, such movements cease as soon as the sperm reaches the egg membrane, or even while it is still separated from the membrane by a layer of jelly surrounding the egg; nevertheless the sperm enters, as though it were being acted upon by some force resident in the egg.

In a marine annelid worm (*Nereis*) it has been shown how the egg behaves during the entrance of the sperm. If the sperm reaches the egg in the brief period during which the egg is fertilizable, the union of the two proceeds as follows (Fig. 92). All but one of the many sperms which may have attached themselves to the egg are usually carried away from its surface by a jelly which flows out from an alveolar zone just beneath

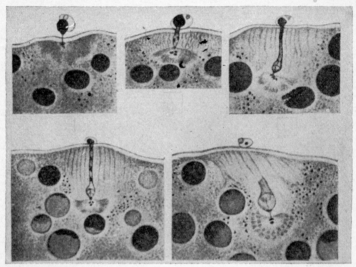

Fig. 92.—Entrance of spermatozoon into egg of *Nereis*. Only the sperm head is drawn in by the fertilization cone; the middle piece and tail remain outside. (*From F. R. Lillie: Problems of Fertilization, University of Chicago Press.*)

the membrane. From the inner region of the egg a transparent *fertilization cone* then extends across this zone and touches the membrane at the point where the single remaining sperm is about to penetrate it. The perforatorium pierces the membrane and becomes attached to the cone which is then withdrawn toward the inner region of the egg, carrying the head of the sperm with it. The sperm's middle piece and tail are left outside the egg. In some sea urchins both head and middle piece enter, while in most animals the whole sperm passes in.

In different animals there is considerable variation in the stage of the egg's maturation at the time when the sperm enters. In sea urchins and starfish both meiotic divisions have been completed, the sperm thus entering a fully matured egg. The frog's egg is entered during the metaphase of the second meiotic division. Entrance occurs during the first metaphase in certain annelids, insects, and mollusks, and even slightly earlier in the threadworm, *Ascaris* (Fig. 85). In these latter cases, there-fore, the cell entered is an oöcyte in terms of nuclear condition but a female gamete in terms of power to undergo impregnation. It will be pointed out shortly that the union of the gametes may in turn be followed so quickly by the first embryonal division that the latter process is begun before the former is completed. This overlapping of the events com-prising the general processes of meiosis, syngamy, and embryogeny com-plicates the cytological study of reproduction in many animals.

One of the first visible effects of syngamy in many eggs is an elevation of the vitelline membrane which begins at the point of sperm entrance and extends rapidly over the egg, forming the so-called *fertilization membrane.* This change and certain further alterations in the egg have

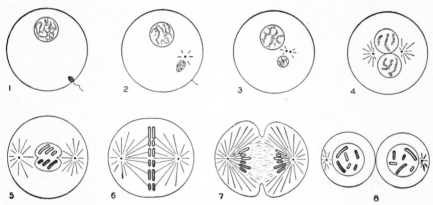

FIG. 93.—Diagram of syngamy and cleavage in an animal that completes meiosis before the entrance of the spermatozoon.

been found to occur in *Nereis* even when the sperm is removed from the egg immediately after it begins to penetrate. In some animals the perivitelline space beneath the raised membrane is wide enough to allow the rotation of the main body of the egg within it. After the fertilization membrane has been formed, no more sperms enter. This is not due simply to the presence of a mechanical barrier, but also to a new physio-logical state in the egg cytoplasm, for sperms will not enter membraneless fragments of eggs in this stage of development.

The behavior of the sperm and egg nuclei (the pronuclei) during syngamy is illustrated in Fig. 93. Soon after entering the egg, the sperm nucleus commonly begins to enlarge and reveal a structure more like that of an ordinary nucleus. Meanwhile the pronuclei approach each other and meet. By this time the sperm nucleus has often, though not always, assumed a size and structure about like that of the egg nucleus. The two now proceed to fuse. As they do so both may have a metabolic type of structure, the resulting diploid nucleus later entering prophase and carrying out the first embryonal mitosis. In other cases both pro-nuclei have passed independently through most or all of the prophasic stages before meeting; hence, when their membranes disappear their two genomes lie together in the achromatic figure of the first embryonal mitosis, and they first become enclosed in a common nuclear membrane at the telophase of this mitosis. This more or less independent behavior of the genomes with no intimate nuclear union before the first embryonal mitosis is known as *gonomery*. In some organisms the two genomes continue to act as two visibly distinct groups of chromosomes through several embryonal mitoses.

This close association of syngamy with the first embryonal mitosis is emphasized further by the behavior of the centrioles. The origin of the centrioles seen at the poles of the achromatic figure in the first embryonal mitosis is not altogether clear, but the characteristic appearance of an aster with a centriole in the cytoplasm near the base of the sperm head is significant. Either the centriole is that known to have been incorporated in the sperm during spermiogenesis, or the sperm in some way induces the formation of an aster and centriole by the egg cytoplasm. It has been shown that by treating echinoderm eggs with certain chlorides the formation of numerous asters can be induced in the cytoplasm and that two of these, especially if they originate near the nucleus, can function in mitosis. Whatever the origin of the aster in normal syngamy, it divides to two which occupy the poles of the first embryonal mitotic figure. The entrance of the sperm is not merely a necessary preliminary to syngamic nuclear union; it also affects the processes leading to the division of the cell.

Syngamy has two effects of cardinal importance. The first of these is *activation*, by which certain physiological processes are set in motion or greatly accelerated. In most cases this leads to the immediate development of the cell into a new individual, but in some animals and plants the cell develops certain protective coats and enters a dormant state from which it emerges later under the appropriate environmental conditions. In either event there is a profound physiological change at the time of syngamy. This is not dependent upon the union of the gametic nuclei, for not only are some of the results of the change manifested long before the union occurs, but complete activation may be induced by various physical and chemical treatments in the absence of sperms. Furthermore, some animal eggs are naturally parthenogenetic, undergoing complete development without syngamy regularly in successive life cycles. The egg has accordingly been termed an *independently activable system* which contains everything necessary to development, even though a stimulus of one kind or another is ordinarily required to initiate its further activity.

The second important effect of syngamy is *diplosis,* the doubling of the number of chromosomes by the union of the two gametic nuclei. *In syngamy two genomes with the monoploid chromosome number are combined into a diploid chromosome complement, each kind of chromosome then being present in duplicate. Every chromosome of this complement divides equationally at every somatic mitosis in the development of the resulting new individual, so that every nucleus in this individual contains a descendant of every chromosome originally present in the zygote.* The peculiar significance of these facts with respect to heredity is evident when it is borne in mind that the two genomes usually come from two parent individuals, that they may exert somewhat different influences upon the characters developed, and that they are to be reshuffled by meiosis to form new genomes before the next sexual generation is produced.

Cleavage.—The rapid succession of meiosis, syngamy, and cleavage in many animals has required frequent mention of cleavage in the foregoing descriptions. This process, also called *segmentation,* is one of much cytological interest and a few features of its early stages will be sketched briefly. The subsequent course of embryogeny lies beyond the scope of this book. It is the early cleavage divisions that furnish such excellent material for studies on mitosis and especially of cytokinesis in animals (page 69).

The animal egg commonly shows a polarity of such a nature that one region, the "animal pole," is physiologically more active than the diametrically opposite region, the "vegetal pole." Also, eggs of different animals differ greatly in the amount and location of their yolk material. These features, to mention only two, exert a strong influence upon the determination of the various cleavage patterns encountered in different classes of animals.

The geometrically most regular cleavage pattern is found in eggs having their yolk uniformly distributed throughout the cell (homolecithal eggs). Among echinoderms, for example (Fig. 94, *A*), the first cleavage division is meridional (through the two poles), the second meridional at right angles to the first, the third equatorial, and the several following divisions in such planes as to result in a spherical mass of cells (*blastomeres*) of uniform size. As development proceeds this sphere becomes a hollow *blastula,* and this in turn is converted into a *gastrula* by an invagination which begins at the vegetal pole.

The egg of the frog is somewhat telolecithal, *i.e.,* its yolk tends to be denser in the region of the vegetal pole than near the animal pole. The first and second cleavage divisions occur as in the homolecithal egg, but the third division is unequal, giving four small cells (*micromeres*) at the animal pole and four larger ones (*macromeres*) at the vegetal pole (Fig.

94, *B*).   From this stage onward the macromeres divide at a slower rate than the micromeres.   Invagination to form the gastrula here begins at the side of the blastula where the regions of large and small cells meet.

The eggs of birds, reptiles, squids, and bony fish are very strongly telolecithal, the yolk being very densely packed throughout most of the cell but absent from the small germinal disc at the animal pole.   The cleavage divisions are restricted to this relatively thin layer of protoplasm and do not extend through the bulk of the cell (Fig. 94, *C*).   After a few divisions have occurred, the young embryo has the form of a plate of cells, the *blastoderm*, lying against a large yolk mass, the distinctness of the

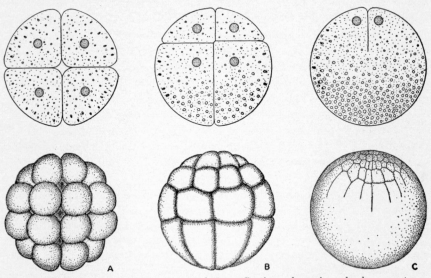

Fig. 94.—Three types of cleavage in animal eggs.   Sections of eggs in early cleavage stages above; surface views of later stages below.   Explanation in text.

boundary between the two regions showing some variation.   This is called *meroblastic* cleavage, in contrast to the *holoblastic* type which extends through the whole egg.

A further type of cleavage is observed among insects (Fig. 88).   The first few mitoses in the fertilized egg are not accompanied by cytokinesis, the embryo being coenocytic during its earliest stages.   Soon after the primordial germ cell has been set apart, the multiplying nuclei in the somatic portion of the embryo move to the periphery along with small masses of cytoplasm, leaving the central region holding most of the yolk (the centrolecithal condition).   Cytokinesis occurs between the peripheral nuclei, but the cells so formed remain open on the side toward the yolk.   Further divisions of these cells produce the ventral plate from which most of the embryo arises.

In the foregoing examples it is evident that there is some correlation between the type of cleavage and such visible features as the location of yolk. The correlation is so far from complete, however, that this feature cannot be regarded as more than a contributing cause of cleavage patterns. Exhaustive studies have shown that the positions assumed by the cleavage spindles and hence of the resulting partitions are determined mainly by some fundamental protoplasmic organization which it is not yet possible to describe.

A most important aspect of cleavage is the relation it bears to the internal differentiation of the embryo. It is evident that differentiation has proceeded much further in some animals than in others at a given stage of cleavage. It has long been known that in a coelenterate (*Clytia*)

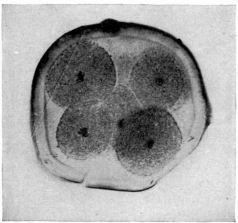

Fig. 95.—Embryo of rabbit in eight-cell stage; five of the cells (blastomeres) visible in the section. (*Courtesy of General Biological Supply House, Inc., Chicago.*)

one of the first 16 blastomeres may produce a complete embryo, whereas in a ctenophore (*Beroë*) it has been observed that the larva is incomplete if a portion of the egg's protoplasm has been removed even before the first cleavage division. In cases like the latter the egg, before its cleavage or even before its fertilization, may have a definite *promorphology, i.e.,* it has developed an internal organization which in some manner foreshadows the morphology of the young embryo. Hence to the three processes which sometimes follow each other so closely as to overlap—meiosis, syngamy, and cleavage—we may now add a fourth, embryonic differentiation.

In some eggs an internal differentiation can be detected in the pattern assumed by certain visible substances. This pattern may be cut up in various ways by the successive cleavage furrows, the ability of any isolated blastomere to produce a whole embryo or only a part of one being in some measure dependent upon the elements of the pattern it includes. The inference that cleavage accompanies internal differentiation but does not produce it is borne out by the striking fact that the larva of an annelid worm has been seen to develop its characteristic form and structure to a certain stage even when the cleavage divisions were suppressed altogether by treatment with KCl. Further discussion of these phenomena would lead us into the fascinating but extremely difficult field of developmental mechanics.

Parthenogenesis.—The development of an egg into an embryo without syngamy is called *parthenogenesis*. An individual so derived is a *parthenote*. This mode of reproduction occurs frequently in lower animals, notably insects, lower crustaceans, and rotifers. In some species, parthenogenesis is the only mode of reproduction, male individuals being unknown, while in others a series of parthenogenetic generations is succeeded under the proper environmental conditions by individuals that reproduce sexually. Eggs of several other groups, including echinoderms, mollusks, amphibians, and even mammals (rabbit), in which parthenogenesis does not normally occur, have been made to undergo parthenogenetic development, at least to a certain stage, by treating them variously with hypertonic sea water, fatty acids, alkaloids, foreign blood serum, and a number of other agencies. Only exceptionally do these artificially induced parthenotes reach the stage of metamorphosis or of sexual maturity.

Some animal parthenotes have the gametic chromosome number, normal meiosis having occurred in the development of the egg. In bees and ants, for example, such eggs are capable of either sexual or parthenogenetic development: when syngamy occurs the result is a diploid female, whereas parthenogenesis leads to the development of a monoploid male. In the majority of cases the parthenotes are diploid, as in aphids and rotifers. The eggs developing in this manner arise from oöcytes in which there are no meiotic divisions, or there may be a single division which is equational in character. These diploid eggs are usually incapable of fertilization.

There is every reason to believe that the parthenogenetic mode of development in these organisms has been derived from the normal sexual cycle, involving a suppression of meiosis in the diploid type and an adjustment of development to a different nuclear constitution in the monoploid type. The suppression of meiosis is suggested by the various observed conditions intermediate between meiosis and ameiosis and between facultative and obligatory parthenogenesis, and also by the fact that in certain plants parthenogenesis occurs only after a failure of meiosis. That the ability to undergo somatic development with a single genome may have been slowly acquired is indicated by the fact that monoploid parthenotes occasionally encountered among plant and animal species do not develop so well as the diploid zygotes. Moreover, when the parthenogenetic development of monoploid animal eggs is induced by artificial means, the few individuals that are successful in developing through metamorphosis have almost invariably become diploid. In the mitoses occurring in parthenogenetic frog embryos, for instance, both the monoploid and the diploid numbers are found, indicating a gradual doubling process. Evidently the embryos not undergoing this change fail to survive. Among salamanders obtained from fertilized eggs subjected to low temperatures there are some that are monoploid at least up to the stage at which ovaries with oöcytes are developed.

Development in the monoploid condition is therefore a possibility in animals as it is in plants, provided the conditions favoring it are present. As a rule monoploid animals derived by such means are almost if not completely sterile. Among natural parthenotes, however, fertility may obtain. In the male honey bee, for example, functional sperms are produced after a single spermatocyte division which is equational in character. All these facts indicate that in the evolution of various groups of organisms there have been adjustments of the reproductive process to a considerable range of variations in the nuclear cycle. This is further evident in plants, most of which have reproductive cycles differing widely from those in animals.

Protozoa.—The Protozoa are a very large group of very small organisms. They are so diversified in structure and type of life cycle that long chapters would be required to describe their cytology fully; hence this discussion must be restricted to a few representative features of special interest.

Protozoa are characteristically unicellular, *i.e.*, the body has the general structure of a typical protoplast, with cytoplasm, membranes, and one nucleus. Some protozoologists prefer to regard them as noncellular, meaning that they are not subdivided into compartments but simply have the structure necessary to a small but complete mass of protoplasm. A tendency to become coenocytic or multicellular does appear here and there in these animals, but evolution within the group has proceeded mainly along other lines. It is customary to say that Protozoa are small because they are unicellular, but as we compare their frequently elaborate structure and behavior with what is seen in Metazoa something may be gained from the concept that they are unicellular because they are small. Effective differentiation in very small masses can occur without a multiplicity of nuclei and cells. Cell division serves them in reproduction, but not in the building of the individual body.

Nuclear conditions vary widely in the Protozoa. Most protozoans have a single nucleus, but probably in all groups the binucleate and multinucleate conditions can be found. In the infusorian cell there are commonly nuclei of two kinds: one or more *micronuclei*, which divide mitotically and are concerned chiefly with reproduction, and a large *macronucleus*, which divides by constriction and is concerned in the physiological activities of the cell, including the mating reaction (Fig. 96). A component of many nuclei in Protozoa and flagellates is the *endosome*, a large, compact central mass which in different cases appears to contain nucleolar matter, chromatin, or both of these substances. At the time

Fɪɢ. 96.—Fission in *Paramecium caudatum.* 1, individual with single macronucleus and single micronucleus above it. 2, the macronucleus is elongating and the micronucleus has divided, constriction beginning at middle of cell. 3, the macronucleus has divided, and fission is nearly completed. (*Courtesy of General Biological Supply House, Inc., Chicago.*)

of nuclear division it elongates and constricts into two (Fig. 97). Its function is not understood.

The aspects presented by protozoan nuclei at the time of division are often very difficult to interpret. The nucleus may be very compact and seem to undergo a simple mass division, or it may show a cloud of small chromatic granules instead of chromosomes with obvious individuality. In many cases, however, chromosomes in definite numbers and essentially like those in Metazoa have been demonstrated, with

Fɪɢ. 97.—Mitosis in a flagellate (*Heteronema*), showing endosome. The division of the chromosomes is longitudinal; late separation at one end makes it appear transverse. (*After J. B. Loefer.*)

kinetochores, spiral chromonemata, longitudinal division, the association of nucleoli with certain members of the complement, meiosis, and even polyploidy. To what extent the less definite types of structure and behavior should be regarded as primitive or as special modifications of the condition generally prevalent in organisms nobody can say. The achromatic figure also presents itself in many forms, with and without asters and centrioles. Centrioles in some groups attain an astonishing size and form (Fig. 99).

The neuromotor apparatus is an unusually interesting specialization in many protozoan and flagellate cells. In some it is absent; in others it consists of a flagellum, a basal granule (*blepharoplast*), and a strand (*rhizoplast*) connecting the latter with a centrosome at the nucleus (Fig. 98). Sometimes a single body acts as both centrosome and blepharoplast. In more elaborate forms there is a central mass, the *motorium*, from which strands run out to the several swimming organs. In Ciliata there are also numerous very fine strands (the "silver-line system") running beneath the rows of cilia and near the stinging organs, or *trichocysts*.

Digestion in the more highly differentiated Protozoa may occur in a special tract running from mouth to anus. Special contractile and supporting structures also occur (Fig. 9). Far from being simple, such protozoans are the most complicated single cells known.

 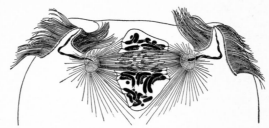

FIG. 98.—
A flagellate
(*Menoidium*).
Explanation in
text. (*After R.
P. Hall.*)

FIG. 99.—Mitosis during fission in a protozoan (*Barbulanympha*). Longitudinal section of anterior end of cell. The two large elongate centrioles are connected anteriorly with the two flagellated areas and posteriorly with the achromatic figure. Some of the astral rays connect at the nuclear membrane with intranuclear chromosomal fibers. (*After L. R. Cleveland.*)

The asexual reproduction of a protozoan by fission may appear to be a simple process externally, but in the more highly organized species it involves a very complicated series of changes. Not only does the nucleus divide mitotically, but the components of the motor apparatus and the other specialized regions are also doubled variously by division and new formation. A prominent part in the process is usually played by the centrosomes or blepharoplasts (Fig. 99).

Sexual reproduction in these small animals involves nuclear divisions and fusions which in many cases have not been fully interpreted. In some genera, however, the details of the process have been made out sufficiently well to show that in certain fundamentals it corresponds to the meiosis-syngamy cycle seen in Metazoa. These changes may occur entirely within one individual cell (*autogamy*). Syngamy involving two individuals may include the complete fusion of morphologically similar or dissimilar gametes, or only a mutual exchange of nuclei between individuals in temporary conjugation (Fig. 100). In *Paramecium caudatum* the latter type of process occurs as follows:

The two animals become united by their ventral sides and the macronucleus of each begins to degenerate, while the micronucleus divides twice to form four spindle-shaped bodies. Three of these degenerate, forming the "corpuscles de rebut," which play no further part. The fourth divides into two, one of which,

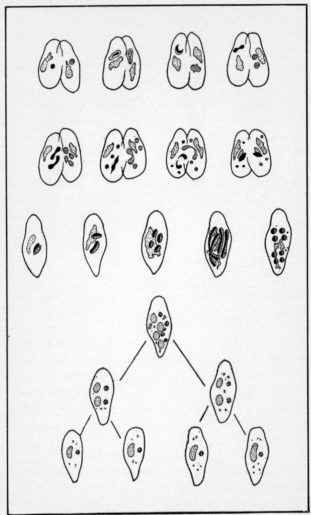

Fig. 100.—Diagram illustrating nuclear behavior during conjugation in *Paramecium*. Explanation in text. (*From T. H. Morgan, after G. N. Calkins.*)

the "female pronucleus," remains in the body, while the other, or "male pronucleus," passes into the other animal and fuses with the female pronucleus. Each animal now contains a cleavage-nucleus equally derived from both the conjugating animals, and the latter soon separate. The cleavage-nucleus in each divides three times successively, and of the eight resulting bodies four become macronuclei and four micronuclei. By two succeeding fissions the four macronuclei are then distributed, one to each of the four resulting individuals. In some other species the micronuclei are equally distributed in like manner, but in *P. caudatum* the process is more complicated, since three of them degenerate, and the fourth divides twice to produce four new micronuclei. In either case at the close of the process each of the conjugating individuals has given rise to four descendants, each containing a macronucleus and a micronucleus derived from the cleavage-nucleus. From this time forward fission follows fission in the usual manner, both nuclei dividing at each fission, until, after many generations, conjugation recurs. (Wilson.)

In these Infusoria there is also another process, *endomixis*, in which the nuclear reorganization closely parallels that in conjugation: it resembles autogamy in occurring entirely within one individual, but it differs from both autogamy and conjugation in involving no nuclear fusion. If the first two divisions of the original micronucleus here accomplish a reduction in chromosome number, as they evidently do in conjugation, it would seem that the diploid number should be restored sooner or later. This point has not been cleared up by cytologists. Both conjugation and endomixis (in species having it) have beneficial effects upon the vigor of the race. In cultures the organisms continue to multiply by fission as long as either process occurs at intervals, but when conditions inducing senile change arise, their vitality decreases and the cultures die out if neither process takes place. Finally, it is of interest to know that researches on *Paramecium* and other genera indicate the presence of a genic basis of inheritance among Infusoria paralleling in some degree that found in Metazoa. The problem of analyzing the experimental data is, however, greatly complicated by the occurrence of several types of nuclear reorganization, the presence of macronuclei, and other factors. Intensive studies now in progress promise to show to what extent genetical principles founded on data derived from higher animals and plants are applicable to Protozoa.

With the above points in mind it becomes unsatisfactory to regard Protozoa merely as simple or primitive organisms. They are small, but not therefore simple. Their organization may not be so complex as that of frogs, but for animals of their size it is probably fully as effective. Which of their peculiar characters are actually primitive can scarcely be stated with confidence at present. Perhaps it is best to think of them as did their discoverer, Anton van Leeuwenhoek, simply as "little animals."

CHAPTER X

CYTOLOGY OF REPRODUCTION IN ANGIOSPERMS

The life cycles of vascular plants, bryophytes, and many thallophytes are complicated by the presence of an *alternation of generations*. By this it is meant that the cycle comprises two phases of vegetative development: one of these, the *sporophyte*, develops from the zygote and produces *spores;* the other, known as the *gametophyte*, develops from the spore and produces *gametes*. Since the chromosome number is reduced at sporogenesis and doubled at syngamy, the sporophyte normally has twice as many chromosomes as the gametophyte.

The two "generations" differ greatly in relative degree of development in the various plant groups. In most bryophytes the gametophyte is the more conspicuous: a moss plant, for example, is a gametophyte, the sporophyte being small and short-lived. In ferns this relationship is reversed, the gametophyte being so small that it commonly escapes notice. In flowering plants the gametophyte is still more obscure and must be studied with the microscope.

The cycles are complicated further by variations in the type of sex differentiation. In mosses and ferns the sperms and eggs may be produced by the same gametophyte (*monoecism, homothallism*), or they may occur on different ones (*dioecism, heterothallism*). In seed plants, male and female gametophytes are always distinct and arise, respectively, from *microspores* and *megaspores*. These spores may be produced by the same sporophyte, in which case the plant is *homophytic* (*monoecious* or *hermaphroditic*). In other species they are produced by different sporophytes; such species are *heterophytic* (*dioecious*). The cytological basis of these sexual conditions will be discussed in Chap. XII.

The present chapter will be devoted entirely to the angiosperms, for these are the plants that have long been most prominent in cytological, cytogenetical, and cytotaxonomic researches.

The Flower.—Under the appropriate physiological conditions the angiosperm sporophyte produces flowers. The typical flower is a group of parts—pistil, stamens, petals, and sepals—of which the first two kinds are directly concerned in sexual reproduction. In the anthers of the stamens, microspores, later becoming pollen, are formed. In the ovarian portion of the pistil, ovules with megaspores are produced, and it is there that the subsequent stages of female gametophyte development, syngamy, embryogeny, and seed formation are carried out.

136

The many families of angiosperms show almost innumerable variations in floral type. Such characteristics as the size, arrangement, and structure of parts often determine the suitability of a species for cytological or cytogenetical investigation. Of special importance is the type of sex differentiation present. Some angiosperms, such as willows, the red campion, and the date palm, are heterophytic (dioecious), the flowers on one plant having only pistils or only stamens. Others are homophytic: of these, some are monoecious, having pistillate flowers and staminate flowers on the same plant, as in maize, while others are hermaphroditic, having pistils and stamens in the same flower, as in buttercups, tulips, and apple trees. Both unisexual and bisexual flowers may be borne by the same plant (some maples), and various other arrangements are known. In some flowers bearing both pistils and stamens the two may not be functional at the same time, so that cross-pollination is favored or made necessary even though the plant is structurally bisexual. Furthermore, some bisexual plants are self-sterile, producing seeds only after cross-pollination. The mode of pollination, *i.e.*, whether by wind or by insects, is often a matter of importance in designing experimental procedures.

Microsporogenesis and the Male Gametophyte (Figs. 101, 103).—The anther commonly differentiates internally into three regions: an outer wall consisting of several layers of cells, a nutritive *tapetum* of one layer, and a central mass of sporogenous cells. The sporogenous cells eventually enlarge as *microsporocytes*, round up from one another, and lie in a fluid filling the enlarged anther. Each microsporocyte then divides into four *microspores*. The two nuclear divisions here are meiotic, each nucleus of the resulting quartet containing the reduced chromosome number. In some plants, cytokinesis occurs after division *I* and again after division *II*, but in most species it does not take place until after *II*, the spherical cell then dividing simultaneously into four tetrahedral spores (quadripartition). The shape of the spores in the quartet often reveals which mode of cytokinesis has occurred. The walls of the microspores become greatly thickened, the characteristic patterns formed often being useful in the identification of species. In many plants this wall thickening involves the activity of the tapetum. This tissue sometimes breaks down into a *tapetal plasmodium* which flows in among the young spores and deposits materials upon them. The wall consists typically of two distinct layers: the thickened *exine* and within this an *intine*.

The male gametophyte of angiosperms is structurally very simple. Its development begins with the division of the microspore into a small *generative cell* and a large *tube cell*. The generative cell may lie against the spore wall at one side, or it may be completely enclosed by the cytoplasm of the tube cell. The generative cell divides into two *male gametes.*   This division may occur before the anther opens, as in maize, or at some later stage; hence the *pollen grains* shed from the anther and transferred to a stigma may contain two or three cells.   The further

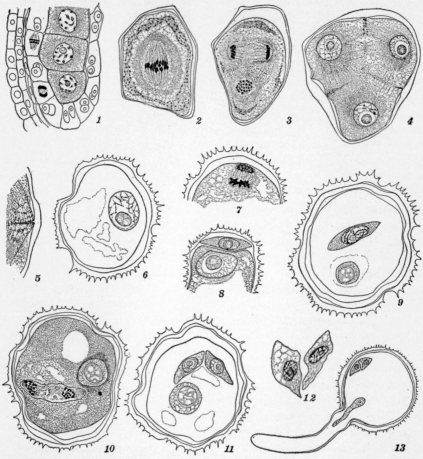

Fig. 101.—Microsporogenesis and development of male gametes in purslane (*Portulaca*). 1, section of anther with microsporocytes; 2, metaphase *I* in microsporocyte; 3, anaphase *II*, with spindles at right angles to each other; 4, cytokinesis beginning; 5, detail of developing partition wall; 6, microspore; 7, division of microspore nucleus; 8, generative cell formed; 9, young pollen grain, with tube nucleus and elongate generative cell; 10, generative cell dividing in pollen grain; 11, pollen grain with two male gametes and tube nucleus; 12, male gametes from older pollen grain; 13, germinating pollen grain; tube nucleus entering pollen tube.   (*After D. C. Cooper.*)

behavior of this small male gametophyte will be described below in the section on syngamy.

   Megasporogenesis and the Female Gametophyte.—The pistil consists typically of an ovary, a more or less elongated style, and a sticky or hairy stigma upon which the pollen will be received.   In the ovary are one or more ovules. Each ovule consists of a central portion, the *nucellus*, surrounded by one or two *integuments* with an opening, the *micropyle*. In the nucellus a subepidermal cell, either at once or after

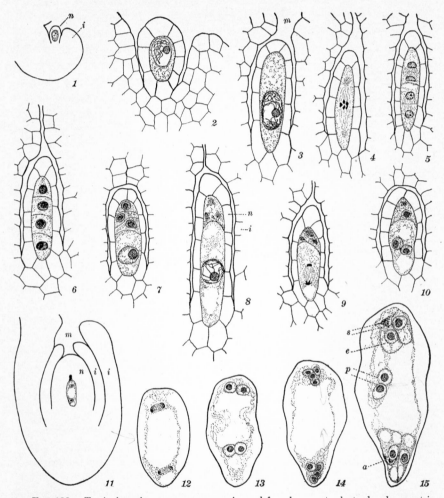

FIG. 102.—Typical ovules, megasporogenesis, and female gametophyte development in angiosperms. 1–10 from lettuce; 11–15 from bloodroot. 1–6, development of megaspore quartet from megasporocyte in ovule. 7–15, development of female gametophyte from one surviving megaspore of quartet. *a*, antipodal cells; *e*, egg; *i*, integument; *m*, micropyle; *n*, nucellus; *p*, polar nuclei; *s*, synergids. (*From preparations by J. Einset.*)

division, enlarges and differentiates as a *megasporocyte* (Fig. 102). This cell divides into a quartet of *megaspores*, each with the reduced chromosome number. Often the outer cell of the two present after division *I* does not divide again, so that the quartet is incomplete. One of the spores then develops into the female gametophyte as the other three degenerate.

This process shows many variations in different genera of angiosperms, although the general structure of the gametophyte is often essentially the same after different modes of development. Typical development occurs as follows. The meiotic divisions in the megasporocyte are accompanied by cytokinesis, the result being a row of megaspores. The innermost of these enlarges greatly as its nucleus initiates a series of three mitoses, yielding eight nuclei lying in the common cytoplasm of the *embryo sac.* Membranes are formed about six of the nuclei, forming a group of three *antipodal cells* at one end of the sac, and another group of three called the *egg apparatus,* consisting of an *egg* and two *synergids,* at the end near the micropyle. In the cytoplasm of the sac lie the two *polar nuclei;* these are not to be confused with animal *polar bodies,* which are immediate products of meiosis.

Certain other types of development occasionally found may be mentioned. (1) The female gametophyte develops from one of the two cells present after meiotic division *I,* two of the nuclei resulting from meiosis thus being involved in the formation of an eight-nucleate sac (*Allium* type) or a four-nucleate sac (*Podostemon* type). (2) A four-nucleate gametophyte arises from a single megaspore (*Oenothera* type). (3) No cytokinesis accompanies meiosis, all four nuclei dividing once to form an eight-nucleate gametophyte (*Adoxa* type). (4) After no cytokinesis the four nuclei divide twice, giving a sixteen-nucleate gametophyte (*Peperomia* type). (5) After no cytokinesis at meiosis one of the four nuclei remains near the micropylar end while the other three pass toward the antipodal end of the sac. All then undergo another mitosis. In the micropylar end this yields two monoploid nuclei as expected, but in the antipodal end the three nuclei undergo fusion just as their division begins, so that instead of six resulting nuclei there are only two, each with three sets of chromosomes. The four nuclei in the sac, two monoploid and two triploid, now undergo another mitosis, giving four monoploid and four triploid nuclei. When cell membranes have been formed, the egg, synergids, and one polar nucleus are monoploid, while the other polar nucleus and the three antipodal cells are triploid. This is the *Fritillaria* type and occurs in several species of *Lilium,* long supposed to develop like *Adoxa.* Since both meiosis and nuclear fusion may result in qualitative differences among nuclei, the importance of these phenomena to the geneticist working with such plants should be obvious.

Syngamy.—A necessary preliminary to syngamy in seed plants is pollination. The pollen is brought by insects, wind, or other agency to the stigma. There it germinates by sending out a pollen tube through one of the special germ pores in the exine. The wall of the tube itself is the greatly extended intine, and into the tube move the cytoplasm and nucleus of the tube cell together with the two male gametes. When pollen is shed from the anther in the two-cell stage, the division of the generative cell to form the male gametes takes place as the pollen tube grows down through the style toward the ovary (Fig. 103). The course of the tube is usually between the thin-walled cells, the intercellular sub-

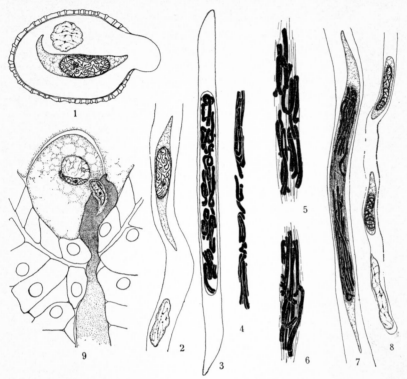

Fig. 103.—Development of male gametes and syngamy in lily (*Lilium regale*). 1, germinating pollen grain. 2, generative cell and tube nucleus in pollen tube. 3–7, stages in division of generative cell and nucleus in pollen tube. 8, tip of pollen tube containing tube nucleus and two male gametes. 9, syngamy; one male gamete near egg nucleus, the other leaving pollen tube (but not entering egg). (*After D. C. Cooper.*)

stance being dissolved by enzymes from the tube. If the style has an open central canal, the tube grows along against the cells lining it. When the style is very long, the style and tube may wither away at the tip before the growing end of the tube containing the cytoplasm and nuclei reaches the ovule. Eventually the tube grows through the micropyle of the ovule into the embryo sac where it ruptures, liberating the male gametes and often the tube nucleus.

Syngamy now occurs (Fig. 104). The male gametes just after entering the sac have been shown in numerous species to be complete cells,

with both nucleus and cytoplasm.   In other species they appear as
nuclei with no cytoplasm distinct from that of the sac or pollen tube.
Often the sperm nuclei have a worm-like form.   One of the gametes

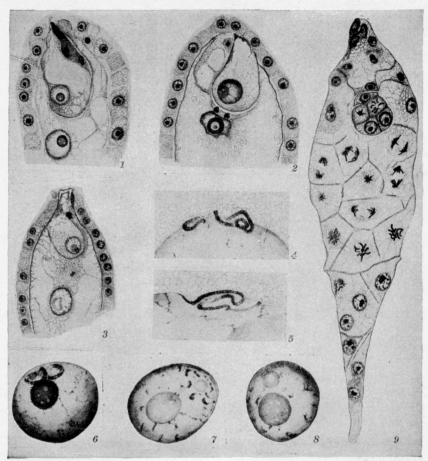

Fig. 104.—Syngamy in *Crepis capillaris*.   1, upper part of embryo sac.   Material just
discharged from pollen tube above egg contains two sperms in one mass and an irregular
body.   Polar fusion nucleus below.   2, two sperms at tip of egg; one synergid visible.   3,
one sperm in contact with egg nucleus, the other moving toward the polar fusion nucleus;
72 minutes after pollination.   4, sperm spread out on surface of egg nucleus.   5, sperm
spread on surface of polar fusion nucleus.   6, sperm beginning to transform inside egg
nucleus.   7, 8, later stages in alteration of sperm in egg nucleus.   9, embryo sac about 32
hours after pollination.   The embryo is developing with a diploid chromosome complement, and the endosperm with a triploid complement.   (*After H. Gerassimova.*)

applies itself to the egg and fuses with it.   The nucleus can be followed
through all the stages leading to its union with the egg nucleus, but the
sperm's cytoplasm, even if it is recognizable before syngamy, has not
been definitely proved by direct observation to enter the egg.   There is

indirect genetical evidence which indicates that it does enter in some species (page 232). As the two gametic nuclei unite, their aspect may vary as it does in animals: both may have a thready structure much like that of the metabolic stage; the male may be smaller and more compact; one or both of them may be in the prophase of mitosis, the maternal and paternal genomes being distinguishable in the next ensuing division. In any case the chromosome complement of the fertilized egg consists of two genomes: diplosis has occurred in syngamy. After a cross in angiosperms, therefore, the nuclear material of the zygote and the individual which it eventually becomes is derived from both parents, whereas its cytoplasm may come from the mother alone.

While the above events are taking place, the other male gamete nucleus takes up a position near the two polar nuclei somewhere in the sac. All three then undergo a triple fusion, forming a primary endosperm nucleus with three genomes. Sometimes the two polars have fused by the time the male nucleus arrives, the male then being added. All orders of fusion of the three have been observed and, as in the egg, they may be in the metabolic state or in some stage of the prophase. In sacs with more than the usual number of nuclei, more than three may unite to form the primary endosperm nucleus. The union of one male nucleus with the egg nucleus while another unites with the polar nuclei is called *double fertilization* and is a process peculiar to angiosperms.

The time elapsing between the arrival of the pollen on the stigma and the syngamic union varies greatly, as the following examples show: rye, 7 hours; maize, 18 to 24 hours, in spite of the length of the style (the silk); Jimson weed, 25 hours; box elder, 40 to 72 hours; Indian pipe (*Monotropa*), 5 days; pecan, 5 to 7 weeks; red oak, 13 to 14 months. These periods vary, of course, with temperature.

Embryogeny and Seed Development.—Pollination and syngamy set in motion a number of reactions in the ovary and ovules which result in the development of a fruit with seeds. This involves alterations in every part, from the fertilized egg to the tissue of the pistil and sometimes the other floral organs.

The fertilized egg develops into the *embryo*, which is to become the sporophytic plant of the next generation. It divides several times transversely, forming a few cells in a row (Fig. 105), and then, beginning in the terminal cell (toward the center of the sac), divisions in the longitudinal and other planes accompany its lateral growth. The stage of embryonic development reached by the time the ovule becomes a mature seed varies widely: in some plants the embryo is a small undifferentiated mass of cells, most of the seed being occupied by endosperm to be described below; in others the embryo is larger, has differentiated its cotyledons, and has digested away some of the endosperm; in still others it fills the entire seed, having digested away all the endosperm and even some of the surrounding ovular tissue. All the mitoses during embryogeny are equational, so that every nucleus contains two genomes, one from each parent.

Even before cell division begins in the fertilized egg, the development of *endosperm* has usually commenced with the division of the primary endosperm nucleus. In many angiosperms there are several of these divisions before cytokinesis occurs, so that the endosperm has an early coenocytic stage. Cytokinesis later converts this into a cellular tissue. In other species the endosperm is cellular from the beginning. The endosperm enlarges along with the whole ovule and may become stored with various nutritive materials. In wheat and other grains the outermost layer contains many aleurone granules. Storage material in some plants is deposited in the form of thick cellulose walls, the endosperm being hard, like wood or even ivory. Such stored material is utilized as the seed germinates and the embryo develops into a young plant.

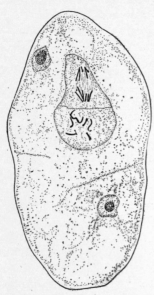

Fig. 105.—Embryo sac or *Crepis capillaris*, showing two-celled embryo with nuclei in mitosis. The endosperm has begun to develop. (*From a preparation by K. Koos.*)

The endosperm is commonly triploid in nuclear constitution, although it often develops with other numbers of genomes depending upon the number of nuclei involved in the previous fusion. Sometimes unfused as well as fused nuclei take part in endosperm development, portions of the tissue being monoploid. Evidently it is neither the derivation of the nuclei nor their fusion, but rather the conditions under which they develop, that determine the formation of endosperm. From the standpoint of comparative morphology it is most logical to interpret the endosperm as gametophytic tissue which, unlike that of gymnosperms, is arrested in development until after the pollen tube enters the sac; it then resumes development with or sometimes without fusions and the incorporation of a male nucleus. A male nucleus may, of course, affect particular characters of the endosperm if it comes from a plant of different genetic constitution.

In most angiosperms the other cells present in the embryo sac before syngamy disintegrate early. The entering pollen tube often destroys one synergid, and the other disappears soon after the egg is fertilized.

The antipodal cells usually degenerate and disappear during endosperm development, but sometimes they enlarge and perform a nutritive function for a time. In maize the antipodals undergo division and eventually form in the kernel an oval mass of monoploid gametophytic tissue lying next to the endosperm, which it closely resembles in cellular organization and contained storage material.

Alterations outside of the embryo sac may be briefly summarized here. The tissue of the nucellus about the sac usually becomes less conspicuous as the endosperm enlarges. In some plant families, however, it may become stored with nutritive substances, in which case it is known as *perisperm*. The tissue of the ovule's integument (or integuments) becomes transformed into the seed coat. The ovarian tissue enclosing the ovule (or ovules) is variously modified into the fruit tissue, or *pericarp*. This is represented by the pod of a bean, the hard covering of an acorn or a maize kernel, the fleshy tissue of the tomato, and the fleshy tissue (*exocarp*) and hard pit covering (*endocarp*) of the cherry. Accessory fruits incorporate flower parts other than the ovary, as in the fleshy tissue of the strawberry, which is developed from the receptacle, and in the plume-like portion of the dandelion fruit, which is formed from the calyx. In multiple fruits, such as the mulberry and pineapple, the tissues of several flowers are combined.

Finally, it should be pointed out that since the pericarp and seed coat develop from tissues already present in the flower before pollination, a given syngamic union does not alter the chromosomal constitution of these parts but it does so affect the fruits and seeds of the next generation.

Aberrations of the Reproductive Process.—In the angiosperms there are encountered a number of modifications of the process of sexual reproduction as described above. These occur only occasionally in some plants, but in certain species one or more of them have become habitual. On the whole they play a minor role in nature, but they should at least be listed here because they do throw much light upon the problem of relationships within some genera and often afford an explanation of unexpected genetical behavior in the breeding plot.

Several of these aberrations fall under the heading of *apomixis*, a term applied to asexual reproductive processes substituted for the sexual process. Apomixis may be vegetative when buds or bulblets of various kinds appear in the place of flowers. Of greater interest, however, are the various types of apomixis involving the formation of seeds. Examples of these are the following: (1) *Reduced parthenogenesis*, in which an unfertilized egg develops with the gametic chromosome number. This phenomenon has been observed in experimental plants belonging to a number of genera, but it is not known to have become an established habit anywhere among angiosperms in nature. (2) *Unreduced partheno-*

genesis, in which an unfertilized egg develops with the diploid chromosome number (Fig. 106). This is probably the commonest mode of apomixis involving seed formation, being known to occur in a number of genera in nature. The female gametophyte and egg in this case are diploid because of a failure of meiosis at sporogenesis in the ovule, or as a result of the development of the gametophyte directly from a somatic cell of the ovule without spore formation (*apospory*). In such cases there is an alternation of gametophytic and sporophytic generations in the life cycle, but no alternation of chromosome numbers. (3) *Apogamy,* in which an embryo arises from a gametophytic cell other than the egg. This has occasionally been observed but is not known to occur regularly

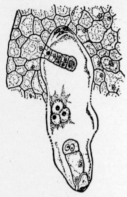

in nature. (4) *Adventitious embryony,* in which a sporophytic cell of the nucellus or the integument buds into the embryo sac and produces an embryo (Fig. 106). This may occur without the stimulus of pollination (*Euphorbia*) or only after syngamy has taken place (orange). (5) *Polyembryony,* in which more than one embryo develops in an embryo sac. One of these may develop sexually in the usual manner, while others arise in one of the ways mentioned above. Another rare mode is the formation of several embryos by proliferation from a single one at an early stage.

Fig. 106.—Embryo sac of *Alchemilla* with one embryo developing by unreduced parthenogenesis (below) and another by adventitious budding (above). (*After S. Murbeck.*)

The following phenomena not included under the heading of apomixis are also encountered at times. (1) *Gynogenesis,* in which the male nucleus enters the egg but then disintegrates, leaving the egg to develop into an embryo with the maternal nucleus only. (2) *Androgenesis,* in which the maternal nucleus presumably disintegrates, for a monoploid plant develops with paternal characters. (3) *Parthenocarpy,* in which fruit development takes place without the egg having been fertilized and in different cases with or without the stimulus of pollination. Parthenocarpy occurs naturally in the banana and some strains of grapes and citrus fruits, and it has been found possible to induce it with a growth hormone in tomatoes, pepper, and tobacco. (4) *Metaxenia,* in which the embryo or endosperm developed after a cross produces a visible modification in the character of the maternal parent tissue enclosing it. This has been observed in apples and the date palm. A visible effect of the male parent on the character of the endosperm (*xenia*) is expected after some crosses, for the male parent contributes nuclear material to the tissue, but effects upon tissues where no such material is present must receive another explanation.

Conclusions.—The foregoing account of the normal angiosperm reproductive cycle, and of various modifications of it which may occur regularly or occasionally in some species, should serve to emphasize the importance of a thorough knowledge of the subject to one who wishes to undertake genetical or cytogenetical researches on this great group of plants.

The typical angiosperm life cycle bears a certain resemblance to that of animals, since each of them includes a diploid body and monoploid gametes. In some studies it may be sufficient to think of them as alike, but to interpret properly certain genetical behavior of the plant one must know that it has a second type of reproductive cell, the spore, and a gametophytic phase, neither of which is present in the animal cycle.

CHAPTER XI

CYTOLOGY OF REPRODUCTION IN PLANTS OTHER THAN ANGIOSPERMS

In nearly all plants of the groups now to be considered—gymnosperms, ferns, mosses, liverworts, algae, and fungi—the life cycle, like that of angiosperms, includes two kinds of reproductive cells: gametes and spores. Diplosis occurs at syngamy, while haplosis, except in certain algae and fungi, takes place at sporogenesis. The following sections will deal chiefly with cytological features of particular interest in each group, although this will entail some consideration of morphological features described in textbooks of general botany.

Gymnosperms.—The reproductive process in gymnosperms is carried out in the cones. The staminate cone bears microsporangia in which microspore quartets and eventually pollen grains are produced. The male gametophyte in these grains has more cells than in angiosperms, but the number of male gametes produced is practically always two. The ovulate cone bears the ovules on the carpels which compose it, but unlike angiosperm carpels these do not form an ovary enclosing the ovules. This is the most fundamental distinction between the gymnosperm cone and the angiosperm flower.

In the ovule one megaspore of a quartet forms a coenocytic and then multicellular gametophyte with archegonia, each containing one large egg (Fig. 107). The female gametophyte in gymnosperms, which has long been termed *endosperm*, thus develops far more extensively than that of angiosperms before syngamy and, in addition to this, archegonia are differentiated. In the Gnetales certain species resemble the angiosperms in differentiating their eggs in the coenocytic stage of the gametophyte, the cellular stage following later, though with nothing corresponding to a polar fusion.

Syngamy in gymnosperms occurs in two main forms which differ chiefly because of the character of the male gametes. In conifers the male cells are nonmotile and are delivered to the egg through a pollen tube which grows inward from the surface of the nucellus. In cycads (Figs. 107, 109) and the ginkgo tree the young pollen tube grows not directly toward the archegonium but into the tissue at the sides of the ovule, while in the pollen grain end of the tube two very large motile spermatozoids are differentiated. Disintegration of the nucellus allows this end of the tube to come into contact with the gametophyte near the archegonia. There the tube liberates the sperms which make their way between the archegonial neck cells into the egg.

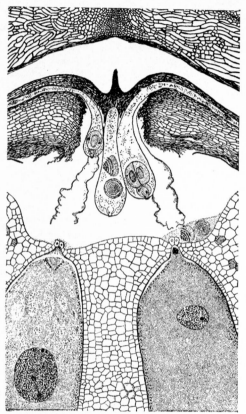

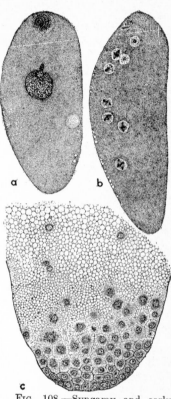

Fig. 107.—Portion of ovule of a cycad (*Dioön*) at the time of fertilization. Pollen tubes growing in the nucellar tissue are developing sperms and discharging them into the pollen chamber above the female gametophyte. The large archegonium at the right is about to be entered by a sperm. In the one to the left the sperm has entered, leaving its cytoplasmic sheath in the upper end of the egg while its nucleus has fused with the egg nucleus. (*Reconstructed from several sections by C. J. Chamberlain.*)

Fig. 108.—Syngamy and early embryogeny in a cycad (*Stangeria*). *a*, sperm nucleus uniting with nucleus of large egg; blepharoplast and cilia in upper end of egg. *b*, nuclear division without cytokinesis in progress in young zygote. *c*, coenocytic embryo becoming cellular. (*After C. J. Chamberlain.*)

The male gamete in conifers may enter the egg as a complete cell or only a nucleus. In cycads the whole sperm enters with its large nucleus, cytoplasmic layer, spirally coiled blepharoplast, and many cilia. The nucleus soon becomes free from the cytoplasm and motor apparatus and advances alone to the egg nucleus, the two then fusing (Fig. 108, *a*).

In conifers a similar course may be followed by the nucleus, but in some cases the male cytoplasm remains with it and eventually surrounds the fusion nucleus. As in angiosperms, the chromosomes of the two gametic nuclei sometimes remain more or less distinct until after the first embryonal mitosis.

Embryogeny in gymnosperms, like female gametophyte development, includes an early coenocytic phase and a later cellular stage (Fig. 108, *b*, *c*). The embryo grows, differentiates its cotyledons, and ceases development before all the endosperm (female gametophyte tissue) has been digested

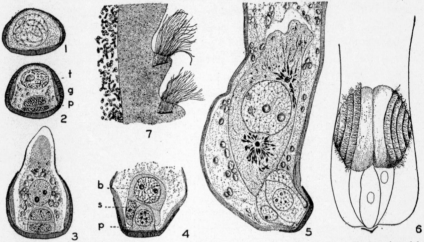

Fig. 109.—Spermatogenesis in a cycad (*Dioön*). 1, microspore. 2, pollen grain with tube nucleus, generative cell, and prothallial cell. 3, germinating pollen grain. 4, generative cell has divided to form body cell and stalk cell. 5, conspicuous blepharoplasts in enlarged body cell in growing pollen tube. 6, two spermatozoids formed by division of body cell; in each of them a spirally coiled blepharoplast runs just beneath the cell membrane and bears the cilia. 7, portion of section through spermatozoid, showing cilia growing from the ribbon-shaped blepharoplast seen as cross sections of two of its coils; portion of large nucleus at left. (*No. 6 after H. J. Webber; others after C. J. Chamberlain.*)

away. In many conifers a remarkable process known as *cleavage polyembryony* occurs. During its period of elongation the original embryo splits into a considerable number, one of which finally survives. Neighboring archegonia in the same gametophyte may also develop embryos, but the mature seed usually has only one. About the embryo is the remaining endosperm; outside of this are a trace of the nucellus and a well-developed seed coat. Since the gymnosperm ovule is not enclosed in an ovary, there is no true pericarp.

Ferns.—Some of the relatives of the ferns produce spore quartets of two morphological kinds which differ in sexual tendency, but in true ferns themselves the spores are of but one morphological type. They are produced in sporangia on the leaves of the sporophyte. The meiotic divisions in the sporocytes proceed in the ordinary way, one interesting feature being the regular arrangement of the proplastids in layers close to the cell plate at each cytokinesis. The chromosome number tends to be high, so that ferns generally are not favorable material for chromosomal studies.

Upon germination the spore produces a small, thin gametophyte, in the large cells of which the chloroplasts appear with admirable clearness (Fig. 18). Ferns in this stage have therefore been used in significant investigations on the genetics of plastids and their mutability in response to irradiation with X rays. The gametophytes develop sex organs of two kinds. In the base of each archegonium one large egg is differentiated. Each antheridium produces a considerable number of spermatozoids, and the stages of this process are of much cytological interest. It is to be remembered that no haplosis occurs in the formation

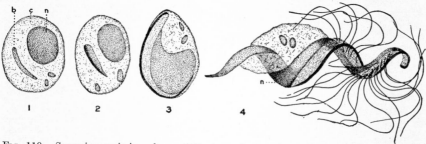

Fig. 110.—Spermiogenesis in a fern. 1–3, stages in transformation of the spermatid; 4, spermatozoid; c, cytoplasm; b, blepharoplast; n, nucleus. (*Based on drawings by A. Yuasa.*)

of these gametes, for the gametophyte from which they arise has itself developed with the gametic chromosome number.

Spermiogenesis occurs essentially as follows (Fig. 110). The spermatid, or cell that is to transform into a spermatozoid, consists of cytoplasm, a nucleus, a blepharoplast, small plastids, and probably other inclusions. The blepharoplast is of special interest, for in several pteridophytes it has been shown to be the centrosome that functioned in the preceding mitosis. It is called a blepharoplast in the spermatid because it bears the cilia of the motor apparatus, recalling thus the parallel behavior of the centrioles in animal spermiogenesis. It apparently differentiates into two longitudinal parts; then from one of these the numerous cilia grow out as the whole structure elongates spirally together with the nucleus, forming the coiled, compact body of the sperm. The spermatid cytoplasm, often containing starch granules, is held mostly as a vesicle in the large posterior coils.

When water is present externally, the sperms are liberated from the antheridium and swim about actively. If open archegonia with recently matured eggs are in the vicinity, the sperms tend to move toward them along a malic acid gradient. Many sperms may enter an archegonium, but ordinarily only one unites with the egg. The fate of the components of the sperm in syngamy is apparently not precisely the same in all ferns, but in general their behavior is as follows. The cytoplasmic vesicle is lost by the swimming sperm before it reaches the egg. The other components enter the egg cytoplasm, although the cilia have been reported in at least one species to remain outside. The nucleus then separates from most or all of the other components (residual cytoplasm and portions of the motor apparatus) and alone unites with the egg nucleus.

The fertilized egg develops into an embryo sporophyte, the early stages being passed through entirely within the archegonium. In ordinary

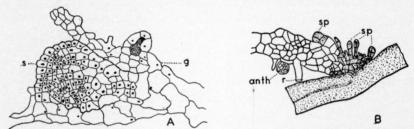

Fig. 111.—*A*, apogamy in a fern: young sporophytic tissue (*s*) developing directly from gametophytic tissue (*g*). (*After Farmer and Digby.*) *B*, apospory in a fern: gametophyte with antheridium arising directly from sporophytic tissue at base of sorus. *sp*, sporangia. *r*, rhizoid. (*After F. O. Bower.*)

ferns the planes of the first few divisions in the spherical cell form a regular geometrical pattern: hemispheres, quadrants, and octants are formed in order. The embryonic parts—stem, root, leaf, and absorbing foot—differentiate in regular positions with respect to the early subdivisions. In some ferns a considerable mass of embryonic tissue is formed before a gradual differentiation of parts becomes visible. Thus it appears that in plants, as in animals (page 129), cleavage and embryonic differentiation may be variously related in time and that the numerical equality of quadrants and embryonic parts in some ferns with early differentiation does not mean that the cleavage divisions determine the differentiation of these parts.

The ferns have long been favorite objects for the study of apogamy and apospory (Fig. 111). These aberrations in the reproductive process have been found to occur more or less constantly in several genera, and they have been induced by cultural conditions in certain others. In apogamy the meristematic region of the gametophyte gradually produces a young sporophyte directly, gametes being in no way concerned. In apospory the meristematic tissue at the leaf margin or the base of a sorus grows out directly into a gametophyte without the intervention of spores. In such cases both generations have the same chromosome number; this is the gametic number in some instances, the zygotic number in others. When one of these aberrations occurs regularly in successive cycles, compensation is made for it by another abnormality elsewhere in the cycle. Apogamy, for example, may be followed by apospory or by spore formation without haplosis.

Mosses and Liverworts.—The bryophytes have a life cycle essentially like that of the ferns, with the difference that the gametophytic phase is in general more prominent than the sporophytic one. In mosses the gametophyte typically passes through an early filamentous stage (the *protonema*) and then the more familiar leafy stage. In the liverworts it is either leafy and moss-like or develops as a broad and branching ribbon. In both groups the sporophyte is usually a stalked spore capsule standing on the gametophyte at the point where it began its development from a fertilized egg in an archegonium. Because of their fairly short life cycle, the prominence of their gametophytic phase, their adaptability to greenhouse culture, their relatively low chromosome numbers, and their response to experimental treatments, the bryophytes hold a prominent place in cytology and have proved to be especially valuable in the genetical study of gametophytic characters.

Some bryophytes are monoecious, both archegonia and antheridia being borne on the same gametophyte, while others are dioecious, with the two sexes in different gametophytes. The latter condition is known to be due to the presence of two kinds of spore in a quartet, their difference being determined at the time of meiosis (page 187). The archegonium bears a single large egg containing relatively little stored nutritive material. The antheridium develops characteristically a very large number of small biciliate spermatozoids.

In spite of the minuteness of the cells concerned, spermiogenesis has been successfully studied in bryophytes, particularly in mosses (Fig. 112). The spermatid, like that of ferns, consists mainly of cytoplasm, nucleus, plastids in some form, and a blepharoplast which has functioned as a centrosome during the last mitosis. The behavior of these cell components is of special interest when it is compared with that observed in animal spermiogenesis (page 121). The nucleus draws out into the form of a curved body within the cell. Meanwhile the blepharoplast also elongates, unites with what is to be the anterior end of the nucleus, and develops two long cilia. The *limosphere*, a large body formed by the plastid material, extrudes a small globule which moves to the anterior end of the nucleus near the blepharoplast and develops into the pointed *apical body*. The remnant of the limosphere takes up a posterior position and may eventually disappear along with a portion of the cytoplasm.

The mature sperm, which straightens out considerably after escape from the antheridium, commonly shows three main parts: (1) a long and slender body representing the condensed nucleus chiefly; (2) a small specialized anterior region composed of the apical body, a small amount of cytoplasm, and the blepharoplast which bears the two cilia, often at different points; and (3) a residual mass of cytoplasm at the posterior end.

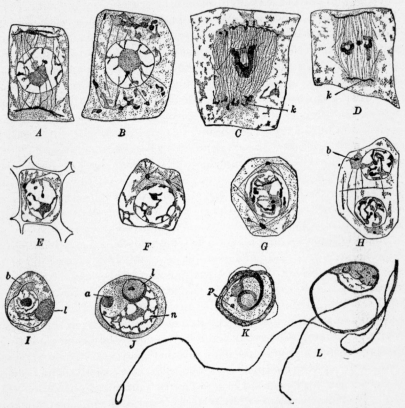

Fig. 112.—Spermiogenesis in a moss (*Polytrichum*). *A–D*, mitosis in spermatogenous cells, showing aspect of plastid substance (*k*). *E–H*, last mitosis in antheridium, showing behavior of centrosome, which in each spermatid becomes a blepharoplast (*b*). *I–L*, transformation of spermatid into biciliate spermatozoid: *a*, apical body; *l*, limosphere; *n*, nucleus. (*After C. E. Allen.*)

The details of syngamy in bryophytes are best known in certain genera of liverworts. The behavior of the motor elements during the process is somewhat uncertain, although it probably parallels that reported for ferns. The nuclear behavior has been closely followed, and it may not be precisely the same in different cases. In *Riccardia* (Fig. 113) the elongate body of the sperm, consisting of the nucleus and possibly a covering of nonnuclear material, applies itself throughout its whole length to the egg membrane and appears to sink through it laterally rather than endwise. This requires 20 to 30 minutes. The sperm nucleus lies without conspicuous change in the egg cytoplasm for 24 to 36 hours, during which time the egg enlarges and becomes more highly vacuolate. Then one end of the sperm nucleus penetrates the membrane of the egg nucleus and at once begins to swell. This process continues until the male nucleus is entirely within the egg nucleus and transformed into a chromatic thready mass with a nucleolus, these lying near the corresponding elements of the egg nucleus. Eventually the sperm and egg chromatin become indistinguishable. The egg continues to grow and undergoes the first embryonal division about 6 to 9 days after syngamy. In *Pellia* the male nucleus undergoes marked alterations as it lies in the egg cytoplasm and shows a structure more or less like that

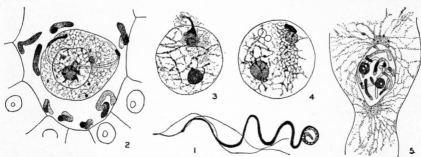

Fig. 113.—Syngamy in a liverwort (*Riccardia*). 1, spermatozoid. 2–4, syngamy. 5, prophase of first mitosis in fertilized egg. Description in text. (*After A. M. Showalter.*)

of the egg nucleus by the time the two unite. Here, as in other groups of organisms, there is some variation in the time relations of the various events: penetration of the egg membrane by the sperm, structural alteration of the sperm nucleus, nuclear union (*karyogamy*), and mitotic division of the zygote nucleus.

The young sporophyte of liverworts contains in the capsule a large mass of sporogenous cells, some of which function as sporocytes while others differentiate as hygroscopic elaters. The sporocyte divisions in some species are noteworthy because of the four-lobed form assumed by the cell before the meiotic nuclear divisions, which occur in rapid succession at the center shortly before cytokinesis is carried to completion. Other liverworts and some mosses show also a very regular behavior of the plastids during these stages. In *Anthoceros* and *Polytrichum*, for example, the single plastid divides twice before the nucleus undergoes its two divisions, with the result that each spore at first contains one (Fig. 114). In *Anthoceros* every gametophytic and sporophytic cell contains one plastid owing to this behavior at sporogenesis and to the further fact that the egg contains one plastid while the sperm contributes none at syngamy.

Apospory and apogamy appear to be very rare in bryophytes in nature. The ease with which apospory can be induced in mosses, however, renders these plants particularly valuable in the study of polyploidy. By placing small pieces of immature sporophyte stalks under suitable cultural conditions, they can be made to produce gametophytes by regeneration. These gametophytes are diploid, and their diploid gametes unite to form tetraploid sporophytes. This process can be repeated, giving tetraploid gametophytes and octoploid sporophytes. Sterility in some degree accompanies these new chromosomal states. By means of hybridization, much higher degrees of polyploidy have been obtained. Chromosome doubling can also be induced by chilling moss protonemata and by injecting young spore capsules of liverworts with certain chemicals.

Fig. 114.—Behavior of plastids during sporogenesis in a moss (*Polytrichum*). *a*, completion of plastid division in sporogenous cell. *b*, thready condition of plastids in sporocyte about to divide. *c*, nucleus divided into four (three visible); immediately after cytokinesis each spore will contain one nucleus and one plastid. *d*, young spore with two plastids formed by division. The cells of the gametophyte have more plastids. (*After T. E. Weier.*)

Algae.—The variety of ways in which asexual reproduction by spores and sexual reproduction by gametes are correlated in the life cycles of algae is of great interest to both cytologists and students of phylogeny, for it affords some basis for speculation as to the origin of the conditions observed in other groups of organisms. In the paragraphs below we shall therefore use the life cycle as a general basis of description, directing attention here and there to special cytological features.

Considering first the *green algae*, it is found that some of the most familiar genera, such as *Ulothrix*, *Oedogonium*, and *Spirogyra*, have the reduced chromosome number throughout the life cycle except in the zygote. They are therefore termed *haplonts* and show no alternation of vegetative generations. The *Ulothrix* plant reproduces asexually by means of motile zoöspores. Under appropriate conditions motile biciliate gametes similar in form to the zoöspores are produced, and these unite two by two to form zygotes. The two which unite, although morphologically alike, are "plus" and "minus" (female and male?) in reaction and come from different filaments: the plants are heterothallic.

The zygote upon germination produces four nonmotile or motile spores with the reduced chromosome number. These in turn develop into new plants.

Oedogonium produces motile asexual zoöspores and male gametes which resemble them in having a crown of many cilia (Fig. 115). The female gamete, however, is a large nonmotile egg with a visibly differentiated "receptive spot" at the point where the sperm is to enter. The nucleus lies near this spot. The sperm passes through a pore in the wall of the cell bearing the egg, and syngamy takes place. The resulting zygote ripens into a resting oöspore, and as it does so meiosis occurs. Upon germination of the oöspore four zoöspores, each with the reduced chromosome number, are produced, and these develop into new plants. Some species are heterothallic, a segregation of the two sex tendencies occurring at meiosis.

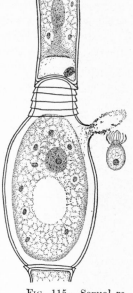

The motor apparatus of the motile cells of *Oedogonium* is noteworthy (Fig. 116). The nucleus of the cell which is to transform into a zoöspore comes in contact with the cell membrane, which there forms a convex thickening. A ring of granules appears in this region, and as the nucleus moves away the ring becomes double, a crown of cilia then growing out from the outer half of the ring. Such cilia-bearing organs formed apparently by the cell membrane are called *plasmodermal* blepharoplasts to distinguish them from the *centrosomal* blepharoplasts of ferns and mosses. It is of interest to observe that the zoöspore resembles the motile gamete morphologically in *Ulothrix* and *Oedogonium*, although the morphology differs in the two genera. This sug-

Fig. 115.—Sexual reproduction in *Oedogonium*. One cell of the filament has enlarged as an oögonium and contains a large egg. A sperm is about to enter the oögonium by way of a pore with an extruded slime papilla. (*Modified from H. Klebahn.*)

gests a common origin of the two types of reproductive cell.

Spirogyra differs sharply from the genera described above in having neither zoöspores nor other ciliate cells. At the time of sexual reproduction two cells become joined by a conjugating tube (Fig. 117). Their two protoplasts with their remarkable chloroplasts then become slightly modified in appearance and behave as gametes. One of them may pass through the conjugating tube to the other, with which it then unites, or both protoplasts may move into the tube and unite there. Contractile vacuoles have been found to play a role in the movement of these gametes by withdrawing water from the central sap vacuole and discharging it between the protoplast and the cell wall. The nuclei of the two gametes fuse, but their plastids do not. It appears that in some species where only one of the gametes migrates the plastids of this gamete degenerate in the fusion cell, leaving those of the other gamete to continue into the next generation. This is more easily demonstrated in the related genus *Zygnema*. As the zygote matures and becomes a thick-walled resting zygospore, the fusion nucleus divides meiotically, three of the four resulting nuclei then degenerating (Fig. 118). Upon germination the zygospore develops into a new plant. Of frequent occurrence in these genera is the formation of parthenospores, outwardly resembling the zygospores, by single cells without fusion.

Chlamydomonas, a unicellular green alga, is also a haplont. The motile vegetative cells under certain conditions unite two by two as

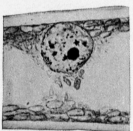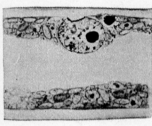

Fig. 116.—Development of blepharoplast in zoöspore of *Oedogonium*.   (*After H. Kretschmer.*)

gametes. The resulting zygote is diploid, and when it germinates meiosis occurs, each of the four new motile cells arising from it having the reduced chromosome number. These organisms, which can be grown in large numbers in a small space, have been the subject of a number of genetical researches. The inheritance of characters exhibited by the vegetative cells and zygotes are as should be expected in an organism with this type of life cycle.

A second general type of life cycle is represented in certain species of *Cladophora* and other genera. In *C. suhriana*, for example, there are two kinds of plants that look but do not behave alike. The plants of one type arise from zoöspores, have the monoploid chromosome number, and produce biciliate gametes. This species is heterothallic. After the union of two gametes, the resulting zygote grows into a diploid plant which bears monoploid zoöspores. Hence this cycle shows a well-marked alternation of generations, and species having it are termed *diplohaplonts*.

A third general type of cycle is found in *Codium* and certain other genera of the coenocytic Siphonales. These plants show no alternation of generations and are *diplonts*, the nuclei being diploid throughout the whole cycle except in the gametes. Meiosis occurs in the male and female gametangia when the nuclei of the biciliate gametes are formed.

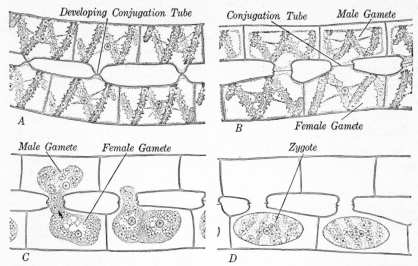

FIG. 117.—Stages in the union of gametes and the formation of the zygote in the green alga *Spirogyra*. Explanation in text. (*From Smith, Overton, et al.: A Textbook of General Botany, 4th ed., The Macmillan Company.*)

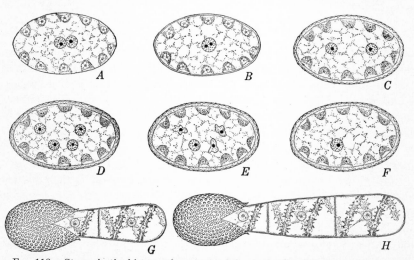

FIG. 118.—Stages in the history of a zygote of the green alga *Spirogyra*. Explanation in text. (*From Smith, Overton, et al.: A Textbook of General Botany, 4th ed., The Macmillan Company.*)

Such gametic meiosis is very rare in plants. The female gamete contains numerous plastids, while the male is much smaller and contains only one. After syngamic union the resulting zygote develops at once into a new plant. *Cladophora glomerata* is also reported to be a diplont, but it differs from *Codium* in having zoöspores: these occur throughout the year, while gametes are formed only in the spring.

The *brown algae* also exhibit life cycles of the three main types described above. *Ectocarpus virescens* is a haplont. The plant body produces biciliate gametes which fuse in pairs, and the resulting zygotes undergo meiosis as they germinate to form new plants. Other types of cycle are shown by certain other species of the genus. Evidently the same species may differ in this respect in the North Atlantic Ocean and the Mediterranean Sea.

Dictyota dichotoma is a diplohaplont. There are three kinds of plant similar in external appearance. Monoploid female plants produce large nonmotile eggs which are liberated into the sea water. These are fertilized by small uniciliate sperms from monoploid male plants. The zygotes germinate in a few hours and develop into diploid plants producing tetraspores. These tetraspores, which are products of meiotic divisions, develop into new sexual plants. In *Laminaria* the gametophytic phase is very minute and consists of only a few cells. The very large body (kelp) is the sporophytic phase.

Fucus and species of certain other genera are diplonts. Here the plant body is diploid and produces large motile eggs and very small laterally biciliate sperms. Some species are dioecious. The zygotes very soon germinate and develop into new diploid bodies. Since meiosis occurs in the divisions of the gametogenous cells in the sex organs, there are no monoploid vegetative cells in the cycle. There are no zoöspores. It is thought that this form of cycle, which is very rare in plants, may have arisen through the assumption of gametic functions by spores. This should not be surprising in view of the fact that the spores in many plant groups show a differentiation into two types correlated with the sex of the plants they produce. It is of further interest to note that in brown algae (*e.g.*, *Cutleria*) having zoöspores these cells and the male gametes are both laterally biciliate.

Of the several cycle types observed among the *red algae* only two will be mentioned here. In *Polysiphonia violacea* there are, as in the brown alga *Dictyota dichotoma*, morphologically similar plants of three kinds: monoploid females, monoploid males, and diploid tetraspore-bearing plants. The female gamete is at the base of a flask-shaped cell with a long hair-like extension, the *trichogyne*. Small nonmotile male gametes (*spermatia*) from male plants become attached to the trichogynes. A spermatium nucleus enters the trichogyne and moves through it to the female nucleus, with which it unites. The diploid nucleus then divides, and the cell sends out short filaments from the ends of which diploid *carpospores* are budded off. About the mass of carpospores the vegetative cells form a cystocarp. The carpospores later develop into diploid plants which bear monoploid tetraspores. These in turn develop into monoploid male and female plants. *Polysiphonia* thus has a regular alternation of sporophytic and heterothallic gametophytic generations in the cycle, and in addition it has a diploid carposporic phase between syngamy and the initiation of sporophyte development. This extra phase is more prominent in certain other genera.

Nemalion and *Scinaia* are haplonts. The only vegetative plants are sexual, and after syngamy meiosis occurs in the zygote. Carpospores soon formed by proliferation from the zygote are monoploid and produce new sexual plants.

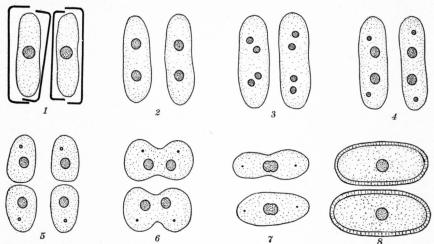

Fig. 119.—Diagram of nuclear behavior during conjugation in a diatom (*Rhopalodia*). Explanation in text. (*Based on drawings by H. Klebahn.*)

Among the *diatoms* the cytology of reproduction is best known in the bilaterally symmetrical Pennales. When ordinary vegetative multiplication by cell division occurs, the two-valved shell is pushed apart and each of the two daughter cells secretes a new valve fitting inside the old one; hence in successive asexual generations the average size of the cells tends to diminish. At the time of sexual reproduction, *e.g.*, in *Rhopalodia* (Fig. 119), two individuals conjugate in a common mass of secreted jelly. In each individual the nucleus undergoes two successive divisions which are meiotic in character. Two of the resulting nuclei become large and two small. Cytokinesis occurs in a transverse plane, giving two cells each with a large and a small nucleus. Then these cells fuse with two similar ones formed in the same manner by the other individual. The large nuclei unite, while the small ones disappear. The two zygotes then grow and become large *auxospores* which secrete a pectic covering and eventually the siliceous wall characteristic of the species. In this process the maximum cell size is restored.   Diatoms with this type of cycle are diplonts.   The radially symmetrical Centrales have been supposed to be haplonts, but recent investigations have shown that at least some of them are diplonts.

In the *blue-green algae* no sexual reproductive cycle has ever been discovered.   The cell in this group multiplies by division and in some genera, *e.g.*, *Oscillatoria*, multicellular filaments are formed.   These filaments multiply by simple fragmentation.   At the time of cell division the problematical central body, which varies widely in distinctness and resembles a nucleus to the extent of containing chromatin, may also divide, but its exact nature and its function are not yet understood.

Fungi.—The fungi, like the algae, show a rather bewildering array of life-cycle types.   This section must therefore be limited to a few of the cytologically better known cases.   These will illustrate the characteristic reproductive behavior observed in the main subdivisions of this great plant phylum.

In the *phycomycetes* the mycelium is coenocytic.   In the order Mucorales abundant asexual spores are produced in sporangia on the mycelium.   The sexual process involves the fusion of the multinucleate contents of two gametangia.   The fusion product becomes a thick-walled resting zygospore.   This germinates to form a mycelium or a "germ sporangium," the spores from which produce new mycelia.   The nuclear behavior during this process is exceedingly difficult to follow, but recent studies indicate several variations in the different species examined: (1) the nuclei fuse in pairs and then undergo meiosis before the zygospore matures (*Mucor genevensis* and others); (2) some of the nuclei fuse, the others degenerate, and meiosis is delayed until zygospore germination (*e.g.*, *Rhizopus nigricans*); (3) the nuclei associate in groups in the zygospore, and some of them fuse in pairs just before germination, meiosis following in the developing germ sporangium (*e.g.*, *Phycomyces Blakesleeanus*); (4) there are no nuclear fusions at any stage (*e.g.*, *Sporodinia grandis*).   In heterothallic species of Mucorales the plus and minus tendencies are segregated in the spores from the germ sporangium.

In the Saprolegniales there are motile asexual zoöspores.   There are also well-differentiated eggs produced singly or in groups in oögonia. An antheridium applies itself to the surface of an oögonium and sends in a tube which delivers a male nucleus to the single egg (*Pythium*). When there are several eggs in the oögonium (*Saprolegnia*), the antheridial tube branches and delivers a nucleus to each of them.   The zygote takes the form of a resting oöspore.   When it germinates, meiosis occurs (demonstrated in *Achlya*), indicating that these plants are haplonts.

In the Blastocladiales there is a genus (*Allomyces*) in which several strains have been shown to be diplohaplonts.   The sexual plants bear uniciliate male and female gametes differing in size. The plants developed from the zygotes bear zoöspores which produce the next generation of sexual plants.

The most familiar *basidiomycetes* are the rusts, which do so much damage to grain crops, and the mushrooms. The latter will furnish our example of nuclear cytology in this group of fungi (Fig. 120). The spores discharged from the gills or pores of the mushroom germinate and produce a septate primary mycelium, usually with one nucleus per cell but sometimes with more. Most species are heterothallic, the spores being of two kinds and producing plus and minus mycelia, respectively. A primary mycelium may produce small asexual reproductive bodies known as *oïdia*, but usually it does not develop the familiar sporophores, or mushrooms. When plus and minus mycelia come in contact, their hyphae unite at one or more points where openings are formed in the intervening walls. At each point of union the plus nucleus divides, one of the daughter nuclei then passing into the minus hypha. At the same time, the minus nucleus divides, one of its daughter nuclei passing into the plus hypha. In this way each primary mycelium comes to have a binucleate cell. In the plus hypha the introduced minus nucleus divides, one of the products passing through a pore in the wall into an adjacent plus cell, rendering it binucleate also. This process is repeated cell by cell until much of the primary plus mycelium becomes *diploidized*. The binucleate mycelium so formed is called a *secondary* mycelium. Meanwhile the same process may be carried out by the plus nucleus delivered to the minus mycelium so that it, too, becomes diploidized. The two mycelia are thus mutually diploidized. As the binucleate secondary mycelium continues its growth, the nuclei, now in pairs, divide in unison (conjugately). Each pair of nuclei is called a *dikaryon*, and this secondary mycelium, which is the stage commonly observed in nature, is accordingly known as the *dikaryophase*. It is often said to be diploid, even though the nuclei are individually monoploid, for the protoplasmic activity is now influenced by two genomes differing in constitution.

Numerous hyphae of the secondary type become much intertwined and differentiated as thick strands (rhizomorphs) which develop the sporophores. At the surface of the gills, or in some species the pores, of the sporophore the ends of some of the binucleate hyphae enlarge as *basidia*. In each young basidium are two nuclei which are descendants of the two brought together when primary hyphal union and diploidization occurred. The two nuclei now fuse (*karyogamy*), doubling the chromosome number. Then the diploid nucleus undergoes two meiotic divisions, and the four resulting nuclei pass into the four basidiospores which are budded off from the basidium. When these spores germinate, two of them produce plus while two produce minus mycelia. This can be determined by removing the quartet of spores from a basidium and cultivating them separately.

In this reproductive cycle, which is paralleled in structures of very different appearance in the rusts, the stage of greatest cytological interest is the dikaryophase. The significance of this peculiar nuclear state will be pointed out below.

The *ascomycetes*, like the basidiomycetes, include forms with cycles including a dikaryophase. The spores, which are borne in sacs, or *asci*,

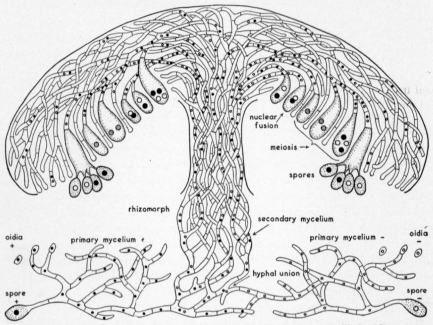

Fig. 120.—Diagram of nuclear history in the life cycle of a heterothallic basidiomycete. At the point of hyphal union the plus and minus nuclei are about to undergo division. One of the products of each division will pass to the other hypha (see text). One primary mycelium is shown partially diploidized as it would be at a later stage; the other is commonly diploidized also. Diploidization has been followed by the formation of a sporophore. The arrangement of successive stages in the basidia is arbitrary. Natural proportions are not represented, and nuclei are not drawn in all cells.

produce septate uninucleate mycelia, which in heterothallic species are of two kinds, plus and minus. The uninucleate mycelium in forms like *Peziza* or *Pyronema* develops the familiar apothecia, or open cup-shaped fruit bodies (Fig. 121). At a very early stage in the development of the apothecium there differentiates in its midst a multinucleate female organ, the *ascogonium*, and a multinucleate *antheridium*. The nuclei of the latter are discharged through a trichogyne into the ascogonium, where they mingle with the nuclei of the ascogonium. The ascogonium then sends out a number of ascogenous hyphae, into which pairs of nuclei (dikarya) migrate. As these hyphae grow, the paired nuclei divide conjugately. Meanwhile the surrounding uninucleate hyphae continue the development of the apothecium.

Eventually an ascus is developed from the subterminal cell of each ascogenous hypha. The two nuclei in this cell unite, and very soon the resulting diploid nucleus undergoes three successive divisions, of which the first two are meiotic in character. Spores are then formed about the eight nuclei as centers. This involves a curious cytokinetic

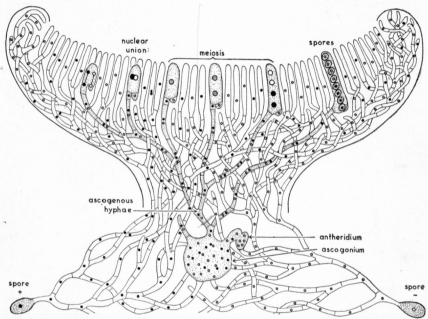

Fig. 121.—Diagram of nuclear history in the life cycle of a heterothallic ascomycete. Early and late stages of the cycle are shown, the early stages being in the lower portion of the diagram and later stages in the upper portion. Long before the apothecium and the spores are mature the sex organs have disappeared. The apothecium is composed of uninucleate hyphae and binucleate ascogenous hyphae. The arrangement of successive stages in the asci is arbitrary. In the ascus at the extreme left the last conjugate division is being completed. Natural proportions are not represented.

activity of the astral rays remaining from the third nuclear division. They curve around from each centrosome and cut out a portion of the cytoplasm about each nucleus, leaving the residual cytoplasm to disintegrate. The eight ascospores sometimes lie in a row, and in some species the positions of the mitotic figures in the three divisions that produced spore nuclei have been so regular that it can be readily determined which portions of the chromatic matter now constituting the eight nuclei were separated at each of the divisions. This has made it possible in certain species to show by genetical evidence that disjunction of homologous chromosomal elements occurs in the first two divisions but not in the third.   This is of special interest in connection with a contention that in some species there are two nuclear fusions in the cycle, one in the ascogonium and another in the ascus, and that a double reduction compensates for this in the three ascus divisions.   It now seems evident that if such a process occurs it is very rare.

An interesting feature of nuclear division in asci is the intranuclear character of the achromatic figure.   As the nucleus enlarges in the prophase, the spindle develops in the karyolymph with its poles at the nuclear membrane.   Asters, when present, lie in the cytoplasm.   The membrane may remain intact until anaphase or even throughout the entire nuclear cycle, constricting between the daughter chromosome groups at the close of division.   Such figures are also present in certain other plant and animal cells.

Conclusions.—The series of three chapters now being concluded should serve several purposes.

1. It should furnish cytological pictures, albeit sketchy ones, of the reproduction and life cycles of organisms representing many natural groups.   These constitute an essential part of the working cytologist's background.

2. It should indicate the great variety of materials available for research projects of various kinds.   The success of a project may depend largely or entirely upon a wise selection of an organism or tissue as a basis of investigation, and there are many of these to choose from in nature.   From what has been set forth in these chapters it should be obvious that one can find materials peculiarly suited to the study of such problems as the role of asters in cytokinesis, the causes and effects of parthenogenesis, the role of cells as units in tissues, the relative effects of monoploidy and diploidy, the process of secretion in cells, the role of the nucleus in development and heredity, and so on.

A single striking illustration of this is afforded by certain fungi described in the preceding section.   Cytologists and geneticists have long wished to know if or in what manner the effect upon development exerted by a fusion nucleus after syngamy differs from that of the nuclei before the fusion; in other words, does the association of two genomes within a common nuclear membrane result in activity differing from that of two unfused monoploid nuclei lying in the common cytoplasm? Material nicely suited to the solution of this problem has been found in the peculiar dikaryophase of basidiomycetes and ascomycetes.   In *Peniophora* and *Neurospora*, representing these two groups respectively, evidence is accumulating that will yield an answer to this important question.   At the present time it appears that at least some of the activities of a fusion nucleus are duplicated by the dikaryon, or unfused pair of nuclei. Hence this peculiar nuclear condition in a part of the life cycle, the possibility of determining the capacities of each spore of a given quartet or octet, and the convenience and rapidity with which the plants may be cultured and subjected to biochemical analysis (page 202), have combined to bring these fungi from obscurity to a prominent position in biological research.

3. These chapters show in what a great variety of ways a given process may be carried out or a given result attained. A recognition of the unity underlying all this diversity should enable one to distinguish more surely what is fundamental from what is accessory or only incidental. Concepts based on only one or two typical cases often require revision when viewed in the light of what occurs in organisms of many kinds. Far too many definitions of biological phenomena are merely descriptions of single examples of a class and fail to indicate what is significant in all cases. The mastery of many definitions is a poor substitute for the possession of a few broadly based concepts.

Finally, an acquaintance with the cytological diversities of plants and animals should contribute something to the value of one's speculations on the origin of the cytological constitutions and reproductive processes characterizing the various groups. This is a part of the great problem of phylogeny, which, because of its complexity and the significance of its conclusions, must be investigated with thoroughness and long suspension of judgment. In no other field of inquiry is it truer that "it is easy to use simple logic when the facts are few."

CHAPTER XII

CYTOLOGY AND MENDELIAN HEREDITY

For two thousand years and more, men have speculated on the causes of likeness and difference between parent and offspring. The fact that some parental characters are transmitted to the immediate offspring while others are not, although the latter may reappear several generations later, exemplifies the puzzles that could not have been solved until recent times. Actually most of the characters exhibited by organisms are not literally transmitted at all: they are developed anew in each generation. The protoplasmic system which performs this development is itself a direct inheritance from the previous generation; hence, what is transmitted is a mass of protoplasm capable of developing the characters under the appropriate environmental conditions. Since each generation begins as a bit of protoplasm derived from the previous generation, similarities between the two are expected, while differences must be due either to the environmental conditions or to an actual constitutional difference between the protoplasms with which the two generations begin their development. Under uniform environmental conditions the similarities and differences have been found to appear according to definite rules. The inference from this is that there is in the protoplasm an organized system of some kind that persists through successive generations, yet undergoes minor orderly alterations affecting the characters developed. The problem of modern cytogenetics is that of describing this system, its transmission, its alterations, and its mode of action in ontogeny.

Before an adequate cytological theory of heredity could be devised, certain prerequisites had to be furnished. (1) There was needed a more precise formulation of the specific facts to be explained. This was supplied by the famous nineteenth-century researches of Mendel, who made mathematical analyses of the manner in which individual characters were inherited after carefully controlled crosses. From these he derived the laws that bear his name. (2) There was needed a more detailed description of the organism's life cycle, especially through the reproductive phases, in terms of visible structural units—cells, nuclei, and chromosomes. This physical framework for a theory was also largely furnished in discoveries made during the nineteenth century: the genetic continuity of protoplasm; the regular presence of the nucleus;

the multiplication of cells and nuclei by division; the presence of chromosomes and their equational division; the disjunction of homologous pairs of chromosomes at meiosis; the fusion of parental nuclei in syngamy; the fact that one of the fusing gametes may be only a nucleus; the presence of a set of chromosomes from each parent in all the offspring's nuclei.

The rise of cytogenetics as a modern branch of biological science began with the opening of the twentieth century, when it was realized that the phenomena of inheritance described by Mendel in 1865 and rediscovered in 1900 could probably be explained on the basis of chromosome behavior. That nuclear elements had a special role of this sort was advocated before 1900 by Weismann and others. Mendel's clear analysis of his data and his interpretation of the results in terms of representative factors, combined with definite findings regarding the chromosome cycle, made it possible in this century for the first time to proceed effectively with an experimental investigation of the whole problem. How intimate the fusion of cytology and genetics has become will be evident in the pages to follow.

Examples of Mendelian Heredity.—We may begin with one of Mendel's own classic experiments with garden peas (Fig. 122). Plants of a pure-bred race of tall peas (6 to 7 feet in height) and plants of a pure-bred dwarf race (¾ to 1½ feet in height) were selected for parents (P_1). When the two types were crossed, all the plants of the first filial generation (F_1) were tall like one of their parents. When these tall hybrids were self-pollinated (or bred to one another), it was found that the second generation (F_2) comprised individuals of the two grandparental types, tall and dwarf, in the ratio of 3:1. It was further found that the tall individuals of this generation, though alike in visible characters, were unlike in genetical constitution: one-third of them, if bred among themselves for another generation, produced nothing but tall offspring, showing that they were pure for the character of tallness; whereas, the other two-thirds, if similarly bred, produced again in the next generation both tall and dwarf plants in the ratio of 3:1, showing that they were hybrids with respect to tallness and dwarfness. The dwarf plants of the second generation (F_2) produced nothing but dwarfs when selfed: they were pure for dwarfness. From these facts it was evident that the plants of the F_2 generation, although they formed only two visibly distinct classes, were in reality of three kinds: pure tall individuals, tall hybrids, and pure dwarfs, these kinds occurring in the ratio of 1:2:1.

The explanation offered by Mendel for these phenomena may be stated briefly as follows. The germ cells produced by the pure tall plant carry something (now termed a *factor*, or *gene*, represented in Fig.

122 by *T*) which tends to make the resulting plant tall. The germ cells
of the dwarf carry something (*t*) causing the dwarf condition. In the
first hybrid generation (*F₁*) both factors are present, *T* coming from one
parent and *t* from the other, but *T* dominates and prevents the expression
of the recessive *t* so that the plants of this generation are all tall. When
the hybrid (*F₁*) produces germ cells, the two factors for tallness and
dwarfness segregate, half the gametes receiving *T* and the other half
t. Each gamete therefore carries either one or the other of the two
factors in question but never both; it is pure either for *T* or for *t*. This
segregation in the germ cells of factors associated throughout the soma
is the central feature of the entire series of Mendelian phenomena and
is the basis of Mendel's first law. Since the gametes, both male and
female, produced by the hybrid plants of the *F₁* generation are of two
kinds (half of them bearing *T* and half bearing *t*), four combinations are

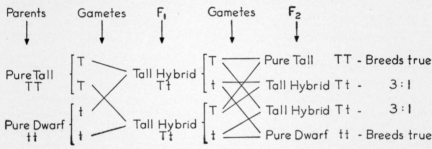

Fig. 122.—A typical case of Mendelian heredity in the garden pea.

now possible: a *T*-sperm with a *T*-egg, a *T*-sperm with a *t*-egg, a *t*-sperm
with a *T*-egg, and a *t*-sperm with a *t*-egg. These four combinations result,
respectively, in a tall plant (pure dominant, *T T*), two tall hybrids (*T t*),
and a dwarf plant (pure recessive, *t t*). It is obvious that in the long run
these three types will tend to occur in the ratio of 1:2:1.

The pure tall individuals and the tall hybrids in *F₂* are ordinarily
distinguished from each other by the *testcross*, or backcross test. It will
be readily seen that when a pure tall plant (*T T*) is crossed with the pure
recessive type (*t t*) all the offspring will be tall (*T t*); whereas, when a tall
hybrid (*T t*) is crossed with *t t*, half the offspring will be tall (*T t*) and
half will be dwarf (*t t*).

The Mendelian proportion of hybrids and pure types is perhaps better
illustrated by characters in which dominance is imperfect or lacking.
In four-o'clocks, for example, certain hybrids are more or less intermediate with respect to flower color and are easily distinguishable from
the pure parental types. When plants bearing pure crimson flowers are
crossed with those bearing pure white flowers, the hybrid plants of the
F₁ generation have magenta flowers. When these hybrids are bred among

themselves, the resulting F_2 generation comprises plants of three visibly different types: pure dominants with crimson flowers, hybrids with magenta flowers, and pure recessives with white flowers; these types tend to occur in the ratio of $1:2:1$.

Two points should be emphasized before proceeding further. (1) It should be understood that the above ratios indicate only the degree of probability of obtaining the various types through random combination of gametes. When the number of individuals is sufficiently large, the ratios tend to be approached rather closely; sometimes they are equalled exactly, even in small populations. The ratios, then, represent statistical expectations. (2) One factor, or gene, is not wholly responsible for the production of a given character. When one gene is singled out as *the* gene for a character, it is either because it is the most influential one known to affect that character, or because it is the only one of the influential genes that exists in both the dominant and recessive states in the material studied. Thus it is the "differential" in a system of factors otherwise uniform throughout the material, the character varying with this one gene. In other strains of material some other gene might be the differential one. When two or more gene pairs are acting differentially at the same time, the characters appear in ratios other than those stated above. From such ratios the geneticist is able to infer the number of genes concerned.

Terminology.—The *genotype* is the entire assemblage of genetic factors, or genes, which the organism actually possesses in its constitution, irrespective of how many of these may be expressed in externally visible characters; or, it is a class of individuals with the same genetic constitution. The *phenotype* is the aggregate of externally visible characters, irrespective of any other factors, unexpressed in characters, which may be present in the organism; or, it is a class of outwardly similar individuals. For illustration: In the case of the tall and dwarf peas there are in the second generation (F_2) three genotypes (with respect to the single character pair discussed): *T T*, *T t*, and *t t*, represented, respectively, by pure tall plants, tall hybrids, and dwarfs; but there are only two phenotypes: tall and dwarf, because the complete dominance of tallness over dwarfness renders the hybrids externally indistinguishable from the pure tall individuals. Thus one phenotype (tall plants) here includes individuals with two genotypic constitutions, and the two can be distinguished only by a study of their progeny. In the four-o'clocks described above, there are represented in the F_2 generation not only three genotypes, but also three phenotypes, since incomplete dominance renders the hybrids externally unlike either of the pure forms. Practically, a phenotype is a class of individuals that look alike, and a genotype is a class of individuals that breed alike (Castle).

Two contrasting characters such as tallness and dwarfness are said to be *allelomorphs* or *alleles*. The same terms are also used for the pair of differential genes influencing them. The corresponding adjectives are *allelomorphic* and *allelic*.

An individual is said to be *homozygous* for a given allelic factor pair if it has received the same type of factor from the two parents—a pea, for example, with the constitution *T T* or *t t*. If it has unlike members in the pair, such as *T t*, it is said to be *heterozygous*. It may be homozygous for some pairs and heterozygous for others, or it may conceivably be either homozygous or heterozygous for all its factors. Thus an organism with the genotypic constitution *A A B b c c* is homozygous for the factors *AA* and *cc* and heterozygous for *Bb*. It is a pure dominant with respect to *A* and *a*, a pure recessive with respect to *C* and *c*, and a hybrid with respect to *B* and *b*. The phenotypic appearance of the organism is here determined by the dominant factors *A* and *B* and the recessive *c*. It is a common practice to represent dominant factors by capital letters and their recessive alleles by the corresponding small letters.

Explanation in Terms of Chromosomes.—The basic reason for the manner in which an allelic pair of characters is inherited becomes evident when factor distribution is compared with chromosome distribution. Each parent furnishes the offspring with one chromosome set, or genome. Referring to Fig. 75, it is seen that in meiosis the two members of any homologous chromosome pair, *e.g.*, the ones marked *A* and *a*, are so distributed that a descendant of *A* lies in half the spores or gametes, while a descendant of *a* lies in the rest of the spores or gametes. If such an organism is self-fertilized or crossed to a similar one, both *A* gametes and *a* gametes being functional in each sex, random unions will result in combinations of three kinds (*A A, A a, a a*) in the ratio of 1:2:1. Hence the inference is that a given allelic pair of genes is located in a homologous pair of chromosomes. If the genes *T* and *t* are so located in a chromosome pair of the garden pea, Mendel's results with tallness and dwarfness are accounted for. His first law was a result of chromosome disjunction at meiosis, although at the time of its formulation almost nothing was known about chromosome behavior.

Mendel also studied six other pairs of heritable characters in peas. He observed that all seven pairs (including tallness and dwarfness) were inherited independently, *i.e.*, while each character gave the usual ratio with its allele, there was no tendency on the part of any character to appear more often with a given nonallelic character than with any other after a testcross. This independence of character pairs was stated in Mendel's second law. A case of this kind is illustrated in the left-hand part of Fig. 123, which shows also the cytological basis for it. The two character pairs are tall vs. dwarf, and green pod vs. yellow pod, the first-named character in each pair being the dominant one. A plant dominant and homozygous for both differential gene pairs ($T\ T\ Gp\ Gp$) is crossed to one that is recessive and homozygous for both pairs ($t\ t\ gp\ gp$). The F_1 plants are heterozygous for both pairs ($T\ t\ Gp\ gp$). When these plants are testcrossed to a $t\ t\ gp\ gp$ plant, plants of four kinds appear in equal numbers in F_2: tall-green, dwarf-yellow, tall-yellow, and dwarf-

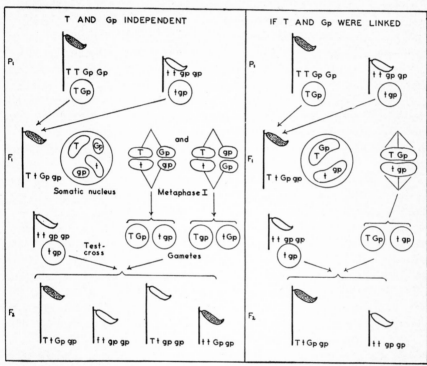

FIG. 123.—Diagram illustrating the cytological basis of independent and of linked inheritance of characters. Vertical lines represent plants; green pods stippled; yellow pods unshaded. Actually, these particular characters are independent, not linked. Further explanation in text.

green. This shows that the F_1 plants must have produced spores and gametes of four kinds in equal numbers: $T\ Gp$, $t\ gp$, $T\ gp$, and $t\ Gp$. The explanation for this lies in the fact that the two gene pairs concerned lie in different chromosome pairs which have two possible relative orientations at metaphase I in the sporocytes of the F_1 plants. Hence Mendel's second law expressed the results of random assortment of chromosome pairs at meiosis.

An important qualification has had to be made in Mendel's second law, now that more character pairs have been studied. Organisms have large numbers of gene pairs, but relatively few chromosome pairs; hence, each chromosome must carry many genes. The inheritance of two character pairs dependent upon differential genes in the same chromosome pair would be unlike that described above, for random assortment of chromosomes would play no part in determining their combinations. This is illustrated in the right-hand part of Fig. 123. If the two gene pairs in the F_1 plant were located in one chromosome pair as shown, there would be formed only two kinds of spores and gametes instead of four, and the F_2 generation would show only the two parental combinations, tall-green and dwarf-yellow. The two characters contributed together by each grandparent are still associated. This phenomenon is known as *linkage*. The number of groups of linked genes equals the number of chromosome pairs; there are, for example, 4 in *Drosophila melanogaster* and 10 in *Zea mays*. Mendel happened to select for special study in garden peas seven independent character pairs associated with genes now known to lie in the seven pairs of chromosomes. It should be added that characters associated with genes in the same chromosome pair show independent inheritance if crossing over between the gene pairs gives a recombination value of 50 per cent (page 175).

Assignment of Genes to a Chromosome.—How is it ascertained in what chromosome of a genome a given gene and those linked with it are located? In plants one of the convenient methods involves the use of individuals occasionally appearing in the breeding plot with one extra chromosome. This condition arises as a result of *nondisjunction*, commonly at sporogenesis. Two members of a pair that should disjoin in meiosis fail to do so, a spore and later a gamete therefore arising with one member of its genome in duplicate. Union of this gamete with a normal one yields a plant with one of its chromosomes in triplicate, all the other chromosomes being in duplicate as usual. At meiosis the three members of the "trisome" usually disjoin two from one, so that some of the spores and gametes carry an extra chromosome. It can readily be calculated that Mendelian ratios in plants obtained when this trisomic plant is testcrossed will not be the same for characters dependent upon genes in the trisome as for characters due to genes in the other chromosomes, provided the trisomic plant is heterozygous for genes in the trisome. For example, when a plant carries the genes *A A a* in the trisome and the factors *B b* in a normal chromosome pair, the population obtained after a testcross to a plant with *a a b b* is expected to show a phenotypic ratio of 5:1 for a character due to *A* and the normal 1:1 ratio for a character due to *B*. Hence, by observing what characters appear in trisomic ratios and by examining the plants cytologically to see which chromosome of the genome is present in triplicate, the conclusion can be drawn that the genes responsible for the abnormal ratios are located in that chromosome. The expected trisomic ratios are ordinarily obtained only when the trisomic plant is used as a female parent, for it has been found that pollen grains carrying the extra chromosome usually do not function well in competition with normal pollen. Moreover, the ratios may be disturbed by the tendency of the extra chromosome to lag in the meiotic anaphase and thus sometimes fail to be included in a spore nucleus.

The first character to be assigned mainly to genes in a given chromosome was sex. This was possible because in many organisms there is a chromosome pair that differs visibly from the other pairs and differs also in males and females. As will be described in a later section, the behavior of this pair is such as to yield two visibly distinct chromosome complements in equal numbers in each generation, and these are found, respectively, in the cells of the two sexes. Nonsexual characters dependent upon genes in the sex chromosomes are said to be sex-linked, and they show a mode of inheritance differing somewhat from characters not so linked. Unlike sex-limited characters, they may appear in either sex, as will be explained further on (page 190).

By these and other methods, genes have been assigned to their proper chromosomes in a considerable number of organisms. In some of those which have been most intensively investigated, this has been done for every chromosome of the genome.

Recombination and Crossing Over.—We have seen that when two pairs of differential genes are located in one chromosome pair the characters dependent upon them are linked, *i.e.*, the character combinations present in the two individuals originally crossed tend to reappear in the F_2 generation following a testcross. In Fig. 123, right-hand part, the F_2 comprises individuals of only two classes, and these show the original combinations. As a general rule, however, there are four classes in F_2: the individuals of the two additional classes show *recombinations*, *i.e.*, the two pairs of characters have, as it were, exchanged partners. The percentage of F_2 individuals showing such recombination tends to maintain a characteristic average in repeated tests involving the same characters, but for different character combinations it varies all the way from 0 to 50. When the value lies near 50, it becomes impossible without other indirect tests to distinguish the results from those of random chromosome assortment (left half of Fig. 123). The mechanism involved, however is a quite different one, since only one chromosome pair is involved. The nature of this mechanism is brought out in the following example (Fig. 124).

Two well-known characters in *Drosophila* cultures are black body and vestigial wings. Each of these is a recessive character, appearing in a fly only when the gene has been received from both parents in the reces-

sive condition *b* or *v*. In the dominant conditions *B* and *V* these genes
produce, respectively, normal gray body and normal long wings. When a
fly, homozygous for both dominant factors, is mated to one with all
the corresponding factors recessive, the offspring all have normal body
and wings, because of the dominance of *B* and *V* over *b* and *v*, respectively.
If the females of this F_1 generation are backcrossed to the homozygous
recessive, flies of four types appear in the next generation: gray-long,
black-vestigial, gray-vestigial, and black-long. Those flies with the
original combinations (gray-long and black-vestigial) together comprise
83 per cent of the total number; only 17 per cent are of the new types

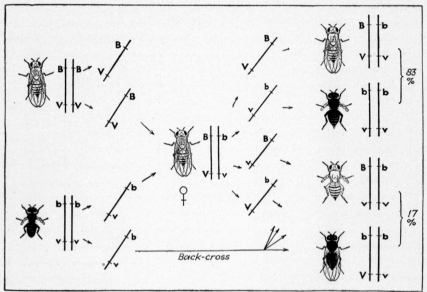

Fig. 124.—Linkage in *Drosophila*.   One pair of chromosomes in each fly represented by
vertical lines; chromosomes in gametes, by diagonal lines.   Explanation in text.   (*Adapted
from T. H. Morgan et al.*)

(gray-vestigial and black-long).   It thus appears that if the two characters, gray body and long wings, are contributed to the offspring by
the same parent, they tend to appear together in the majority of the
individuals resulting from the backcross; in other words, they are
linked.   This is explained by the fact that the differential genes concerned are located in one chromosome of a pair.   The same is obviously
true of the allelic characters, black body and vestigial wings, for their
genes are carried in the other chromosome of the pair.   Hence in the F_1
fly one chromosome of a homologous pair carries *B V*, while the other
carries *b v*, and they tend strongly to continue thus into the next generation.   Were the two pairs of genes in question, *B b* and *V v*, carried by
different pairs of chromosomes instead of by the same pair, there would

be no linkage: the two characters, gray and long, and likewise the two characters, black and vestigial, would then be exhibited together in the next generation by about 50 per cent of the flies, the chance frequency based on random assortment, rather than 83 per cent.

We have next to inquire into the origin of the new combination appearing in 17 per cent of the flies after the backcross. In the original female both chromosomes carry B V; hence every egg has this combination. The male has b v in both chromosomes of the pair; hence every sperm has b v. All flies in F_1 will therefore have B V in one chromosome of the pair and b v in the other; they are heterozygous for both pairs of genes. When the females of the F_1 generation mature their eggs, the two chromosomes disjoin in meiosis so that half of the eggs carry one and half the other. If the chromosomes are passed along unaltered, no new combinations appear in the next generation.

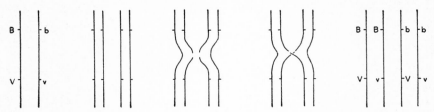

FIG. 125.—Diagram of crossing over between Bb and Vv responsible for recombinations in case illustrated in Fig. 124.

Now let it be supposed that in some of the oöcytes two nonsister chromatids exchange portions 'at some point between the two pairs of genes (Fig. 125). Some eggs will then carry unaltered chromosomes $(B$ $V)$ $(b$ $v)$, while others will carry altered ones $(B$ $v)$ $(b$ $V)$. Fertilization of these four classes of eggs by sperms carrying b v will obviously result in flies of four classes, two of which are of new kinds. The percentage of recombinations appearing depends upon the proportion of the oöcytes in which chromatid exchange (*crossing over*) occurs between the two pairs of genes. If it occurred in every oöcyte, only 50 per cent of the resulting flies would show the recombinations, since two normal as well as two altered chromatids would result in each oöcyte. From this it can readily be seen that the frequency (17 per cent) of recombination in the present example is due to the fact that the proper chromatid exchange occurred in 34 per cent of the oöcytes. Such crossing over between pairs of linked genes is a phenomenon occurring generally in plants and animals, although in some cases, notably in the males of *Drosophila*, it is absent.

Position of Genes in the Chromosome.—One of the theories of inheritance propounded late in the nineteenth century stated that "ancestral germ plasms" are arranged in a linear series in the chromosomal thread and that the significance of longitudinal chromosome division lies in the division of these numerous units. The confirmation of this view during the twentieth century has involved the answering of two questions: "In what particular order are the various genes arranged?" and "What is the precise location of each gene in the chromosome?"

The determination of the *serial order of the genes* has been made possible mainly through studies on recombination. Soon after Morgan and his coworkers had their intensive investigations of inheritance in *Drosophila* well under way, certain cases of recombination of linked characters were observed in the flies. It was then (1911) suggested that this might be a result of chromatid exchange (crossing over) such as had been reported for salamander chromosomes by Janssens (1909). This hypothesis was employed with notable success in the further development of cytogenetics, although the complete proof of its correctness was not available until 1931. The determination of serial order was based upon the fact that different couples of allelic character pairs yield recombinations in different percentages. The hypothesis was advanced that the frequency of crossing over simply varies with the distance separating the two gene pairs concerned, exchanges occurring with uniform frequency throughout the length of the tetrad. For convenience it was assumed that when recombinations appear in 1 per cent of the individuals in F_2 after a testcross the two gene pairs are separated by one "crossover unit" in the threads. On this basis a diagram, or "linkage map," was gradually built up showing the arrangement of the various genes as indicated by recombination percentages. The same procedure has since been followed in the case of a number of other animals and plants. The method used in constructing such maps is illustrated in the following example from maize.

Among the mutant characters known to be linked and assignable to chromosome 4 in maize are the following: sugary endosperm (su_1), which is recessive to the normal starchy endosperm (Su_1); tunicate ear (each kernel with a pod) (Tu), dominant to normal ear (tu); glossy leaf (gl_3), recessive to normal leaf surface (Gl_3). When plants heterozygous for all three pairs are testcrossed to plants homozygous and recessive for all three, the results are as follows (Fig. 126). The recombination percentage of sugary and tunicate is 29; hence these two genes are placed 29 units apart on a line representing the chromosome. Between tunicate and glossy the recombination percentage is 11; hence gl_3 is 11 units from Tu, but on which side? This is decided by the recombination percentage given by sugary and glossy, which is 34: gl_3 must therefore be located to the right of Tu. In this way the relative order of these three genes in the chromosome is determined. Recombinations between further characters likewise indicate the positions of other genes.

It will be noted that the recombination percentage for su_1-gl_3 is somewhat less than the sum of the percentages for su_1-Tu and Tu-gl_3. This is because genes, when rather widely separated in the chromosome, may have two crossovers between them, leaving them still in the same chromatid. This makes the observed recombination percentage lower than it would have been if no such double crossing over had occurred. Linkage maps, like those for *Zea* and *Drosophila* (Figs. 127, 128), are built up by plotting positions only on the basis of closely linked genes, thus without taking double crossing over into consideration. This means that map distance (number of units) between two genes represents recombination percentage only when these genes are rather closely linked—within about 10 units in *Drosophila* and maize. Thus the map may exceed 100 units in length, whereas the upper limit of observed

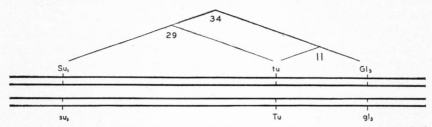

Fig. 126.—Diagram illustrating the method of determining the serial order of linked genes by comparing recombination percentages. The four parallel lines represent the chromatids in the tetrad at pachytene in the plant to be testcrossed. Further explanation in text.

recombination is 50 per cent owing to the fact that each crossover alters only two of the four chromatids. At the present time the most fully developed linkage maps for insects, vertebrates, and plants are those of *Drosophila melanogaster*, the common fowl, and maize, respectively.

The map as just described is a convenient record of the linkage relationships and serial order of the genes in the chromosome, but there are limits to its reliability as a picture of the chromosome itself. This is because such a map, especially when only a few genes have been placed upon it, does not necessarily show the *actual position of the genes in the chromosome*. If, after numerous linkage studies, no gene has to be given a place beyond the one already at the end of the map being constructed, it is a reasonable inference that this gene is actually at the end of the chromosome, but it might be that the chromosome beyond this point is inert or occupied only by unmutated genes. A gene is detectable in normal material only when it is present in the mutated as well as the unmutated form, thus giving a character contrasting with the normal one and revealing the fact that a corresponding normal gene exists. Another method, therefore, must be used to ascertain actual gene position.

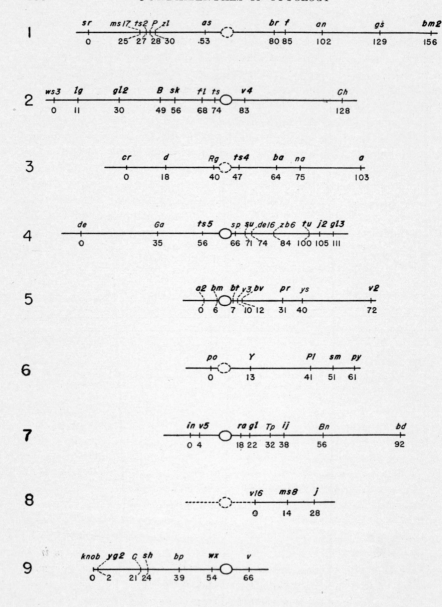

Fig. 127.—Linkage map for *Zea mays*. The kinetochores are assigned tentatively to positions with respect to the genes; those shown with broken lines are less definitely placed than the others. (*After L. F. Randolph.*)

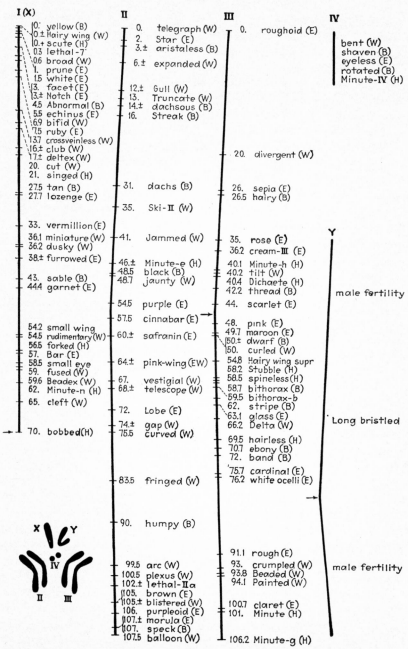

I (X)

0.	yellow (B)
0.±	Hairy wing (W)
0.+	scute (H)
0.3	lethal-7
0.6	broad (W)
1.	prune (E)
1.5	white (E)
3.	facet (E)
3.±	Notch (E)
4.5	Abnormal (B)
5.5	echinus (E)
6.9	bifid (W)
7.5	ruby (E)
13.7	crossveinless (W)
16.±	club (W)
17.±	deltex (W)
20.	cut (W)
21.	singed (H)
27.5	tan (B)
27.7	lozenge (E)
33.	vermillion (E)
36.1	miniature (W)
36.2	dusky (W)
38.±	furrowed (E)
43.	sable (B)
44.4	garnet (E)
54.2	small wing
54.5	rudimentary (W)
56.5	forked (H)
57.	Bar (E)
58.5	small eye
59.	fused (W)
59.6	Beadex (W)
62.	Minute-n (H)
65.	cleft (W)
70.	bobbed (H)

II

0.	telegraph (W)
2.	Star (E)
3.±	aristaless (B)
6.±	expanded (W)
12.±	Gull (W)
13.	Truncate (W)
14.±	dachsous (B)
16.	Streak (B)
31.	dachs (B)
35.	Ski-II (W)
41.	Jammed (W)
46.±	Minute-e (H)
48.5	black (B)
48.7	jaunty (W)
54.5	purple (E)
57.5	cinnabar (E)
60.±	safranin (E)
64.±	pink-wing (EW)
67.	vestigial (W)
68.±	telescope (W)
72.	Lobe (E)
74.±	gap (W)
75.5	curved (W)
83.5	fringed (W)
90.	humpy (B)
99.5	arc (W)
100.5	plexus (W)
102.±	lethal-IIa
105.	brown (W)
105.±	blistered (W)
106.	purpleoid (E)
107.±	morula (E)
107.	speck (B)
107.5	balloon (W)

III

0.	roughoid (E)
20.	divergent (W)
26.	sepia (E)
26.5	hairy (B)
35.	rose (E)
36.2	cream-III (E)
40.1	Minute-h (H)
40.2	tilt (W)
40.4	Dichaete (H)
42.2	thread (B)
44.	scarlet (E)
48.	pink (E)
49.7	maroon (E)
50.±	dwarf (B)
50.	curled (W)
54.8	Hairy wing supr
58.2	Stubble (H)
58.5	spineless (H)
58.7	bithorax (B)
59.5	bithorax-b
62.	stripe (B)
63.1	glass (E)
66.2	Delta (W)
69.5	hairless (H)
70.7	ebony (B)
72.	band (B)
75.7	cardinal (E)
76.2	white ocelli (E)
91.1	rough (E)
93.	crumpled (W)
93.8	Beaded (W)
94.1	Painted (W)
100.7	claret (E)
101.	Minute (H)
106.2	Minute-g (H)

IV

bent (W)
shaven (B)
eyeless (E)
rotated (B)
Minute-IV (H)

Y

male fertility

Long bristled

male fertility

X   Y

IV

II   III

Fig. 128.—Linkage map for *Drosophila melanogaster*, showing serial order of many of the known genes as determined by genetical methods. Letters in parentheses indicate portions of fly in which characters appear: *B*, body; *E*, eye; *H*, hairs; *W*, wings. Arrows indicate kinetochore position. Genes in chromosome IV are very closely linked. Positions of genes in *Y*-chromosome not well determined. (*Adapted from T. H. Morgan, A. H. Sturtevant, and C. B. Bridges and from C. Stern.*)

The solution of the problem of gene position, like that of numerous other cytogenetical questions, is being greatly facilitated by the use of abnormalities in chromosome behavior.   In the next chapter, abnormalities of various types will be described.   Our present purpose will be served by one of them, *deletion*.   Occasionally there appears spontaneously or in experimentally treated material a chromosome with a portion missing.   This portion may have been deleted from the end (terminal deletion) or from some other region (intercalary deletion). Most deletions render a monoploid cell inviable.   The same is true of a diploid cell if both chromosomes of the pair carry the deletion, but if only one member of the pair carries it the cell is often functional.   By observing the characters affected by the absence of a chromosome portion, it can be inferred what genes were lost at the time of deletion. Obviously the most useful deletions are those which are small and which do not prevent the development of the cells concerned.   Two examples illustrating the procedure will now be described.

In maize there is a mutant gene (yg_2) in the linked group occupying chromosome 9.   Plants carrying this gene in the homozygous recessive condition ($yg_2\ yg_2$) are yellow-green, while homozygous dominant ($Yg_2\ Yg_2$) and heterozygous ($Yg_2\ yg_2$) plants have the normal green color. In some strains of maize, chromosome 9 has a small terminal knob, while in other strains the knob is large; hence the chromosome can be easily distinguished in certain stages of the nuclear cycle.   The position of the yellow-green gene in the map already made on the basis of linkage relationships was near one end.   That it was also near the end of the actual chromosome was demonstrated in the following cross (Fig. 129).

A yellow-green plant homozygous for yg_2 and a small knob was used as a pistillate parent, whereas the staminate parent was normal green and homozygous for Yg_2 and a large knob.   Pollen from the latter plant was given X-ray treatment, which is known to induce chromosomal aberrations, and then placed upon the silks of the pistillate parent. When the resulting kernels were sown, they produced a population comprising plants of several classes.   Most of them were normal green in color, as expected in heterozygotes, and cytological examination showed the members of their ninth pair of chromosomes to have been unchanged by the irradiation.   Plants of a second class were yellow-green and had the large-knobbed chromosome (from the pollen parent) considerably shortened, evidently by the deletion of a region near the knob.   A third class, also yellow-green, had the large knob reduced in size, indicating a deletion including a portion of the knob.   In all cases the maternal chromosome remained unaltered.   These cytological and genetical data showed that the deletions had removed the dominant normal gene, Yg_2, from chromosome 9 in some of the pollen and also that the gene

when present lies very close to the terminal knob.   In addition to the
above three classes there was a single individual that was partly normal
green and partly yellow-green.   In the normal-green portion of the plant
the ninth chromosome pair was unaltered, as in the first class, whereas
in the yellow-green portion the paternal chromosome was shortened and
had no knob.   Evidently, therefore, the deletion in this case was truly

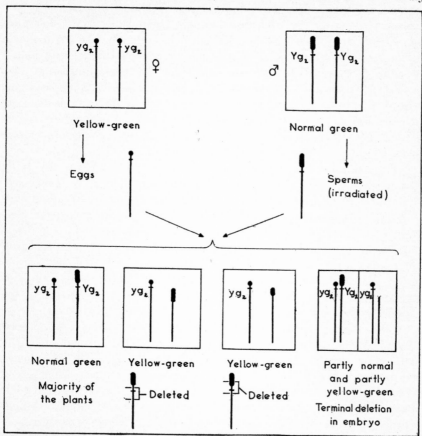

Fig. 129.—Diagram illustrating the method of determining gene location by the use of
deletions.   Explanation in text.   (*Based on work of H. B. Creighton.*)

terminal, a rare condition; moreover, it must have occurred in the
embryonic stage of the plant, since only a portion of the plant was
affected.   This plant was of further interest from the standpoint of the
physiology of genic action, for the particular effect of each of the two
genotypes was restricted to the portion of the plant containing it.
Relatively few exceptions to this type of genic action are known.

Gene location by the deletion method is most precisely determinable
in organisms having chromosomes that are large and distinguishable on

the basis of characteristic morphology. In the above example the condition of the chromosomes was determined chiefly in the micro-sporocytes, for although the chromosomes in the somatic cells of maize are not large, they are beautifully displayed in a greatly extended form at the pachytene stage in microsporocytes (Fig. 79). Not only do they show well their minute structural features there (page 92), but they are present as synapsed pairs, which makes it possible to compare minutely the two parental members part for part.

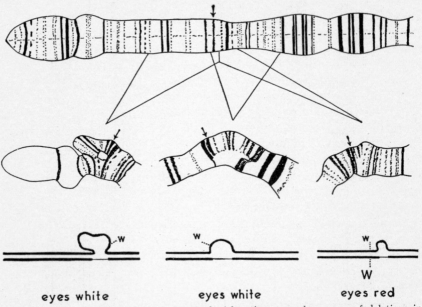

eyes white   eyes white   eyes red

Fig. 130.—Diagram illustrating the method of locating genes by means of deletions in salivary-gland chromosomes. Explanation in text. (*Based on drawings by O. Mackensen.*)

A second example illustrating this method of locating genes is taken from the literature on *Drosophila*. The somatic chromosomes in the fly are very small. Gross alterations in them can be detected, and the approximate positions of certain genes have been determined by such alterations. The rediscovery of the giant chromosomes in the salivary glands of the larva (page 94) has now made it possible to carry on such researches with far greater speed and precision. The method used in the case about to be described parallels that used in the case of maize. Male flies carrying dominant genes including W (normal red eyes) in their chromosome I were X-rayed with the purpose of inducing deletions or other aberrations in this chromosome. These flies were then mated to females carrying recessive genes, including w (white eyes, recessive), in their chromosomes I (the X-chromosomes). F_1 females were then selected for study because they contained two X-chromosomes, one from each parent. Some of them had white eyes, indicating a loss or mutation of the dominant W originally present in the father's X-chromosome. When these and other females were tested by further crosses, the chromosomes in the salivary glands revealed the conditions shown in Fig. 130. These chromosomes, it will be recalled (Fig. 67), are synapsed pairs, each of them representing two parental homologues in intimate lateral union. Since the union is so precise, band for band, dissimilarities in the two can be clearly analyzed.

The three cases in the diagram include deletions in the same general region of the paternal X-chromosomes, and by comparing these with the normal maternal chromosomes with which they are in synapsis it can be seen that where the band indicated by an arrow is present in the lower (paternal) longitudinal half of the chromosome pair the eyes of the fly are red, indicating the presence of W, whereas the eyes are white when this band is lacking in this half. From this it is concluded that the gene W was removed in the portion deleted in two of the three cases, leaving the recessive w to function alone and produce white eyes. This gene affecting eye color is accordingly assigned to a small region occupied by this band. This region represents considerably less than 1 per cent of the length of the chromosome. In this manner a large number of genes have now been located with various degrees of accuracy in the chromosomes of *Drosophila*.

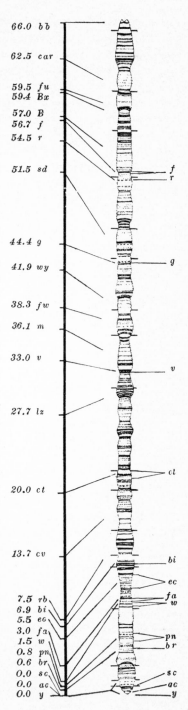

FIG. 131.—Diagram comparing the linkage map of the X-chromosome of *Drosophila melanogaster* with the salivary-gland chromosome map for some of the genes that have been located. Explanation in text. (*Adapted from T. S. Painter and O. Mackensen.*)

When the chromosome map constructed on the basis of such data is compared with the linkage map for the same chromosome, it is found that the two agree with respect to the serial order of the genes (Fig. 131). This is gratifying proof of the value of the crossover method long used for the determination of such order. The spacing of the genes, however, differs in some regions, showing that the occurrence of crossing over is not uniform in frequency throughout the length of the chromosome as was originally assumed in constructing the linkage map. A lower frequency in certain chromosomal regions, notably near the kinetochore, yields recombination percentages lower than the average; hence the genes in such regions appear closer together in the linkage map than they do in the chromosome map showing the true positions. The successful construction of such chromosome maps accurately summarizing large bodies of observational data is surely one of biology's major achievements. Their usefulness and appearance suggested an earlier remark (page 97) that the salivary-gland chromosome is a sort of "biological spectrum" indicating the genetical composition of the organism.

The Special Case of Sex.—Sex, like other characters of the organism, has a genic basis. Its inheritance in dioecious organisms, however, differs from that of other characters because of a special type of chromosomal mechanism. This specialization is manifested in the differentiation of one chromosome pair from the others in its influence upon sex and often in its visible morphology. The members of this pair are therefore known as *sex chromosomes*, although the other chromosomes, called *autosomes*, may also have some share in the determination of sex. In addition, there is a further differentiation of the sex chromosomes into two kinds, usually designated as X and Y (Figs. 132–136). The individuals of one sex, nearly always the female, have two similar chromosomes (XX), while those of the other sex have two unlike ones (XY). In a few organisms, notably birds and lepidoptera, the females have the XY pair. In some species there is no Y, one sex therefore having only one sex chromosome. Again, the X or the Y may comprise two or more elements. In certain monoploid organisms, *e.g.*, bryophyte gametophytes and some algae, the single genome includes an X in the female and a Y in the male, both X and Y being present in the zygote and the sporophyte into which it develops.

In all the above cases the behavior of the sex chromosomes in meiosis and syngamy normally results in an approximate numerical equality of the two sexes. This is shown in the following examples.

The XY type referred to above is the one of most frequent occurrence, being found in plants and animals of many natural groups. In Fig. 132 it is seen that the disjunction of the two X-chromosomes in the female animal yields gametes of but one class: every egg carries an X. Disjunction in the male, however, yields gametes of two classes: half the sperms carry X and half carry Y. The autosomes are the same in all gametes, excepting of course any differences due to ordinary heterozygosity in the individuals producing them. Syngamic unions of two kinds are now possible, X with X and X with Y. These yield, respectively, offspring of two sexes: females (XX) and males (XY). This type of mechanism is found in man (Fig. 133), although the large number

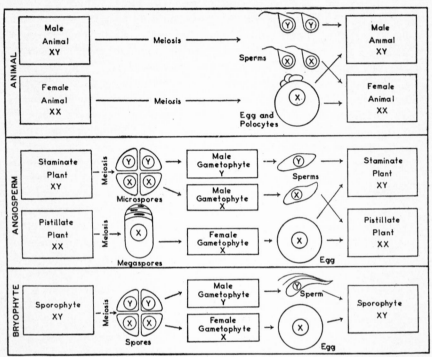

FIG. 132.—Diagram illustrating the relation of the X- and Y-chromosomes to sex in the life cycles of an animal, an angiosperm, and a bryophyte.

of chromosome pairs (24) and their small size have made it difficult to identify the sex pair, particularly the Y.

Many dioecious angiosperms have the same mechanism (Figs. 134, 135). Here the pistillate plant has XX and the staminate plant XY. All megaspores, female gametophytes, and eggs are alike in carrying X. Half the microspores, pollen grains, and male gametes carry X, while the other half carry Y. Here again two sorts of combination are possible: X with X, giving pistillate offspring, and X with Y, giving staminate offspring.

An example of the operation of the XY mechanism in monoploid organisms is afforded by the liverwort *Sphaerocarpos*, the first plant known to have sex chromosomes (Fig. 136). Here the female plants (gametophytes) have in their single genome one large X, while the male plants (gametophytes) have a very small Y. After syngamy the zygote with XY develops into the asexual sporophyte. When meiosis occurs at sporogenesis, disjunction of the X and Y results in the presence of two spores with X and two with Y in each quartet. These develop, respectively, into new female and male gametophytes. It is of interest to compare this case with that of the angiosperm in the preceding paragraph. In the liverwort X and Y are correlated, respectively, with femaleness and maleness in different gametophytes and gametes, with XY in the asexual phase of the cycle; whereas, in the angiosperm the male gametophytes and gametes have either X or Y, this difference determining in turn which of the sporophytes shall be female (XX) and which male (XY).

Fig. 133.—*XY*-chromosome pairs disjoining in first meiotic division. *a*, in spermatocyte of man. *b*, *XY* pairs in opossum, monkey, and man. (*After T. S. Painter.*)

A characteristic feature of sex chromosomes is their degree of heteropyknosis (page 86). About half the X-chromosome in *Drosophila* is heterochromatic, the numerous genes that exert an influence toward femaleness being arranged all along the euchromatic portion. In some organisms practically the entire sex chromosome is heterochromatic and is visible during the metabolic stage as a dense, stainable body in the midst of the chromonemata of the other chromosomes. Experiments have shown that in *Drosophila* the Y exerts practically no influence upon

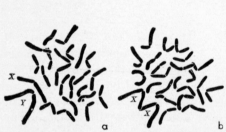

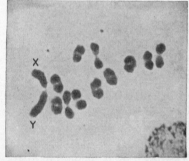

Fig. 134.—Somatic chromosome complements from staminate (*a*) and pistillate (*b*) individuals of a dioecious angiosperm (*Melandrium album*). (*After M. Westergaard.*)

Fig. 135.—Metaphase of first meiotic division in microsporocyte of *Melandrium. XY* pair about to disjoin. (*Photograph by H. E. Warmke.*)

the kind of sex developed, although it does influence fertility. In *Melandrium*, a genus of angiosperms, on the other hand, the large Y seems clearly to exercise a strong influence toward maleness. Another notable feature is the frequent absence of crossing over between the X and Y.

The significance of all these facts is by no means well understood, but there is a tendency to associate them with the advantages of dioecism. It has been pointed out above that the sex chromosome mechanism results in the production of males and females in equal numbers, even though this ratio may be disturbed by other causes. The 1:1 ratio is expected not only for sex but for all allelic character pairs in each generation in monoploid organisms. In diploid organisms the sexes also appear 1:1 in each generation, even though most of the other character pairs show a 1:0 ratio in the F_1 generation and a 3:1 ratio in F_2. This numerical equality of the sexes in spite of inequality in other characters is a significant result of the differentiation of a special sex chromosome pair with unlike members. If X and Y exert different influences upon the

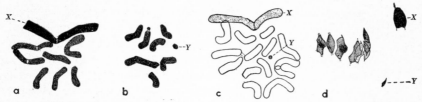

Fig. 136.—Sex chromosomes in a liverwort (*Sphaerocarpos Donnellii*). *a*, genome in female gametophyte. *b*, genome in male gametophyte. *c*, diploid complement in sporophyte. *d*, first meiotic division in sporocyte. (*After G. Lorbeer.*)

type of sex developed, it can be realized that crossing over could impair the distinctness of the two sex differentiating processes and lead to deleterious sexual states; hence the value of the lack of crossing over between these chromosomes, at least in some organisms. Also suggestive is the further fact that heteropyknosis evidently interferes with or prevents crossing over.

It is to be emphasized that the chromosomes are not alone responsible for the type of sex developed. As in the case of all other characters, the sex expressed is a result of the interaction of genetical and environmental factors. The significance of the sex chromosomes lies in the fact that they automatically maintain two genotypes in the species, these resulting in the development of two types of organism, male and female, under the range of environmental conditions normally encountered. This is all that nature requires for the successful operation of the mechanism: absolute distinctness between males and females in all cases and under all possible conditions is not to be expected. The fact that abnormal environments may sometimes alter the sex is accordingly no argument against the sex-determining role of the chromosomes as properly conceived. Under normal conditions the genotype is the sufficiently decisive differential factor; under other conditions the environmental factor may be differential; under all conditions both factors share in determining what the organism does. It should be evident that the same principle holds for inorganic systems.

Thus the behavior (curved flight) of a pitched baseball depends upon the combined influences of a constitutional factor (rotation) and an environmental factor (air resistance). The decisive role of differential factors in the chromosomes is strikingly shown in gynandromorphic insects, in which portions of the body differing in the number of *X*-chromosomes differ also in sex and sex-linked characters (Fig. 137).

Fig. 137.—A *Drosophila* gynandromorph. The left side is female and has two *X*-chromosomes in its nuclei. The right side is male and has only one *X*-chromosome as a result of the loss of the other *X* in an early embryonic mitosis. (*After T. H. Morgan et al.*)

Sex-linkage.—An interesting example of the inheritance of a nonsexual character depending upon differential genes located in the sex chromosomes is that of Daltonism, a type of color-blindness that prevents some people from distinguishing properly red from green. The defect occurs in relatively few individuals in affected families and appears less frequently in women than in men because it is both recessive and sex-linked. The chromosomal basis for its inheritance is illustrated in Fig. 138.

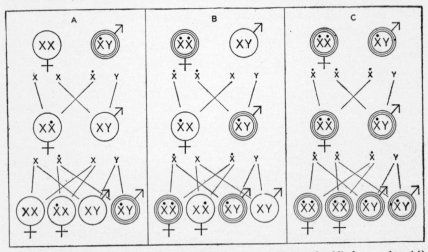

Fig. 138.—Diagram illustrating the inheritance of red-green color blindness, when (*A*) the father, or (*B*) the mother, or (*C*) both parents manifest the defect. ♀, female. ♂, male. Recessive (defective) gene indicated by dot above *X*-chromosome carrying it. Individuals manifesting the defect indicated by triple outlines.

The gene responsible for the defect when in the recessive state is located in the *X*-chromosome; hence females may have either one or two such recessives, while males can have only one. The Y-chromosome has no influence on the character. When a male has the recessive gene, he is color-blind, for no normal allele is present to dominate it (first part of diagram). His offspring by a normal female all have normal vision: the daughters are heterozygous, carrying one recessive gene dominated by a normal one, while the sons have only a normal gene. If one of the daughters mates with any normal male, the probabilities are that half of her daughters will resemble her in carrying the hidden defect, while half of her sons will be color-blind.

A female is color-blind only when she carries the recessive genes in both of her X-chromosomes (second part of diagram). When mated to a normal male, her daughters all have normal vision but carry the hidden defect, while all her sons are color-blind. When one of these heterozygous daughters mates with a color-blind male, the probabilities are that half of the offspring of both sexes will be color-blind. What happens when a normal male is involved has been shown in the preceding paragraph.

When a color-blind female mates with a color-blind male, the results are even more serious (third part of diagram). In such a case every X-chromosome carries the recessive gene, and all the offspring are color-blind. This is the fifth of six possible crosses, the sixth being normal by normal. Fortunately the fifth type occurs very rarely.

Among organisms that have been extensively studied cytogenetically many such sex-linked characters have been identified.

Summary and Conclusions.—The characters exhibited by an organism are determined by the constitution of the protoplasm and by the environmental conditions, external and internal, in cooperation with which the protoplasm undergoes development. Character relationships of successive generations, when attributable to protoplasmic composition, constitute organic heredity.

The data on the inheritance of many different characters show the dependence of those characters upon constitutional factors located in the nucleus, and they suggest that the factors, or genes, are individualized organic units or semi-independent portions of the chromosomes. That a given gene is present is indicated when it exists in two forms producing two effects. When both forms are present together, one commonly dominates the other in character production. A given gene affects several characters, while a given character results from the action of numerous genes acting at the same or different stages of ontogeny.

The Mendelian rules according to which characters are inherited have their cause in the distribution of the chromosomes through successive life cycles. The association of chromosomes beginning at syngamy results in a combination of parental characters in the offspring. The segregation of their controlling genes pair by pair when spores or gametes are formed is due to synapsis and disjunction of homologous chromosomes. The independence of many character pairs in inheritance has its basis in the random assortment of the various pairs of chromosomes in meiosis. The linked inheritance of many characters is a result of the location of their differential genes in the same chromosome pair. Recombinations of the characters composing two linked pairs are due to crossing over of chromatids somewhere between the two differential gene pairs.

Sex inheritance in dioecious plants and animals has its basis in the behavior of a chromosome pair specially differentiated with respect to genes influencing sex and often in visible morphology. Nonsexual characters are linked with sex, though not restricted to one sex, when their controlling factors are located in the X chromosome.

Which chromosome of a genome carries a given gene or linked group of genes can be ascertained by using trisomic strains. The chromosome observed to be present in triplicate is responsible for characters showing special trisomic ratios in inheritance. Other methods involving further chromosomal aberrations also are available.

The serial order of the linked genes in a single chromosome pair is found by comparing the recombination percentages obtained after crosses involving various couples of character pairs.

The actual positions of the genes in the chromosome are determined by relating abnormalities of characters depending on these genes to visible abnormalities in chromosome structure, such as deletions.

As a result of the normal operation of the chromosomal mechanism, members of a human family resemble each other and their ancestors because they bear many similar genes in chromosomes derived from common sources. They differ from one another in particular ways because of the orderly reshuffling of the chromosomes at each meiosis and the various combinations resulting from syngamy. The human race is so highly heterozygous that complete similarity is to be expected nowhere except in identical twins, which arise from the same fertilized egg and therefore carry identical genic outfits, barring new mutations. Extensive studies on such twin pairs reared together and apart have strongly emphasized the fundamental role of genetical constitution in determining the results of development. Unlike environments may influence the development of different capacities, but the experimental evidence indicates that the initial potentialities in identical twins are similar to a degree rarely approached in other pairs of individuals. The naïveté of attempts to explain the development of characters without reference to the genetical nature of the material should be obvious.

CHAPTER XIII

CHROMOSOMAL ABERRATIONS

Exceptions to the normal mode of chromosome behavior are frequently observed, particularly when large numbers of individuals are being examined in experimental work. Often one is led to discover them by suggestive abnormalities in the characters of one or more individuals. Some types of aberration occur only rarely, while others appear much more frequently; and it has been found that by various experimental treatments, such as irradiation with X rays or ultraviolet light, the frequency of occurrence can be markedly increased. Some aberrations involve whole genomes and result in polyploidy (Chap. XIV). Others affect a single whole chromosome, as in the nondisjunction leading to the trisomic condition found so useful in assigning genes to their proper chromosomes (page 174). Still others produce alterations involving breakage of the chromosome. It is this last group of alterations that will concern us in this chapter.

Abnormalities of several kinds have proved their value in cytogenetical research, for not only do they furnish material for tests of hypotheses founded upon normal chromosomal and genic behavior, but to certain questions they often yield answers not obtainable in normal material. They also throw a most interesting light upon the fundamental problem of the nature of the gene. Finally, they afford important additional clues to the role of intrachromosomal changes in the evolution of diversity among organisms in nature.

Deletion.—A *deletion* is the removal of a portion of a chromosome, the remaining portion with the kinetochore then continuing as a deficient chromosome (Fig. 139). A deleted segment, if it does not include the kinetochore, cannot function in mitosis and is soon lost. Just how this alteration is accomplished is not known, but the evidence indicates that while two portions of a chromonema lie very close together two breaks may occur there, the four freshly broken ends then reuniting two by two in a new way. The loss of a portion usually leads to the inviability of cells having no corresponding normal chromosome, although there are some small deletions that are not lethal even in monoploid cells. Deletions are nearly always intercalary, as shown in the diagram; terminal deletions are relatively rare.

When a deficient chromosome meets a normal one in synapsis, homologous regions pair closely, leaving a region of the normal chromosome extending as an unpaired loop. Some degree of sterility is expected among the resulting spores or gametes. The great value of deletions in determining gene location has already been emphasized (page 182). Of special interest is the fact that they also reveal the presence and position of unmutated genes which would not be detected in crosses of

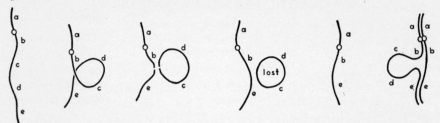

FIG. 139.—Diagram illustrating the production of a deletion (of the *cd* region) and the synapsis of the resulting deficient chromosome with a normal chromosome. If the ring had included the kinetochore (small circle), it would have remained functional and the ends of the chromosome would have been lost. Such ring-shaped chromosomes disappear eventually because of difficulties in mitosis.

normal individuals, for in normal material both the normal gene and its mutant allele must be present before the presence of either is suspected.

Inversion.—An *inversion* is a reversal in the position of a portion of a chromosome. Most inversions are intercalary (Fig. 140); a few are terminal. The mode of formation is apparently like that of deletions, except that the four broken ends recombine in a different pattern. The behavior of a chromosome carrying an inversion is normal in mitosis.

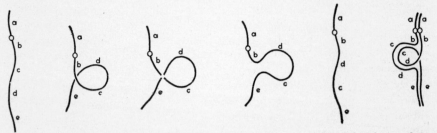

FIG. 140.—Diagram illustrating the production of an inversion (of the *cd* region) and the synapsis of the chromosome carrying it with a normal chromosome.

Its genetical effects are like those of an uninverted chromosome, except for differences in linkage relations and, in some cases, a modified effect upon characters due to the altered relative positions of certain genes (*position effect*). Inversions can be used for the purpose of locating genes when linkage relations within the chromosome are well known.

At the time of synapsis in individuals heterozygous for the inversion, the association of homologous regions results in the looped configuration shown in the diagram. Meiosis may be carried through, yielding spores or gametes with and without the inversion. Frequently, however, there is sterility, sometimes in a high degree. This is due in part to the disturbing effects of crossing over in the region of the inversion, for this may produce a chromatid with two kinetochores and a chromatid with none. The akinetic chromatid is lost, while the dikinetic one either forms a "bridge" between the two groups at anaphase (Fig. 141) or goes in its entirety to one pole. In either case an abnormal complement and sterility result.

Fig. 141.—Anaphase *I* in microsporocyte of maize showing a chromatid bridge due to crossing over in the region of an inversion. The crossover resulted in a chromatid with two kinetochores and one with none. The latter is seen as a small fragment near the bridge. (*Courtesy of B. McClintock.*)

Such sterility is of special interest in connection with the origin of diverse types in nature, for it has been found that certain geographical races of *Drosophila* differ in being homozygous for different inversions. These races are meiotically regular and fertile, but heterozygotes formed by crossing two of them are not; hence, two such races are kept distinct by this internal mechanism and can proceed independently with their differentiation into more widely divergent types.

Translocation.—The transfer of a portion of one chromosome to another except by normal crossing over is known as *translocation*. It may involve homologous or nonhomologous chromosomes. In nearly all cases the translocation is reciprocal, *i.e.*, parts of two chromosomes are exchanged (Fig. 142). These parts may be of any relative length, for breaks and recombinations evidently can occur at many places in the chromosomes. Sometimes one of the resulting chromosomes has

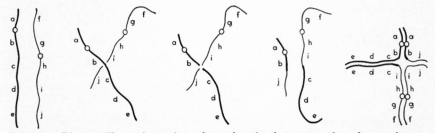

Fig. 142.—Diagram illustrating reciprocal translocation between nonhomologous chromosomes and the synapsis of the resulting chromosomes with their normal homologues.

two kinetochores while the other has none, but in the successful cases each translocated chromosome has one only and behaves normally in mitosis. The simple translocation of one piece without exchange seems to occur very rarely.

The meiotic behavior typical of plants in which reciprocal translocation of nonhomologous chromosomes has occurred is shown in Figs. 143-145. An individual carrying the two translocated chromosomes and the two normal chromosomes with which they are homologous is called a *structural hybrid:* it is "heterozygous for the translocation." In its sporocytes these chromosomes form a cross-shaped configuration by the synapsis of homologous parts and then open out into a ring-of-4 at diakinesis. Such ring or chain formation is known as *catenation.* While

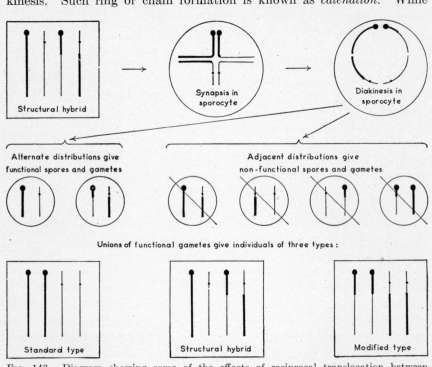

Fig. 143.—Diagram showing some of the effects of reciprocal translocation between nonhomologous chromosomes (distinguished by heavy and light lines and unlike knobs.)

the other chromosomes of the complement form bivalents and disjoin as usual, the chromosomes in the ring disjoin in two ways. In some sporocytes, alternate members go to the same pole, giving spores and later gametes of two kinds. Since both kinds contain all the chromosomal elements, although in unlike arrangements, they are both functional. In other sporocytes, adjacent members of the ring go to the same pole, yielding spores and gametes all of which lack certain elements of the genome and are nonfunctional. Hence such plants are said to be semisterile, although the percentage of sterility differs considerably in different cases. When such a plant is selfed, male gametes of the two functional kinds meet female gametes of the same two kinds and produce offspring

of three classes: (1) standard plants with normal chromosomes in duplicate, (2) structural hybrids, and (3) modified plants with the translocated

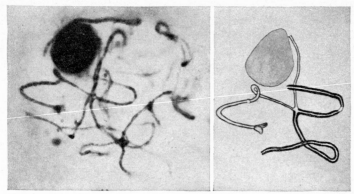

FIG. 144.—Synaptic complex formed in microsporocyte of maize plant heterozygous for a reciprocal translocation. (*After B. McClintock.*)

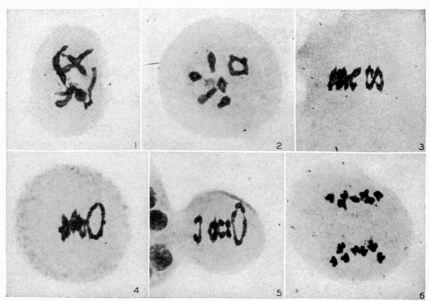

FIG. 145.—First meiotic division in microsporocytes of a strain of wheat (*Triticum*) heterozygous for a reciprocal translocation. 1, cross configuration in prophase. 2, ring-of-4 at diakinesis. 3, metaphase; members of ring about to disjoin alternately. 4, 5, adjacent disjunction; metaphase and early anaphase. 6, anaphase. (*After L. Smith.*)

chromosomes in duplicate. These three types tend to occur in the ratio
of 1:2:1.

Among plants, both types of homozygote, standard and modified,
commonly show a regular formation and disjunction of bivalent chromo-

somes and breed true. They differ, of course, in the linkage relations of certain characters controlled by genes in the chromosomes involved in the translocation. In *Drosophila* the "modifieds" are for some reason sterile. Modified lines with all the chromosomes of the genome altered by translocations have been established in *Crepis tectorum* by crossing strains carrying different translocations, and these new lines are kept distinct by the sterility of hybrids formed between them and the original standard line.

A second reciprocal translocation may follow a first in the same line, or two translocations may be brought together from different lines. In

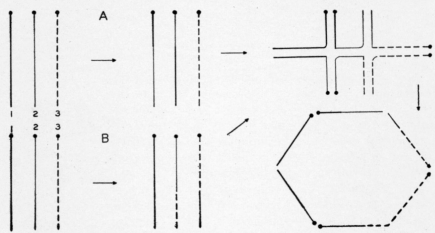

FIG. 146.—Diagram illustrating formation of ring-of-6 by two reciprocal translocations. In line *A*, chromosomes 1 and 2 are translocated. In line *B*, chromosomes 2 and 3 are translocated. Union of gametes from these two lines may give a group of six chromosomes forming a double-cross configuration at synapsis and a ring-of-6 at diakinesis. If the two translocations had occurred at corresponding levels in the chromosomes, the synaptic complex would have been a six-rayed star. Chromosomes are marked with knobs to distinguish ends.

either manner, rings of more than four chromosomes may be built up (Fig. 146). In extreme cases all the chromosomes of the complement are combined in one large ring or chain in the meiotic prophase (Fig. 147, *b*). Fertility in such plants tends to vary with the percentage of alternate chromosome distribution in anaphase *I*.

Reciprocal translocation and its effects have been found in a considerable number of plant genera in nature. In a species of peony (*Paeonia californica*), which has 10 somatic chromosomes, there have been found seven types showing respectively in sporocytes five independent bivalent pairs, a ring-of-4 and 3 pairs, a ring-of-6 and 2 pairs, a ring-of-8 and 1 pair, a ring-of-10, 2 rings-of-4 and 1 pair, and a ring-of-4 with a ring-of-6. Near the center of the range of the species in California the types with free pairs and small rings are more abundant, whereas near its periphery the types with larger rings are more numerous. It seems likely that such translocation has been a factor in the differentiation

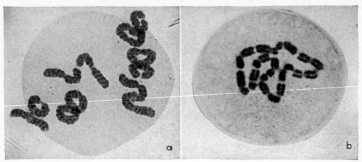

Fig. 147.—*a*, Rings and chains-of-4 in microsporocyte of *Tradescantia*. (Some of the chromosomes have been pressed out of the cell in making the preparation.) *b*, ring-of-12 in microsporocyte of *Rhoeo*. Each chromosome shows its two arms. (*Courtesy of K. Sax.*)

of races and species, although its importance in this respect cannot yet be measured. It is held to be a major factor in the genus *Crepis*. In *Datura* it has been found in investigations extending over many years that the same fundamental genome of 12 chromosomes has its parts arranged in numerous ways in the various species from different parts of the world. They appear to be homozygous translocants, or modifieds, derived from one or more main chromosomal types. Within the species *stramonium* there are several such natural races, or *prime types*. The arrangement of chromosome parts in the genome of a given race is determined by observing the meiotic configurations (rings, etc.) in crosses between this race and one or more others in which the arrangement is known in terms of an arbitrarily chosen standard. Since prime types in the same species are so closely similar morphologically, it seems best to regard reciprocal translocation as supplementary to mutation, hybridization, and isolation as a factor in speciation in such genera.

Fig. 148.—Catenated chromosomes in an evening primrose, *Oenothera franciscana sulphurea*. *a*, late meiotic prophase, with a ring-of-12 and one free pair. *b*, first meiotic anaphase, showing alternate distribution of members of ring. (*After R. E. Cleland.*)

The genus *Oenothera* is of unusual interest in this connection because of its relation to the mutation theory propounded many years ago by Hugo de Vries, the great Dutch botanist. *Oenothera lamarckiana*, a truebreeding type, was observed to produce occasional offspring unlike itself. This was interpreted as the production of new species by sudden large steps, or mutations, from a pure parent species. Since that time cytogeneticists have developed another interpretation of the phenomenon.

The principal cytological element in the new explanation is the fact that 12 of the 14 chromosomes occupy constant positions in a ring at meiosis and show a regularly alternate mode of disjunction in a high percentage of the sporocytes (Fig. 148). The main genetical element in the explanation is the evidence that there are two groups of genes, known as *Renner complexes*, that segregate in sporogenesis and that each complex carries a gene which prevents development when in the homozygous state (Fig. 149). If the two Renner complexes (designated as *gaudens* and *velans* in this species) are located, respectively, in the two groups of seven chromosomes regularly passing to opposite poles in meiosis (six from the ring, plus one member of the free pair carrying similar Renner complex factors), it is possible to account for the production of

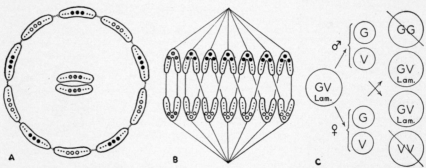

Fig. 149.—Diagram of cytogenetic constitution of an evening primrose, *Oenothera lamarckiana*. *A*, ring-of-12 and one free pair at diakinesis. Factors of Renner complex gaudens (*G*) represented by large dots, those of velans complex (*V*) by circles, those common to both complexes by shaded circles. Factors ordinarily recombining by crossing over represented by small dots. *B*, segregation of two Renner complexes by alternate disjunction of chromosomes in ring at anaphase *I*. *C*, effect of lethal factors in Renner complexes: of three possible combinations only the heterozygotes (*GV*) survive.

spores and gametes of two main classes: those carrying the *gaudens* complex and those carrying the *velans* complex. Random combinations of male and female gametes of these two kinds produce zygotes of three kinds, but since the development of two of these is prevented by homozygosity of lethal genes, the only plants appearing are of the original heterozygous *O. lamarckiana* type. Thus the type breeds true not because it is a pure species, but because it is a hybrid whose homozygous offspring do not survive.

The mutations which occasionally appear in *O. lamarckiana* have been found to have several causes: (1) gene mutation of the ordinary kind; (2) the removal of a lethal gene from a Renner complex by crossing over; (3) the occasional nonlethal action of a lethal gene; (4) nondisjunction, giving trisomic and other types; (5) chromosome doubling.

Other species of *Oenothera* also exhibit the results of reciprocal translocation, and relationships are strongly suggested by the ways in which the various genomes and Renner complexes present in the genus interact when brought together by hybridization.

Duplication.—Occasionally a chromosome comes to have a certain portion represented two or more times instead of once. This is known as *duplication.* The extra portion or portions may lie next to the one

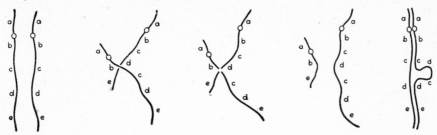

Fig. 150.—Diagram illustrating a duplication (of the *cd* region) and the synapsis of the chromosome carrying it with a normal chromosome.

normally present or at some distance from it. Their orientation may be normal or inverted, depending upon the manner in which they were added. Evidently they originate by one or more translocations (Fig. 150). The presence of duplications has in some cases been revealed by genetical data, and in salivary-gland chromosomes they can be readily seen and correlated with abnormalities in characters and breeding behavior. A significant point regarding duplication is that it may produce a genetical effect like that of gene mutation. The dominant mutation known as bar eye in *Drosophila* has turned out to be a result of duplication (Fig. 151).

Aberrations and the Nature of the Gene.—The chromosomal aberrations described briefly in these pages are leading toward a needed improvement in our understanding of the gene. For many years the gene concept has been of inestimable value in the task of reducing to order the multifarious data of genetics. The theory that the organism has within it discrete units with a special role in the inheritance and development of characters rests upon the

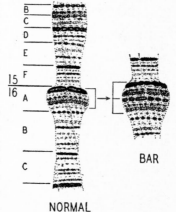

Fig. 151.—Portion of salivary-gland chromosome of *Drosophila*, showing the duplication responsible for the bar-eye mutation. (*After T. S. Painter.*)

independent "Mendelizing" of various small character differences in sexually reproducing organisms, and upon the further fact that different characters can be correlated with the activity of definitely localized small regions in the chromosomes. Evidence for the occasional mutation of the units is found in the sudden alterations of characters ascribed to them.

The gene has been generally regarded as a minute body with a considerable degree of structural and physiological independence, perhaps the last member of the series organism-cell-nucleus-chromosome-chromomere-gene, the gene itself being possibly a single protein molecule or small group of molecules. There have been various conjectures regarding the nature of its chemical and physical activity, and attempts have even been made to estimate its size. Most geneticists have, however, been content to employ the gene concept mainly as a useful tool in research and to define it, if at all, in terms of its effects, leaving the future to furnish an adequate description of it in physicochemical terms. This is a situation in biology comparable with that in physics and chemistry, where the concept of the atom was long employed with conspicuous success when far less was known about its actual nature than is known today. The hope that our knowledge of the gene is to become more intimate is encouraged by researches now in progress on the biochemical aspects of genic action. In the ascomycetes, for example (page 167), are nuclear conditions that are making it possible to associate particular chemical reactions with certain genes, and from the nature of these reactions it is expected that much can be learned concerning the physicochemical constitution of the genes involved. This association of cytogenetics with biochemistry promises to be as useful in leading us toward a solution of the problem of the role of genes in ontogeny as the union of genetics and cytology 40 years ago has been in elucidating their role in heredity.

Discussion of the nature of the gene has been stimulated anew by the discovery that certain aberrations in the visible structure of the chromosome produce effects similar in many respects to those of gene mutations. Three illustrative cases are the following. A color character, brown midrib, which had been ascribed to bm_1, a recessive gene located near the kinetochore in chromosome 5 of maize, has been found to develop even when the region carrying this gene is removed altogether by a small deletion. In *Drosophila* the character roughest-3 mutated when the small region carrying its differential gene in the X-chromosome was inverted; moreover, when the former alignment was reestablished by a reinversion, the normal character was restored. The dominant mutant character, bar eye, in *Drosophila* is now known to be due to a duplication. This character may increase in intensity when a second duplication adds still another like portion, and it may revert to normal when the extra portion or portions are removed. An additional observation of importance is that in some X-rayed cells both gene mutations and chromosomal deficiencies show the same response to variations in irradiation dosage, the frequency of both varying as a linear function of the total energy applied. The two processes are also similarly affected by dormancy as opposed to activity in tissues at the time of irradiation.

Such phenomena have led to a current theory that a gene is any small portion of a chromosome having an effect upon character development differing from that of neighboring portions, so that when this portion is unlike in the two chromosomes of a pair Mendelian behavior is exhibited by characters influenced by it. Any change in this portion affecting its influence, whether the change be a loss, gain, or rearrangement, represents a mutation. In other words, genes are not all elements of the same nature, even though their effects are generally comparable. The extreme form of this view is that genes as discrete biological units do not exist and that the only real genetical unit is the chromosome, in particular the chromonema. This may be regarded as a sort of gigantic chain molecule whose various parts alter the action of the whole in some manner whenever they are sufficiently modified. Opponents of this extreme view have cited phenomena in normal and aberrant material which would not be expected in a single molecule. For example, the positions of crossovers and induced breaks and the relatively small amounts of energy required to produce them indicate the presence of numerous distinct units not bound together by strong intramolecular chemical bonds. They regard the evidence as indicative of a process of gene mutation distinct from chromosomal aberrations, although both may share in producing the phenomena studied by the geneticist.

In any event, genes are localized constitutional conditions that can be treated as units in genetical research. Such conditions are the physical basis of Mendelian phenomena, and any stable modification of their character-influencing power may be regarded as a mutation. We continue to look to the future for a determination of the precise physico-chemical nature of these conditions and the manner of their association in the chromosome. In this search for further light on the nature of the gene, few developments are more suggestive than the increasingly close association of genetics, protein chemistry, and virus research. It seems that genes, proteins, and viruses have much in common, and the clarification of their relationships, when achieved, should be of immense value in many branches of biological science.

CHAPTER XIV

CHROMOSOME NUMBERS AND THEIR ALTERATION

In earlier chapters it has been shown that in the life cycle of sexually reproducing organisms there is an alternation of two chromosome numbers, one of them being double the other. In typical cases the numerically smaller chromosome group consists of one genome, while the larger consists of two. It has also been mentioned that higher numbers of genomes are sometimes present. For reasons not well understood this condition is very rare among animals, but it is of frequent occurrence in plants, especially among angiosperms. In many genera of this group it characterizes certain species of a genus or even all of them. Sometimes a single altered individual appears in a population of diploid plants in the field or breeding plot. An individual may show the increase in number only in a portion of the body, this portion constituting a sector or sometimes a layer of tissue overlying the normal portion.

Plants with increased numbers of certain chromosomes or of whole genomes are valuable in many ways. They furnish material for the study of the action of individual chromosomes, since they may have the various members of a genome present in different numerical relations. Again, differences in chromosome number and the characters sometimes correlated with them are often useful in classifying related species and in determining their probable origin (Chap. XVII). Finally, the change in chromosome number is sometimes accompanied by morphological or physiological alterations that render the plant more valuable commercially. This point has increased in interest since the discovery that such chromosomal changes can be induced by experimental means.

Terminology.—A nucleus with some number other than the true monoploid or diploid number of chromosomes is said to be *heteroploid*. This term and others given below are also applied to cells, tissues, individuals, races, or species with such nuclei. When the number is an exact multiple of the monoploid, the nucleus (or tissue, etc.) is *euploid*. The terms designating the multiples up to 10, beginning with the triple number, are as follows: triploid, tetraploid, pentaploid, hexaploid, heptaploid, octoploid, enneaploid, decaploid. The higher multiples, which are of rarer occurrence, are usually designated as eleven-ploid, twelve-ploid, etc. Euploid types are often said to be *polyploid*. In such species the zygotic and gametic chromosome numbers are, for example, hexaploid and triploid, or tetraploid and diploid, rather than diploid and monoploid as in the types selected for discussion in foregoing chapters.

A nucleus (or tissue, etc.) with some number other than an exact multiple of the monoploid number is *aneuploid*. When the number is a little lower than some multiple, it is *hypoploid;* when it is a little higher, it is *hyperploid*. Obviously, a number falling between the diploid and triploid numbers, for example, may be called either hyperdiploid or hypotriploid.

A chromosome complement in which heteroploidy is due to the multiplication of a single kind of genome (or of some of its members) is said to be *autoheteroploid;* whereas one in which specifically different genomes or members are combined, as in an interspecific hybrid, is *alloheteroploid*. Although this distinction cannot always be sharply drawn, it is of considerable importance, as will appear later. This chapter deals with the first type of heteroploidy. The second type is discussed in the following chapter.

Unfortunately, authors have not agreed in their use of symbols denoting chromosome numbers. At present it seems best to let x and $2x$ stand, respectively, for the gametic and zygotic numbers in the life cycle, regardless of whether the organism is heteroploid or not. The symbols n and $2n$ have often been used in the same sense, but the present tendency, which should be followed in the interest of uniformity, is to use n for the true monoploid number (one genome), $2n$ for the true diploid number (two genomes), $3n$ for the true triploid number (three genomes), etc. Obviously, there are cases in which one cannot determine without special study whether a gametic complement of x chromosomes is made up of one, two, or more genomes. Some writers apply the term *haploid* to any gametic number; others use it as a synonym for monoploid.

Tetraploidy.—Next to diploid plants, tetraploids constitute the commonest chromosomal type in nature. The doubling of the chromosome number occurs in two principal ways. The first of these is by *somatic doubling*, in which the chromosomal division cycle and the spindle mechanism lack their normal correlation, so that the divided chromosomes at the close of the resulting aberrant mitosis are enclosed in one nucleus instead of two. If this aberration occurs in a very young embryo, the whole plant into which it develops has the tetraploid number, whereas its occurrence at a later stage results in a plant with tetraploidy in one or more branches or other portions. The second way is by *ameiosis*, in which failure of haplosis leads to the formation of diploid spores and gametes, a union of two such gametes then giving a tetraploid plant.

The principal methods used for inducing tetraploidy artificially are temperature treatment, decapitation, and treatment with colchicine. When, for example, young maize ears are kept unusually warm during the stages when the embryos are beginning their development, some of these embryos may develop into tetraploid plants instead of diploids. Abnormal temperature, either high or low, may induce ameiosis in flower buds, so that diploid spores and gametes become available for crossing. When some plants, notably tomatoes, are decapitated, the shoots arising from the callus tissue are often tetraploid. At present the most popular method for inducing tetraploidy and higher stages of heteroploidy is the one employing colchicine. This substance, which is an alkaloid

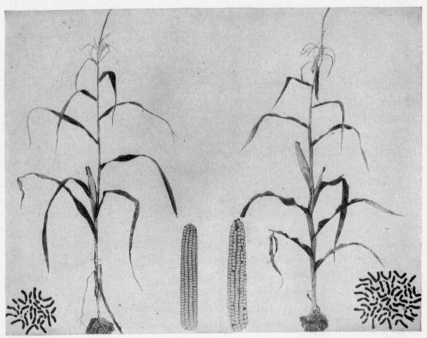

Fig. 152.—Induced autopolyploidy in maize. Left: normal diploid plant, an ear from such a plant, and diploid chromosome complement in root tip. Right: tetraploid plant from kernel on ear subjected to heat-treatment during early stages of embryo development; also mature ear and tetraploid chromosome complement in root tip. (*Courtesy of L. F. Randolph.*)

derived from the autumn crocus, may be applied by painting very young buds with a lanolin emulsion containing it, or by standing cut shoots or roots in an aqueous solution for brief periods, or by spraying young plant parts with such a solution, or by treating seeds before planting. Many useless malformations may result from such treatments, particularly when the dosage is too high, but when the technique is sufficiently refined tetraploid shoots may appear. Colchicine produces its effect by preventing the formation of the mitotic spindle. The chromosomes pass through their division cycle as usual, but since no spindle is developed their halves undergo no anaphasic separation and reorganize as a single tetraploid nucleus. When the influence of the drug has declined sufficiently for normal nuclear and cell divisions to occur, development of the tissues continues with the altered chromosome number.

The characters exhibited by tetraploid plants derived by doubling as described above often serve to distinguish them from their diploid relatives (Figs. 152, 155). In many instances they are stockier in habit,

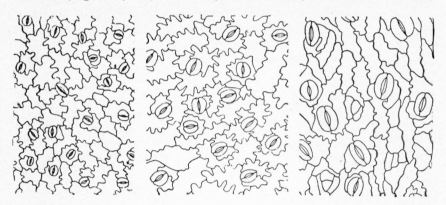

Fig. 153.—Stomates and epidermal cells of diploid, tetraploid, and octoploid *Nicotiana* hybrids. (*After W. H. Greenleaf.*)

darker green in color, bear larger flowers and seeds, and have larger nuclei and cells. With a hand lens one can often tell the polyploids from the diploids by the size and arrangement of the stomates (Fig. 153). In mature vegetative organs such as leaves the cells may be larger and fewer than in the diploids; sometimes they are not. In the meristematic

Fig. 154.—Synaptic configurations in heteroploid plants. *a*, trivalent at zygotene in triploid tulip. *b*, postdiplotene trivalent in triploid tulip. *c*, quadrivalent at zygotene in tetraploid hyacinth. *d*, postdiplotene quadrivalent in pentaploid tulip. (*After W. C. F. Newton and C. D. Darlington.*)

tissues of maize the number of cells is the same as in the diploids, but with the greater cell size is associated the development of larger organs. There are also physiological differences between diploids and tetraploids. Some tetraploid plants are able to grow well in a wider range of ecological habitats than the related diploids. Fruits borne on tetraploid tomato plants derived from diploids have a higher vitamin C content than those borne on the diploids.   Similarly, yellow kernels produced by tetraploid maize plants have more vitamin A than those from diploids.

Chromosome behavior in autotetraploid plants is normal throughout somatic development.   At meiosis, however, certain irregularities arise when all or some of the chromosomes form quadrivalent groups at synapsis (Fig. 154).   This may lead to some irregularity in distribution at anaphase *I* and add thus to the sterility attributable to other genetical causes.   In colchicine-induced autotetraploids, fertility ranges from a fairly high value comparable to that in many natural tetraploids down to complete sterility.   Later it will be pointed out that in allotetraploid

Fig. 155.—Selfed ears from diploid (above) and tetraploid (below) plants heterozygous for the color-factor pair *Rr*.   Segregation for color is about 3:1 in the diploid and 35:1 in the tetraploid.   Note difference in size of kernels.   (*After L. F. Randolph.*)

plants the fertility may be much higher than in the diploids from which they are derived (page 221).   In tetraploid lines, diploid individuals appear on rare occasions as a result of parthenogenesis, just as haploids sometimes appear among diploid organisms.

Genetical ratios for characters of autotetraploid plants tend to be unlike those of diploids, for each chromosome is present in quadruplicate. Assuming a random distribution of the four chromosomes bearing a given gene, the expected phenotypic ratios after selfing are 1:0 for a plant with *AAAA* or *AAAa*, 35:1 for a plant with *AAaa*, 3:1 for a plant with *Aaaa*, and 0:1 for one with *aaaa*.   The corresponding testcross ratios are 1:0, 5:1, 1:1, and 0:1.   These expectations are for characters controlled by genes in regions near the kinetochore, where the four chromosomes are distributed at random but the eight chromatids are not, owing to the fact that sister chromatids tend to pass regularly to the same pole (see page 106).   Chiasmata liberate the chromatids from this restriction in regions far from the kinetochores; hence in such regions they are distributed at random.   On the basis of such random distribution of eight chromatids in these regions, the ratios for genes located there would be the following.   After selfing: $AAAA$, 1:0; $AAAa$, 783:1; $AAaa$, 21:1; $Aaaa$, 2.48:1; $aaaa$, 0:1.   After a testcross the corresponding ratios would be 1:0, 27:1, 3.7:1, 13:15, and 0:1.   In a number of researches expected ratios have been found to be rather closely approximated (Fig. 155).

The breeding behavior of autopolyploids differs markedly from that of diploids because of the relative infrequency with which recessive characters reappear in succeeding generations.   Thus the F_2 generation is more uniform than in diploids.   Another fact of genetical and practical interest is that tetraploid lines in many cases are kept distinct from the diploids by cross incompatibility and, in case fertilization is accomplished, by the failure of the resulting triploid lines to compete successfully with the diploids and tetraploids.

Triploidy.—Triploid plants almost always arise from the union of a monoploid and a diploid gamete, the latter having been produced regularly by a tetraploid plant or after a failure of haplosis in a diploid plant. Such plants, like tetraploids, show good vegetative growth and are frequently somewhat larger than the diploids.   Although the sexual fertility of some triploids is low because of the irregular meiosis where three genomes are present, others, *e.g.*, maize and iris, show good fertility. Progenies derived from triploid plants tend to have a low survival value because of their aneuploid chromosome numbers, and this greatly restricts the value of triploidy in the development of new types.   As a general rule triploid plants are unsuccessful in nature unless they have some form of asexual reproduction upon which they can rely; hence they are rarely found established among sexually reproducing species in the field. Numerous highly valued plants of the orchard and garden, *e.g.*, certain varieties of apples, tulips, iris, and hyacinths, are triploid, but they are normally propagated by vegetative methods.

Higher Degrees of Polyploidy.—Species with 6, 8, and 10 or more genomes are found in nature and show a high degree of fertility.   That their establishment probably was accomplished gradually and may have involved some hybridization is suggested by experimentally produced autopolyploids with such numbers of genomes.   In maize, to select an example from a considerable number of known cases, induced octoploid plants are far less vigorous than the tetraploids and are completely sterile. Again, when doubling is induced in commercial varieties of potatoes, which are tetraploids, the resulting octoploid plants and tubers are inferior to the tetraploids; whereas, when related diploid species are doubled, the

resulting tetraploids tend to be more vigorous and highly fertile.   The
sterility of higher autopolyploids is due in part to a tendency to form
multivalents (Fig. 156) which are distributed with some degree of irregularity in meiosis.

In general the results obtained so far with agricultural and ornamental
plants indicate that a limit of improvement through induced chromosomal
doubling is ordinarily reached at or near the tetraploid level.   Furthermore, a deleterious effect of the chromosomal change may offset the
improvement.   Thus doubling in tobacco plants results in an increase of
as much as one-third in the percentage of nicotine in the leaves, but this
is more than offset by a reduction of 50 per cent in the dry weight of the
leaves.   In several cereals it has been found that although the doubled
varieties bear larger kernels the total yield is not larger, for an accompanying reduction in fertility decreases the number of kernels obtained.

Fig. 156.—Chromosomes from normal and colchicine-induced polyploid *Petunia* plants
at first meiotic metaphase: two bivalents, two trivalents, two quadrivalents, two quinque-
valents, one heptavalent, and one octovalent.   (*After A. Levan.*)

The problem of plant improvement by chromosomal doubling is therefore far from being a simple one.   It is found that different kinds of
plants (species, varieties, inbred lines) often show widely different
responses to the doubling, for the type and degree of change exhibited
evidently depend in part upon the genic composition and physiological
state of the material treated.   At present the results of a given experiment cannot be predicted with any degree of certainty, nor can the limits
of the method's usefulness be stated.   Nevertheless, investigators are
confident that with proper attention to the genotype and a judicious use
of selection and crossing much of value will be accomplished, even though
the ratio of error to trial may still remain high.   We shall revert to this
topic in a discussion of hybridity in the next chapter.

Although clear cases of polyploidy are relatively rare among animals,
the high numbers in some genera strongly suggest changes in number
in the evolution of certain natural groups.   Known somatic numbers in
carnivores range up to 78 in the dog, and a comparable range is found in
rodents.   Most of the investigated primates including man have 48.
Single individuals or strains with increased chromosome numbers are
occasionally encountered in the field and in the laboratory.   Diploid,
tetraploid, and octoploid races of the brine shrimp (*Artemia*) exist in

nature, and it has been found that the development of tetraploid individuals can be induced in the laboratory by refrigerating eggs that would normally have developed parthenogenetically into diploids.   Another notable case is a series of polyploid salamanders that appeared spontaneously in laboratory cultures (Fig. 157).   A beginning has also been made on the investigation of colchicine-induced chromosome doubling in animal cells.

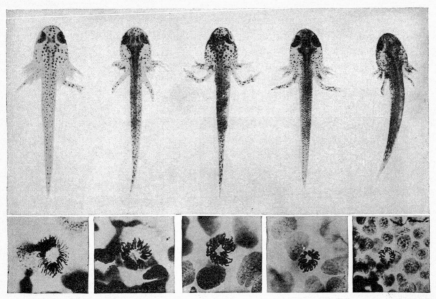

F<small>IG</small>. 157.—Larvae of the common newt (*Triturus viridescens*) with different numbers of genomes.   From left to right: pentaploid, tetraploid, triploid, diploid, and monoploid specimens.   Below them are mitotic metaphases observed in bits of tail fins stained and mounted without sectioning.   The normal diploid larva has 22 chromosomes.   The size of nuclei and cells increases roughly in proportion to the chromosome number, but the body size does not; this indicates a lower cell number in the polyploids.   (*Courtesy of G. Fankhauser.*)

Other Types of Heteroploidy.—In the sporophytes of plants true *monoploidy* occurs very rarely.   Such plants have appeared in cultures in the case of several angiosperm genera (*Datura, Zea, Crepis, Nicotiana, Oenothera, Triticum,* and others), but nowhere have such monoploids become established in nature, so far as we know.   The main reason for this appears to be their high degree of sexual sterility.   Although they are usually somewhat smaller and less vigorous than diploids, they often grow well, but at the time of meiosis the chromosomes of the single genome, having no synaptic partners, behave so irregularly that practically no functional spores or gametes are produced.   Rarely all the chromosomes are included in a single spore, so that after many trials a diploid plant is sometimes obtained by selfing a monoploid one.   Such a plant is of interest in genetical studies, for it is completely homozygous, except for possible new mutations. It seems possible that a monoploid race might be established in nature if the plant had efficient means of vegetative reproduction, but no such case has been discovered.

Among the many types of *aneuploidy*, in which one or more full genomes are accompanied by one or more additional chromosomes not constituting a full genome, the commonest and probably the most important is the *simple trisomic* condition $(2n + 1)$. Here the plant has all its chromosomes in duplicate except one, which is present in triplicate. If two members of the genome are in triplicate, the plant is said to be *doubly trisomic* $(2n + 1 + 1)$, etc. Simple trisomic plants are of special value, for they have normal fertility, transmit the extra chromosome to

Fig. 158.—Flower heads borne on monoploid individuals of *Crepis capillaris*. Left: monoploid head. Middle: diploid head, after chromosomal doubling. Right: head with monoploid and diploid sectors arising after local doubling. (*After L. Hollingshead.*)

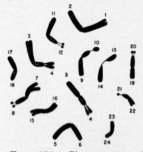

Fig. 159.—Chromosomes in pollen grain from trisomic *Datura stramonium*. This grain carries an extra 3.4 chromosome. (*After S. Satina, D. Bergner, and A. F. Blakeslee.*)

some of their progeny, though only rarely from the pollen parent. They thus serve to reveal the special functions of each chromosome of the genome. This point has been explained on page 174, where the effect upon genetical ratios was described.

Since each chromosome of the genome differs from the others with respect to the group of genes it carries, plants trisomic for different chromosomes are expected to differ in visible characters. This expectation is met in some degree in the species investigated. In *Datura stramonium* each of the 12 possible trisomic types can be distinguished from the others (Figs. 159, 160). The same is true of the trisomic types, also 12 in number, in *Nicotiana sylvestris*. In *Zea mays* 9 of the 10 possible trisomic types have been obtained, and most of these are distinguishable, although the differences are less than might be expected. Moreover, there are certain features, notably the reduced size of the plants and seeds, that characterize all the maize trisomics in common. In addition to these primary trisomic plants, in which the three chromosomes composing

NORMAL

ROLLED   GLOSSY   BUCKLING   ELONGATE

ECHINUS   COCKLEBUR   MICROCARPIC   REDUCED

POINSETTIA   SPINACH   GLOBE   ILEX

Fɪɢ. 160.—Seed capsules of normal and primary trisomic types of the Jimson weed (*Datura stramonium*). Each of the 12 members of the genome (see Fig. 72) produces a characteristic visible effect when present in triplicate. In "rolled" the extra member is chromosome 1.2, in "glossy" it is 3.4, and so on to "ilex" with 23.24. The plants show other differences also. (*Courtesy of A. F. Blakeslee.*)

the trisome are all alike, *Datura* has been found to have a number of secondary trisomic types, in which the extra chromosome consists of two similar arms as the result of some form of aberration (Fig. 161).   Since there are 12 chromosomes in the genome, 24 secondaries should be possible if each of the two arms of every chromosome were to give rise to such a chromosome with similar arms.   More than half of these have actually been found in *Datura*.   The same phenomenon is also known to occur in maize, although not so many of the secondaries have yet been discovered. The special characters of these plants show that each half of each chromosome has its own distinctive effect upon the many reactions involved in development, which is what one should infer from the fact that they carry different groups of genes.

Monosomic plants, with one less than the normal diploid chromosome number ($2n - 1$), are rarely encountered, evidently because of the serious

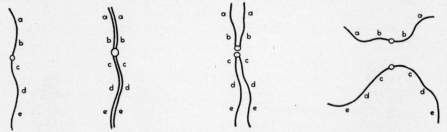

FIG. 161.—Diagram of the production of chromosomes with two similar arms ("secondary" chromosomes) by the misdivision of the kinetochore.

unbalance in the chromosome complement caused by the loss of one member.   Autopolyploids, however, are frequently found with a chromosome missing as a result of irregular disjunction of multivalents; here the loss of a single member causes less unbalance.   In tobacco plants, which are allotetraploid (page 222), nearly all the 24 possible types lacking one chromosome have been found.

Other aneuploid types with varying numbers of additional chromosomes are found in considerable variety, especially in hybrids between members of a polyploid series.   The number of extra chromosomes in some of these is rather high.   Ordinarily fertility and vigor among aneuploids approach the normal as the composition of the complement approaches that in a plant with complete genomes.

Significance of Autoheteroploidy in Nature.—After observing the alterations in characters following the spontaneous or induced doubling of the chromosome number, and after considering the prevalence of polyploidy among angiosperms in nature as revealed by lists of reported chromosome numbers, the conclusion that doubling and character differentiation have been causally related in the natural evolution of these plants is one that can hardly be escaped. To what extent the poly-ploidy in nature has arisen by doubling in relatively pure strains (auto-polyploidy), or by the doubling in hybrids (allopolyploidy) to be discussed in the next chapter, is a difficult problem to solve. At present the relative importance of the two processes is a subject of debate, and it is well realized that much observational and experimental work must be done before the tangled situation in nature can be very thoroughly understood. In the meantime it is to be borne in mind that the two forms of natural polyploidy differ in degree rather than in kind: to form a hybrid at all, two species must have a considerable degree of similarity in their genomes.

The significance of autopolyploidy in the origin of polyploid species in nature is strongly suggested by the fact that experimentally produced polyploids and those in the field show many resemblances. They tend to differ morphologically from related diploids in the same way; they often show similar physiological peculiarities and ecological adaptability; both show the same type of meiotic irregularity, including multivalent associa-tions and sterility among the spores or gametophytes. The natural polyploids are irregular in a less degree, presumably because of the past action of natural selection.

Whether induced autopolyploids gradually improve in fertility and regularity of meiotic behavior after many generations is a significant question now being studied. Should they do so and become distinct new types with regular bivalent formation, it is possible that they might have greater genetic stability than their ancestral diploid types, for the reason that a new recessive mutation would remain hidden longer and affect the phenotype only in those rare individuals having all the increased number of controlling factors in the recessive state.

The role of allopolyploidy is suggested by the absence of multivalents in many natural polyploids, for when the high chromosome number results from a combination of genomes each of which is present only twice, bivalents only are expected at meiosis. Furthermore, as will be pointed out in the next chapter, chromosomal doubling in diploid hybrids is often, though not always, accompanied by increased fertility, and this, together with the increased vigor and new character combinations due to the hybridity, should contribute much to the success of such newly formed types in nature.

Answers to many questions like those suggested above will be required before the evolutionary role of heteroploidy can be described with any degree of precision. A role it surely has, but just how it should be ranked among other factors of speciation in different families of organisms we do not know.

CHAPTER XV

CYTOLOGICAL ASPECTS OF HYBRIDITY

The traditional conception of a hybrid was that it was the offspring of parents belonging to different species. From a practical point of view, a hybrid was an individual manifesting a combination or blend of characters from those species. The advances in modern genetics and cytology have led to an interpretation that is at once broader in its basis and more specific in its designation of what constitutes hybridity. It is now usually stated that a hybrid is the product of the union of two genetically unlike gametes, whatever their source. They may come from two species, varieties, or inbred lines, or even from the same heterozygous bisexual individual. They may or may not manifest combinations or blends of characters, for dominance often renders them indistinguishable from one parent. Hence, in the modern view, the essence of hybridity lies in the genetical constitution of the individual itself rather than in the taxonomic relationship of the parents which contributed to this constitution, although it is of course realized as fully as ever that the crossing of individuals with greater than varietal differences is of special importance in the evolution of natural types.

The essential constitutional state of an ordinary diploid hybrid lies in the unlikeness of its two genomes. The smallest degree of difference between them is seen in an individual heterozygous for only one gene. (It may be pointed out in passing that this condition may also arise by mutation in the individual, rather than by gametic union.) Heterozygosity in its many possible degrees thus constitutes hybridity in modern genetics. The two genomes may also differ in the arrangement of the genes in regions of certain chromosomes, as in the plants heterozygous for translocations and inversions described in Chap. XIII. Such plants are referred to as *structural hybrids*, even though they may conceivably contain no heterozygous pairs of genes. Furthermore, one genome may have genes with no counterpart in the other, as in plants with a deletion in one genome, or in a hybrid between two rather distantly related types. The number of chromosomes may even differ in the two genomes. The present tendency is, therefore, to include a wider variety of cases under the heading of hybridity, but to state more specifically what is common to all of them: a dissimilarity in the genomes responsible for their cytogenetical behavior.

The genomic composition of a hybrid usually has well-known consequences. Among these are the appearance of certain parental characters to the exclusion of others, the appearance of a condition intermediate between the parents as in "blending" or quantitative inheritanee, the production of gametes unlike in genetical constitution, and often a reduction in the degree of fertility. Hybrids resulting from narrow crosses, such as those cited as illustrations of Mendelian heredity in Chap. XII, commonly show regular chromosome behavior and good fertility. It is mainly in hybrids resulting from wider crosses, *i.e.*, in hybrids in the traditional sense, that more extensive genic and structural differences in the chromosomes lead to the cytological and genetical abnormalities to be reviewed in this chapter.

Chromosome Behavior in Diploid Hybrids.—The fundamental reason why it is often difficult or impossible to obtain hybrids between members of different species or genera lies in the genic dissimilarity of the parents. The effects of this dissimilarity are various. The pollen of one species may not grow successfully in the style of the other; the gametes, if they meet, may not actually fuse; if fusion does occur, the zygote may fail to develop because of disharmony within its chromosome complement or between it and the surrounding tissues. In certain cases, on the other hand, the cross results in a hybrid that develops well, even with greater vigor than was shown by the parents. The two parental genomes, in spite of their differences, may thus constitute a single harmonious system during ontogenetic development.

In most such hybrids, abnormalities appear at some stage in the development of reproductive cells that render them partially or completely sterile. Although degenerative changes may set in at an early stage of flower development, the most characteristic cytological aberrations appear during the meiotic prophase and affect especially the course of synapsis. Synapsis may be normal, indicating a close genic similarity in the genomes. More often synapsis fails to occur between some or all of the chromosomes (*asynapsis*), or after synapsing the chromosomes may separate prematurely (*desynapsis*). Although asynapsis usually indicates a considerable degree of genetical dissimilarity in the genomes, it does not always do so, for even in pure lines and narrow crosses synapsis sometimes fails because of certain mutant genes influencing the course of meiosis or because of temporary physiological conditions induced by the environment. Obviously, caution must be used in depending upon synapsis as a criterion of relationship.

The usual consequence of normal synapsis is regularity in the anaphasic distribution of the chromosomes, each spore and gamete bearing a complete genome. This is distinctly favorable to fertility, yet it does not guarantee it, for some of the genomes produced may have chromosomes that do not constitute a harmonious system. Some of the foregoing points are illustrated in the following cases.

Maize (*Zea mays*) and Mexican teosinte (*Euchlaena mexicana*) each have 10 chromosomes in the gamete. When the two are crossed, the resulting hybrids vary in fertility depending in part upon what race of teosinte is used. Synapsis tends to be regular (Fig. 162), and crossing over takes place. In subsequent generations some of the plants show various parental character combinations, while others are precisely like maize or teosinte. This indicates a degree of cytological and genetical similarity unusually high for plants assigned to different genera. On the basis of a variety of evidences it has recently been proposed that the two species of *Euchlaena* be transferred to the genus *Zea*.

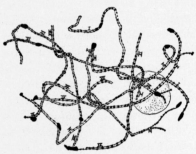

Fig. 162.—Pachytene stage in microsporocyte of a teosinte-maize F_1 hybrid, showing the nearly perfect synapsis of the chromosomes. (*After A. E. Longley.*)

Chromosomal compatibility and fertility are also shown in various degrees in crosses of European and American species of grape, sycamore, and larch, as well as in certain intergeneric moth hybrids. After crossing the garden pea (*Pisum sativum*) with *P. humile*, each with seven chromosomes in the gamete, the hybrids in subsequent generations show regular meiosis, but the occurrence of abnormal types and much sterility indicates disharmonies in many of the complements produced by the random assortment of the parental chromosomes.

When the foxglove (*Digitalis purpurea*) is crossed with *D. ambigua*, each having 14 chromosomes in the gamete, the number of bivalents formed at meiosis in the hybrid varies from 5 to 12, the rest of the chromosomes remaining univalent. Such behavior is exhibited by many other interspecific hybrids, and the irregularity may vary in amount with the cultural conditions. One result of this partial asynapsis is irregular anaphasic distribution: the bivalents disjoin normally, but the univalents either pass in various numbers to the poles or undergo equational division. Further irregularity follows in the second division, so that numerous abnormal complements and much sterility result. Irregularity in chromosome distribution often leads to the formation of microspore groups comprising spores varying in size and number (*polyspory*) instead of normal quartets. Such a condition can, however, arise from temporary environmental causes such as extreme fluctuations in temperature; consequently, nonuniform pollen is not a sure sign of hybridity. Along with the inviable chromosomal combinations are some that are successful.

This may be the case even when the genomes of the parents differ in the number of members. Thus in F_1 pansy hybrids between *Viola arvensis* ($n = 17$) and *V. tricolor* ($n = 13$) the number of bivalents varies and there is some sterility, but later generations are made up of both the parental types and a number of new ones that are fertile and breed true.

When asynapsis is complete, total sterility may be expected. Occasionally there is a different result: all the chromosomes may undergo a single equational division, two large spores then being formed each with the hybrid's diploid complement. Rarely such a spore may function in the production of polyploid offspring.

Hybridity Involving Polyploidy.—Hybrids containing different numbers of genomes may be obtained by intercrossing members of a polyploid series. For example, crosses of diploid and tetraploid species may yield triploid hybrids, those between tetraploids and octoploids may produce hexaploid hybrids, etc. Polyploid hybrids may also be obtained by inducing chromosome doubling in plants already hybrid in constitution. The characters exhibited by such plants, provided they develop successfully, depend not only upon the kinds of parental genes and their interaction, but often upon the relative number of parental genomes as well. Thus in maize-teosinte hybrids the tetraploid type with two genomes from each parent resembles the diploid hybrid, whereas the triploid hybrid with one maize and two teosinte genomes looks more like teosinte. The same tendency is strikingly shown in more extensive series of radish-cabbage hybrids and moss hybrids.

The breeding behavior of these allopolyploid plants depends of course upon the number of genomes, the type and regularity of synapsis, the viability of spores, gametes, and zygotes, the ratio of genome numbers in embryo and endosperm, and other factors. The calculation of expected genetical ratios becomes a complex matter, yet for certain types, notably the one in which there are two genomes from each parent (see next section), the expectations have in several instances been approximated by ratios observed in the breeding plot.

Chromosome behavior at meiosis in polyploid hybrids is illustrated in the following cases. In a fertile hexaploid hybrid poppy formed by crossing the diploid *Papaver nudicaule* (7 chromosomes in gamete) with the decaploid *P. striatocarpum* (35 chromosomes in gamete) the microsporocytes showed 21 bivalents: all the chromosomes found mates. In contrast to this, a hexaploid hybrid rose formed by crossing a diploid form (7 in gamete) with a decaploid form (35 in gamete) showed only 7 bivalents, the remaining 28 chromosomes appearing as univalents. In hybrids like the latter the chromosomes often show a very characteristic type of subsequent behavior: the bivalents disjoin and pass poleward, after which the univalents, now longitudinally double, occupy the equator and separate equationally. All may succeed in reaching the poles in time to be included in the telophase nuclei, or some may fail and become the nuclei of small extra microspores (Fig. 163). Such irregularity results in various degrees of sexual sterility.

The difference in behavior shown by the poppy and rose hybrids is interpreted on the basis of chromosomal homology as follows. The genomes involved in the poppy cross are of five kinds: A B B_1 C C_1. The diploid species has in the soma two A genomes only, one being transmitted by each gamete. The decaploid species has all five in the gamete. Hence after a cross the pairing in the hybrid is AA BB_1 CC_1, making 21 bivalents in all. In the roses there are also five genomes, A B C D E, but their degree of difference is great enough to preclude synapsis between them. The diploid type furnishes a gamete with A

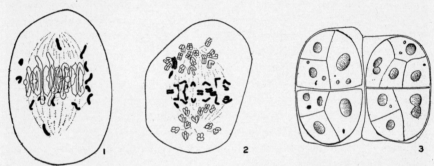

Fig. 163.—1, 2, meiosis in microsporocytes of an interspecific wheat hybrid. After the bivalents disjoin and pass poleward in division *I*, the univalents occupy the equator and separate equationally. 3, supernumerary microspores in a wheat-rye hybrid. (*After K. H. von Berg.*)

and the decaploid type one with A B C D E, so that in the hybrid only the two A genomes form bivalents. The hypothesis that a differentiation of the fundamental genome of a genus into several kinds has occurred in different strains with the passage of time has the support of other similar cases. From such synaptic behavior, conclusions are drawn regarding the degree of residual homology in these genomes and the degree of relationship of the plants containing them. This method of analysis has been carried out on a very extensive scale with different types of wheat, goat grass (*Aegilops*), rye, and their various interspecific and intergeneric hybrids. Here, as in the roses, there are genomes of several types each consisting of seven chromosomes, and these are combined in different ways in the genera, polyploid species, and hybrids.

Amphidiploidy.—Special consideration should be given to the type of polyploid hybrid having two genomes from each of two species. Such a plant is said to be *amphidiploid*, since it is diploid for both parental genomes. (It is also allotetraploid, but a plant combining three genomes

from one parent with one of the other is likewise allotetraploid.) Amphidiploid hybrids are of special importance because they are usually fertile,
occur rather widely among angiosperms in nature, afford clues to the
relationship of certain species, and open a new path to the improvement
of cultivated plants.

Amphidiploidy commonly arises through a doubling of the chromosome number in the somatic cells of a diploid hybrid. Such doubling may
occur spontaneously, and in numerous cases it has been induced with

Fig. 164.—Hybridity and polyploidy in *Calendula*. From right to left: flower heads
of *C. suffruticosa*, *C. officinalis*, a diploid *officinalis* × *suffruticosa* hybrid, a tetraploid
officinalis × *suffruticosa* hybrid resulting from colchicine treatment. (*Courtesy of C.
Weddle.*)

colchicine. If it takes place in the zygote very soon after syngamy, the
whole plant is amphidiploid; if later, *e.g.*, in a bud, only a branch or other
portion shows this condition. The most valuable feature of these plants
is the increased fertility that many of them show over the diploids from
which they arose. It is largely in the hope of conferring some degree of
fertility upon sterile hybrids with desirable combinations of characters
that the doubling technique is applied in plant-improvement programs,
and in many cases the results have been successful. In addition, the
plants obtained may show certain characters associated with tetraploidy
itself, such as sturdier habit or greater flower size (Fig. 164). They also
frequently exhibit pronounced hybrid vigor.

One of the earliest known amphidiploid hybrids appearing in culture was the fertile *Primula kewensis*, with 36 somatic chromosomes. A cross between *P. floribunda* ($2n = 18$) and *P. verticillata* ($2n = 18$) had yielded the sterile diploid *P. kewensis* ($2n = 18$) with one genome from each parent species. From a lateral bud on this plant there arose spontaneously a tetraploid shoot with two genomes from each parent, and this proved to be fertile. The numerical changes may be represented as follows: $(9 + 9) \times 2 = 36$.

An example of doubling which evidently occurred after syngamy is afforded by a fairly fertile amphidiploid columbine that appeared after a cross of the two diploid species *Aquilegia chrysantha* and *A. flabellata nana*: $(7 + 7) \times 2 = 28$. A general formula for such cases would be $(n + n)2 = 4n$. Among commercially important plants evidently having such a constitution are the pink-flowered ornamental tree, *Aesculus carnea*, and tobacco, *Nicotiana tabacum*. The former arose in cultivation as a hybrid between the horse chestnut, *A. hippocastanum*, and *A. pavia*: $(20 + 20) \times 2 = 80$. The latter has been shown by a long series of studies to represent in all probability an amphidiploid hybrid derived from a cross of *N. sylvestris* and another species which now appears to have been *N. otophora*: $(12 + 12) \times 2 = 48$.

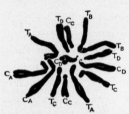

FIG. 165.—Somatic chromosome complement in an amphidiploid hybrid between *Crepis capillaris* and *C. tectorum*. It comprises two genomes of four members each from *tectorum* (*T*) and two genomes of three members each from *capillaris* (*C*). Satellites on *tectorum* *D*-chromosomes do not show at metaphase in this hybrid. (*After L. Hollingshead.*)

Some plants spoken of as amphidiploids have arisen from crosses of species differing in chromosome number. The chromosome complement of such an amphidiploid *Crepis* plant is shown in Fig. 165. *Nicotiana "digluta"* arose from a cross of *N. glutinosa* (24 somatic chromosomes) and *N. tabacum* (48 somatic chromosomes): $(12 + 24) \times 2 = 72$. If, as indicated in the preceding paragraph, *N. tabacum* is tetraploid with 2 genomes from each of two species, *N. "digluta"* in terms of the basic number for the genus, 12, would be allohexaploid with 4 genomes from one species and 2 from the other. The general formula for such cases would be $(n + 2n)2 = 6n$. Whether such plants are regarded as amphidiploid because they carry the combined somatic complements of the parents or as allohexaploid because of their number of basic genomes, they have the degree of fertility exhibited by other hybrids in which each genome has a duplicate with which to pair at meiosis. Further examples of this type of hybrid are the domestic plum, $(8 + 16) \times 2 = 48$; certain hybrid mints, $(48 + 12) \times 2 = 120$; and certain hybrid cottons, $(26 + 13) \times 2 = 78$. In the mints and cottons the new types were developed with the aid of colchicine.

Amphidiploids sometimes arise in ways other than by somatic chromosome doubling. Diploid spores and therefore gametes may appear after haplosis has failed in sporogenesis in a diploid hybrid, two diploid gametes then uniting. Although the chance of obtaining such plants in this manner seems to be relatively small, they have evidently arisen thus from interspecific diploid hybrids in *Nicotiana*, *Triticum*, and *Digitalis*, and in a *Raphanus-Brassica* hybrid. A recently observed case is that in *Madia*, a genus of western composites. Two rare and self-sterile species, *M. nutans* ($n = 9$) and *M. Rammii* ($n = 8$) produced a nearly sterile diploid hybrid ($2n = 17$). Among several types in F_2 there were two plants with 34 chromosomes which showed almost perfect synapsis into 17 bivalents. After four generations the plants of this line were vigorous, fertile, true breeding, and different in several morphological characters from their parents and all other species of the genus.

A third important method is illustrated by amphidiploid snapdragons (*Antirrhinum*) obtained by crossing two different autotetraploid strains.

It should now be evident why polyploid hybrids confront the geneticist with difficulties, as suggested earlier in the chapter. Even in the typical amphidiploids with two genomes from each parent, much depends upon the manner and degree in which synapsis is carried out. In the most nearly true breeding of them the homologous chromosomes from the same parent form bivalents, while those from the other parent do likewise (*autosynapsis*). The result is that the genomes of the parent species remain distinct in successive generations, the hybrid therefore breeding true for characters due to interspecific hybridity. The genetical results in such a case, where the two parents seem to have had relatively few genes in common, are as though the plant were diploid with a large chromosome number: the Mendelian characters of each original parent continue to show disomic ratios. If the particular genes concerned are present in the chromosomes from both parents, there appear certain tetrasomic ratios like those in experimentally induced autotetraploids (page 208). When some or all of the chromosomes from one parent synapse with members from the other parent (*allosynapsis*), the genetical data become even more difficult to analyze. Since two crossable species may have genes in common as well as unlike genes, the type of synapsis, degree of fertility, and genetical ratios tend to be variable in polyploid hybrids generally, even in the most regular amphidiploids.

Cytological Types of Hybridity.—The foregoing descriptions have been based upon the essential feature of hybridity as it appears in plants or animals with two or more genomes: the presence in the nucleus of genomes differing in genic constitution and therefore in influence upon characters. This difference arises in practically all cases from the union of nuclei from two sources, each nucleus in the individual having a "hybrid" chromosome complement when the two sources contribute unlike sets of genes. This is evident enough in the ordinary diploid hybrid employed in most cytogenetical researches, but because there are other ways in which unlike outfits of genes may be associated in an individual, it will be well at this point to pass them in brief review, beginning with the ordinary intraspecific hybrid (see Fig. 166).

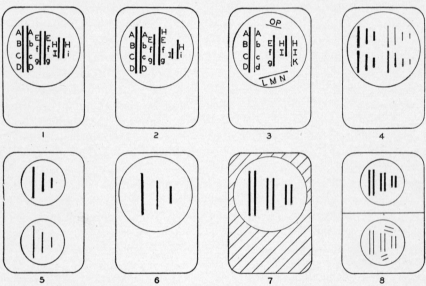

Fig. 166.—Diagram illustrating various ways in which unlike genetical elements may be combined in an organism. Rectangles and circles represent cells and nuclei, respectively. Explanation in text.

(1) Two similar genomes with one or more genes in the heterozygous state. (2) Two genomes similar in their genes but differing in the arrangement of these in the chromosomes: "structural hybrids" with chromosomal regions translocated or inverted in one of the genomes. (3) Two genomes with wider genic differences and often differing in chromosome number: diploid interspecific hybrids with synapsis and reassortment of specific characters, or with asynapsis and sterility. (4) More than two genomes from two species with regular or irregular cytogenetical behavior: polyploid hybrids, most of whose gametes are themselves "hybrid" in constitution. (5) Two unfused monoploid nuclei carrying different genomes: dikaryotic hybrids in certain fungi (page 163). (6) One genome only, this being composed of chromosomes and genes from different sources: "monoploid hybrids," or "haplomicts,"

in monoploid algae and in bryophyte gametophytes which exhibit combinations of characters from two unlike parents. (7) A nucleus from one species in cytoplasm of another species, the cytoplasm carrying a nongenic element having a distinct and persistent effect upon characters: cases of "cytoplasmic inheritance" described in the next chapter. (8) There is no hybridity within the protoplast, yet two genetically unlike kinds of protoplast are so intimately associated in a body that both share in determining its characters.

Examples of the last condition in the foregoing list may be given here. In a *chimera* two genetically unlike tissues together constitute an individual plant as a result of local somatic mutation or of a graft involving two species. In periclinal chimeras, which have one type of tissue overlying the other like a glove over a hand, the plant may combine characters of the two species involved. The form of the leaf, for example, may be determined by the inner component, while the character of its surface is that of the outer component. Sometimes the characters of the outer component are apparently affected by the genotype of the inner component. The chimeral condition may be reproduced vegetatively but not sexually, since the spores are developed solely by one component or the other—normally the one constituting the subepidermal cell layer. Another example of such cellular association is afforded by certain slime molds in which the numerous ameboid cells do not lose their boundaries when they unite to form a pseudoplasmodium from which fruiting bodies (sorocarps) develop. When pseudoplasmodia of two species are thoroughly mixed and grown under certain cultural conditions, the mixture produces not only sorocarps of the two specific types but also some combining in various ways the characters of the two species. An extreme example of the association of unlike protoplasts is seen in lichens, whose bodies are made up of a fungus and an alga living in symbiotic union.

This section is included in the chapter not to confuse our conceptions of hybridity, but rather in the hope of supplying them with a broader basis. The physical basis of heredity shows a striking fundamental similarity throughout practically the entire organic world, yet it has several variants in different groups of organisms. Cytogenetical researches are being extended into more groups as time goes on. Hybridity, the presence of unlike genetical protoplasmic elements from different sources, exists in some degree nearly everywhere, but if the investigator expects the physical mechanism of inheritance to be of exactly the same standard type in every organism he will meet many puzzles. It has sometimes happened that an elaborate and ingenious hypothesis has been formulated to account for aberrant genetical data when an awareness of a peculiar cytological or histological condition in the organism would have suggested a much simpler explanation.

Conclusions.—We may summarize here the contributions that cytology has made to our understanding of hybridity.

It has revealed much of the physical basis of peculiar modes of genetical behavior and grades of sexual sterility in known hybrids.

It has furnished a means of detecting hybridity and probable origin in some organisms not giving other clear evidence. For example, it has shown why some plants that breed true must be regarded as hybrids.

It has shown that a significant association often exists between hybridity, heteroploidy, apomixis, and certain types of mutation.

It has afforded a partial explanation of how unstable hybrids may, after some generations, yield new stable and fertile types.

It has revealed in chromosomal alterations an inner evolution which plays some role in the evolution of external diversity among organisms.

It has offered suggestions as to modes of procedure in attempts to produce new fertile types through hybridization.

It has devised artificial methods of conferring fertility, with tetraploidy, upon desirable but sterile hybrids.

It has revealed a number of variants of the fundamental physical basis of hybridity among organisms.

Finally, it has given us a far better conception of the cytogenetical history of present organisms, enabling us better to predict what their future may possibly be. Change is the rule in nature, and cytogenetics has shown us some of its inner causes.

CHAPTER XVI

THE ROLE OF THE CYTOPLASM IN DEVELOPMENT AND HEREDITY

In the preceding chapters it has been shown why and how the chromosomes have been assigned a special role in the development and inheritance of the organism's characters. When two individuals develop similar characters under the same environmental conditions, it is concluded that their protoplasmic constitutions are alike, for development is the result of interactions of the protoplasmic system with its environment and among its own components. When the interactions and characters are the same in successive generations, the characters are said to be inherited, although this actually means that they have been redeveloped in the offspring because its protoplasm is like that of the parent. When two individuals, whether they are brothers or parent and offspring, develop different characters in the same kind of environment, the differences are attributed to dissimilarities in the constitution of their protoplasms, in particular to differential factors in their chromosomes. It is largely the Mendelian phenomenon and the numerous refinements in experimental procedure that have made this correlation possible. We now face the question, "Are there differential factors elsewhere in the protoplast?"

Reciprocal Crosses.—A method for ascertaining whether cytoplasmic elements participating in character formation ever act differentially is that of comparing the results of reciprocal crosses. In angiosperms the cytoplasm is derived mainly or entirely from the maternal parent. When, therefore, two inbred types of plant are crossed reciprocally, the offspring of the two crosses have nuclei that are alike but cytoplasms that are different. Differences between the two classes of offspring might then be attributed to the differential action of the parental cytoplasms. This is the converse of the situation in crosses employed in most cytogenetic investigation, where the nuclear constitution is made to vary in a uniform cytoplasm. The usual absence of differences between such reciprocal intraspecific hybrids indicates the absence of such cytoplasmic differences between the two types crossed as would lead to differences in character development. In some interspecific and intergeneric hybrids, however, such differences are frequently observable. Often the difference disappears in the course of one generation or more. This is interpreted to mean that the egg carries in its cytoplasm a lingering effect impressed

227

upon it by the plant which bore it and that this effect is soon nullified as new cytoplasm is produced under the influence of the hybrid nuclei in the plant into which the fertilized egg grows.

An example of the brief temporary effect of the maternal cytoplasm upon the offspring is seen in seeds of stocks (*Matthiola*) (Fig. 167). The epidermis of the embryo is dark blue in *M. incana* and yellow in *M. glabra*. When the two are crossed, with *incana* as the maternal parent, the hybrid's seeds are dark blue. When the reciprocal cross is made, the seeds vary from clear yellow to light blue. Thus the cytoplasms of the two species react differently to the same heterozygous genes in the hybrids' nuclei: *incana* cytoplasm develops a blue color strongly and at once, whereas *glabra* cytoplasm does so weakly or not at all. When the two kinds of hybrid are selfed, they behave alike in yielding blue seeds with varying depth of color and yellow seeds in the ratio of 3:1.

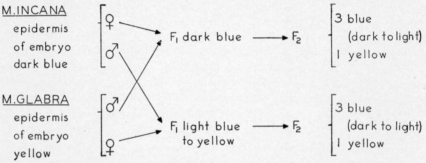

Fig. 167.—Effect of reciprocal crossing in *Matthiola* (stocks). Explanation in text. (*Based on data of C. Correns.*)

The same phenomenon is observed among animals in the case of certain larval characters. For example, in cross-fertilized sea urchin or fish eggs the rate and the type of cleavage are the same as in the mother, no matter what the direction of the cross. They are characters impressed upon the egg during its ovarian history, and the male nucleus fails to change the condition already induced in the egg by maternal nuclear factors. When the hybrid matures and produces eggs, however, it is found that these all show the dominant rate and type of cleavage, no matter which parent contributed the dominant factor. This shows that the male does affect the character in the second generation. Breeding experiments with moths and butterflies have given similar results with respect to some embryonic characters. The conclusion is that certain characters whose differentiation is initiated in the egg cytoplasm before syngamy, although fundamentally Mendelian in their inheritance, may be peculiar in that the visible effect of the male gamete is delayed for one generation.

An instance of cytoplasmic influence enduring for a longer period is afforded by the protozoan, *Paramecium*. When individuals of two races unlike in size are allowed to conjugate and then to multiply by fission, the individuals of both exconjugant lines gradually come to be of the same size after about 22 fissions. The inference is that there is here a lingering cytoplasmic influence slowly being overcome by genes affecting size. This inference is supported by the further observation that the size eventually attained is not the same after different pairs of individuals of the same clones have conjugated, for this indicates the formation of various genic combinations in the meiosis and syngamy occurring at the time of conjugation.

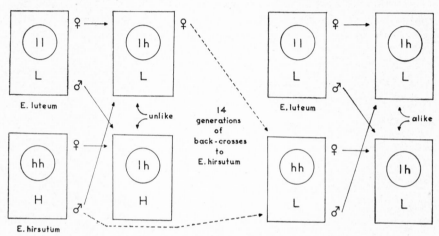

Fig. 168.—Diagram illustrating cytoplasmic inheritance in species of *Epilobium* (willow herbs). Rectangles represent plants; circles represent their nuclei. *L*, *luteum* cytoplasm; *H*, *hirsutum* cytoplasm; *l*, *luteum* genome; *h*, *hirsutum* genome. The third plant in the second row is a "nucleocytoplasmic hybrid" (compare Fig. 166, 7). Further explanation in text. (*Based on data of P. Michaelis.*)

In another class of cases the story is a different one: the cytoplasmic effect does not disappear, but persists indefinitely even in spite of attempts to increase the influence of the genes. In *Epilobium* (Fig. 168) the hybrids derived from reciprocal crosses of *E. luteum* and *E. hirsutum* are unlike in various vegetative characters and fertility. The hybrid type containing *luteum* cytoplasm retains its distinctive characters even after back crossing to *hirsutum* for 14 generations. After such a number of backcrosses the nuclei in all probability have only *hirsutum* chromosomes, yet the effect of the original maternal cytoplasm persists. When such plants containing *hirsutum* chromosomes and *luteum* cytoplasm are crossed reciprocally with *E. luteum*, the hybrids obtained are alike in spite of the fact that the nuclear relations are the same as in the original cross between the two species, where the reciprocal hybrids were not alike.

This supports the conclusion that the characters involved have a differential basis in the cytoplasm.

A comparable example is furnished by certain moss hybrids, in which gametophytic characters are involved. When *Funaria hygrometrica* and *Physcomitrium pyriforme* are crossed reciprocally, the resulting hybrid sporophytes show characteristic structural differences, as do the diploid hybrid gametophytes produced from them by regeneration. Some of these gametophytic characters, notably the length of the leaf midrib, persist throughout subsequent backcross generations of monoploid offspring grown from spores, indicating a strong and persistent cytoplasmic effect.

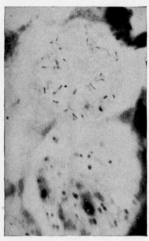

FIG. 169.—Two sporocytes in a partially male-sterile individual of maize. Normal cell above, affected one below. See text. (*Courtesy of M. M. Rhoades.*)

The shape of the leaf shows the effect somewhat less strongly, and the form of the paraphyses shows it still less. The conclusion is that in these mosses, and presumably in other plants showing strongly persistent cytoplasmic effects, there is a stable element in the cytoplasm that acts differentially upon characters. This element in mosses is called the *plasmone*. In the case of some characters, such as midrib length in the above-mentioned hybrids, it is the plasmone that is responsible for differences in the character, while other characters may be acted upon differentially by both plasmone and genome or by the genome alone.

Peculiar interest attaches to a case of cytoplasmic inheritance in *Zea* because of a visible difference in the cytoplasm correlated with the character involved. In a certain race of maize the pollen degenerates partially or completely, usually after the formation of the generative cell. This character, male sterile, is transmitted through the eggs to the next generation, but not by the few good pollen grains from partially sterile plants. That the cause of the defect is actually in the cytoplasm and not in the genes has been shown by a series of crosses involving each of the 10 chromosomes. In cells that are to yield normal pollen, certain bodies, presumably the proplastids, are rod-shaped, whereas in cells about to produce degenerating pollen they are spherical (Fig. 169). These bodies, if not the cause of the defect, are at least indicators of a determining influence in the cytoplasm.

Chlorophyll Characters.—Two successive generations of cells reproducing by division resemble each other partly because the organs of a given cell may actually continue as the corresponding organs of its daughter cells.   In a unicellular green alga the daughter individuals are like the mother in being green because the chloroplast of the mother cell is divided and passed on directly to them.   In those algae in which a swarm spore germinates to produce a multicellular individual or associates with others of its kind to form a colony, the color of the successive colonies or individuals is a character transmitted directly by the repeated division of chloroplasts.

A somewhat similar interpretation has been placed upon the inheritance of chlorophyll characters in the higher plants, the supposition being that plastids, multiplying only by division, are responsible for the distribution, in the individual plant and through successive generations, of those characters which manifest themselves in these organs.   Abnormalities in chlorophyll coloring, such as pale greenness, whiteness, and variegation, are accordingly attributed to an abnormal condition in the chloroplast or the surrounding cytoplasm.   Since the color itself is not present in the plastids of angiosperm gametes, this character may resemble ordinary Mendelian characters in being developed anew in each generation, but it differs from them in depending upon the reproduction and distribution of differentiated cytoplasmic organs, the plastids. Indeed, it has been shown that the various known chlorophyll characters, even those appearing much alike, fall into two categories: (1) those inherited according to ordinary Mendelian rules, which is taken to mean that the processes concerned in their color development are under the influence of differential nuclear factors; and (2) those not so inherited and therefore having their differential in the cytoplasm.   Both types may appear in the same genus or species, as in maize.   It is to be emphasized that the characters in both categories are developed under the influence of both nucleus and cytoplasm but that they differ with regard to the location and nature of the factors acting differentially.

A classic example of the non-Mendelian type is a variegated four-o'clock, *Mirabilis jalapa albomaculata*.   Plants of this kind have some branches with normal green leaves, some with white leaves, and some with variegated leaves.   Flowers are borne on branches of all three types. Crosses between unlikes result in seedlings with the color of the maternal parent or branch.   For instance, when a flower on a green branch is pollinated with pollen from a flower on a white branch, the offspring are all green.   In the reciprocal cross the offspring are all white and soon die because of the lack of chorophyll.   If flowers on variegated branches are pollinated, offspring of all types may result.   In no case does the pollen affect the color of the progeny.

The hypothesis proposed to account for these facts is that there is present in the plant an abnormal cytoplasmic condition that prevents the normal development of the chloroplasts.   It is delivered directly to the next generation through the egg cytoplasm but is not transmitted by the male parent because the male gamete brings no functional cytoplasm into the egg at syngamy. If the condition were under the differential control of nuclear factors, it would be transmitted equally well by male and female gametes, since the nuclear contributions of the two are equivalent. There are other plants in which chlorophyll characters of this non-Mendelian type are inherited from the male parent as well as from the female, indicating a participation of the male gamete's cytoplasm in the formation of the zygote.

There is much concerning the inheritance and development of chlorophyll characters that is not well understood. The cytological mechanism of variegation is particularly obscure in cases like the above, especially where the color pattern does not coincide with the pattern of tissue development. There is much more to be learned about plastids, the nature of the cytoplasmic differential factor, and the causes of differentiation in general before such problems can be solved.

Conclusions.—The subject of this chapter leads us back to a concept stressed in early pages of the book, *viz.*, that of the living individual as an organized protoplasmic system with many specialized regions contributing to the orderly activity of the whole. Accounts of the remarkable role of the nucleus in heredity like that in the more recent chapters sometimes suggest that the nucleus is the sole arbitrary determiner of the protoplast's activities and their consequences, the cytoplasm being merely a complex organic culture medium in which it performs its functions. Whatever may have been the historical origin of the nucleus-cytoplasm type of organization—and what it was we should like very much to know —the fact that the cytoplasm participates in at least the development of characters is now obvious.

That the cytoplasm also shares in determining what kind of characters shall develop is evident in the phenomena reviewed in this chapter. Nuclei never develop alone: it is always a nucleocytoplasmic system that undergoes development. When the type of cytoplasm associated with the nucleus is sufficiently altered, as in certain wide crosses, the characters are also altered, showing the importance of nucleocytoplasmic interaction in character development. Hence in pure lines the cytoplasm at least contributes to the similarity of individuals, whether these are brothers or parent and offspring, and similarity is a principal feature in heredity. The visible results of a strongly differential action of the cytoplasm sometimes observed in reciprocal interspecific crosses, and the fact that in attempted crosses between very distantly related organisms the nucleus and cytoplasm will not interact at all, indicate that the cytoplasm is in some measure responsible for the differences between those organisms. They also suggest that if such very wide crosses were successful and the hybrids obtained were fertile, the cytoplasm would be found to play a more prominent differential role in character determination than it does in pure lines and intraspecific hybrids.

Emphasis upon the nucleus as a system of elements necessary to development and upon its chromosomal organization as the key to the Mendelian phenomenon is surely warranted, but it should not obscure the fact that "the physical basis of heredity" in a broad sense includes all relatively stable protoplasmic elements affecting the characters developed, wherever these elements are located and whether their activity results in likeness or unlikeness in the characters. Even if one inclines to view the cytoplasm as a "culture medium" in which the nucleus somehow works out the characters, it must be remembered that this medium, even more than the characters themselves, is a direct inheritance from previous generations.

CHAPTER XVII

CYTOLOGY AND TAXONOMY

In recent years, cytology has found a new field of usefulness as an ally of taxonomy. As every student of biology is aware, the task of taxonomy is that of arranging animals and plants into a hierarchy of systematic units—species, genera, families, orders, etc.—according to the degree of their relationship. In earlier days "relationship" meant merely resemblance in externally visible characters or nearness of approach to certain ideal standards. Modern taxonomy is much more than this. It strives to improve systems of groupings made for the sake of convenience, but it also seeks the natural causes of the likenesses and differences in character observed, and it does this knowing that true relationship has its basis in community of origin.

Modern taxonomy differs from that of earlier centuries in two other important respects: it makes use of a greater diversity of evidence, and like other branches of biology it has supplemented observation with experiment. In its effort to discover true relationships and origins, it not only makes use of the usual morphological characters, but is quick to seize upon evidence afforded by physiological behavior, ecological relations, geographical distribution, serological interactions, cytological characters, genetical behavior in controlled crosses, and, in some measure, the fossil record. In short, it is now more conscious of its integral share in accounting for the distribution of organic types in space and time.

This chapter affords a glimpse of *cytotaxonomy*, in which cytological characters, chiefly the number, morphology, and behavior of chromosomes, are employed in the task of determining true natural relationships. The immediate aim of this new alliance of cytology and taxonomy is to establish and measure correlations between such cytological characters and the natural taxonomic units founded on field observation and controlled experiment. Its further aim is to evaluate alterations in chromosome complements as factors in the development and diversification of these units, and so to gain a more broadly based conception of the origin of the diversity observed in the living world.

This type of study has been carried on more extensively with plants than with animals. This is due in large measure to the fact that polyploidy occurs very widely in plants, especially among angiosperms, whereas among animals it is comparatively rare. In both kingdoms, however, significant results are being achieved.

Cytological Evidence of Relationship.—Cytological evidence of value to the taxonomist is of four chief kinds: chromosome number, chromosome morphology, chromosome behavior in crosses, and aberrations in reproduction.

Chromosome Number.—The number of chromosomes has now been ascertained in many hundreds of species of animals and plants. The reported numbers have been assembled in lists which every worker in this field must have ready to hand. Unfortunately, the usefulness of many original reports is impaired by a lack of completeness in the taxonomic designations and by failure to make permanent records of the plants in the form of herbarium specimens or photographs. Furthermore, the reliability of the numbers varies, for in many cases the counts have been made upon too few or sometimes atypical specimens. As the science of cytotaxonomy develops further, it is obvious that more care will be required with respect to these points.

One does not look far in a general list of chromosome numbers without being struck by the fact that the species of a genus tend strongly to show numbers that bear some characteristic arithmetical relation to one another. This is most evident where the numbers constitute a regular series of multiples. In other genera the numerical correlations are less complete, and in still others no significant correlation can be detected between numerical and specific differences. Such diversity is, of course, to be expected in view of the many ways and degrees in which chromosome numbers may be altered. Such ways have been described in previous chapters. It is to be borne in mind that it is primarily the kinds of genes present that determine characters, the number of chromosomes in which they are carried being a secondary factor in producing diversity.

A few examples of such numerical relationship will now be listed. In the pond lilies of the genus *Nymphaea* the species *stellata, lotus, odorata, candida,* and *gigantea* have the following somatic numbers, respectively: 28, 56, 84, 112, *c.* 224. It may be suspected that the basic number, or original monoploid number, for this genus is 7, but no species with a somatic number of 14 has yet been reported. In the genus *Plantago,* the plantains, the 40 species examined include 24 diploids with 12 somatic chromosomes, four diploids with 10, one diploid with 8, one diploid with 18, eight tetraploids with 24, one tetraploid with 36, one octoploid with 48, and one sixteen-ploid with 96 (Fig. 170). Here it appears that there is more than one basic number, and it is of interest to observe that the sections of the genus can be arranged in three groups: (1) those comprising only diploids with six as the basic number, (2) those containing both diploids and tetraploids with this basic number and types with a lower basic number, and (3) those containing polyploid species only. The original basic number is probably 6, with 5, 4, and 9 as derivatives.

This conclusion is supported by the morphology of the chromosomes (page 238).

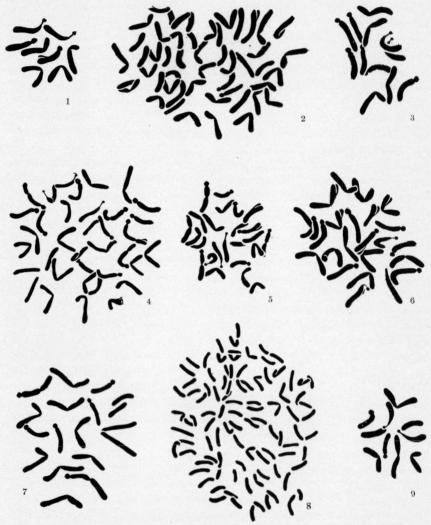

Fig. 170.—Somatic chromosome complements of several species of plantains (*Plantago*). 1, *ovata*, with 8 chromosomes; 2, *Brownii*, with 48; 3, *major*, with 12; 4, *japonica*, with 36; 5, *alpina*, with 24; 6, *media*, with 24; 7, *Raoullii*, with 18; 8, *lanceolata* var. *altissima*, with 96; 9, *serraria*, with 10. (*After D. McCullagh.*)

Frequently the sections of a genus show characteristic differences in chromosome number. In *Verbena*, the section Glandularia with a basic number of 5 includes five diploids with 10 chromosomes and three triploids with 30. In the section Verbenaca, with 7 as a basic number, the Leptostachya group is made up of nine diploids with 14 chromosomes, while the Pachystachya group comprises one triploid with 21, two tetraploids with 28, and one hexaploid with 42. In the genus *Triticum* (wheats) the species of the einkorn group have 14 somatic chromosomes, those of the emmer group 28, and those of the spelta group 42. The highly important agricultural wheat species belong to the spelta group. In the violets (*Viola*) the morphological characters determining the sections are not well correlated with chromosome number, other factors evidently having been more important in differentiation within this genus. In the sedges (*Carex*) the species have a great variety of chromosome numbers that do not form any definite type of series, although it is possible that they represent a combination of several definite series with their modifications.

Within a species there is sometimes a small amount of variation in chromosome number. In lists based on many collections and counts there frequently appears a "variety" with some multiple of the number characteristic of the species. Its rarity and association with the prevalent type may indicate recent origin. In other cases its distribution and characters suggest its independence as an established subspecific unit. Most often such plants are tetraploids, though higher multiples sometimes occur. Aneuploids are very rare.

Within a family the related genera often reveal their relationship in their chromosome numbers. Sometimes their numbers are the same. When different numbers occur, these usually do not distinguish the genera as clearly as they do related species in a genus. Very often a polyploid series runs through a considerable group of genera, with one or more of the multiples of the basic number appearing in each genus. In the Ericaceae (heaths), for example, at least ten of the genera show one or more numbers of the series 6, 12, 18, 24, 36, and 48, with 24 as the commonest somatic number. Four of the genera, together with a genus in the neighboring Empetraceae, show 26 somatic chromosomes. In the Malvaceae (mallow family) as many as five polyploid series are represented, with 5, 6, 7, 11, and 13 as the basic numbers. These series, singly or in combination, are more or less distinctive of certain groups of genera within the family. In the Leguminosae (pea family) polyploidy appears far less frequently. Of the genera studied, 42 are completely diploid, 18 are more than one-half diploid, none is predominantly polyploid with a few diploids, and 10 are completely polyploid with the occasional exception of one species. Polyploidy in this family, although occurring in about 23 per cent of the species examined, does serve to differentiate certain related genera more clearly than is usual in the angiosperms.

Chromosome number becomes less valuable as an indicator of relationship when groups larger than genera and families are considered. There appears to be little if any significant correlation of chromosome number and form on the one hand with structural complexity and the major divisions of the plant and animal kingdoms on the other. It is true that certain great groups show definite tendencies: most fungi have very low numbers; true ferns have high numbers; plants of the lily family and amphibians have large chromosomes. It seems evident, however, that the major evolutionary lines are distinguished by kinds and assortments of genes rather than by the number, size, and form of chromosomes.

Chromosome Morphology.—Species may differ in the number of their chromosomes, or in their visible morphology, or in both. In plants or animals with very small or very numerous chromosomes it is often impossible to use chromosome form as a character in the study of relationships. The value of the character increases as the chromosomes become larger and fewer. The genus *Crepis* has long been one of the most valuable to the cytologist, for although the chromosomes are of only medium size they are well differentiated morphologically and occur in genomes composed of very few members. In a majority of the species the gametic number is 4, while in most of the rest it is only 5 or 6. The characteristic morphology of these chromosomes in several of the species with the lower numbers is illustrated in Fig. 71. It is plainly evident here that each species is characterized by a chromosome complement that is not only like those of its relatives in general features but also unlike them in certain respects. The particular kind of chromosome complement characteristic of any individual or group of related organisms is called a *karyotype*. The diagrammatic representation of a karyotype is an *idiogram*.

Another example of distinctive karyotypes in a genus of plants is afforded by *Plantago* (Fig. 170). The chromosome complements in this genus are composed of members differing in size as well as in morphology and number. It is their morphology that makes it possible to decide that the complement of 18 somatic chromosomes in one of the species mentioned on page 235 consists of two genomes of 9 members each rather than three genomes of 6, and that each genome of 9 may in turn represent a combination of two basic genomes with 4 and 5 members.

In related genera the morphology of the chromosomes may, like their number, be strikingly similar or unlike in various degrees. In maize and its relatives the densely staining knobs characteristic of the chromosomes of these plants aid in cytological comparisons of the various genera. The genomes of maize (*Zea mays*), annual teosinte (*Euchlaena mexicana*) from southern Guatemala, and gamagrass (*Tripsacum floridanum*) are represented as idiograms in Fig. 171. Inspection of these idiograms shows that maize and gamagrass differ in chromosome number, knob position, and arm ratio. Maize and Mexican annual teosinte are very closely similar in the morphology of their chromosomes, including the position of their knobs. Southern Guatemalan teosinte has a genome like that of maize except for knob position which is like that of gamagrass. These features, together with chromosome behavior in the crosses mentioned below, have an important bearing upon the question of the origin of maize. A proposal to transfer the two species of *Euchlaena* to *Zea* has already been mentioned (page 218).

The use of chromosome morphology and number in the determination of generic relationships is especially well illustrated in a recent study of the Ranunculaceae (buttercup family). The conclusions reached in this study are summarized in the lower phylogenetic chart reproduced in

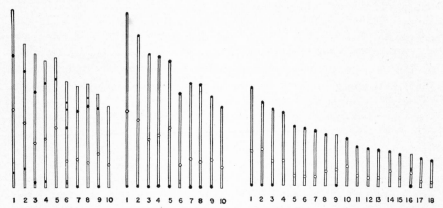

1 2 3 4 5 6 7 8 9 10   1 2 3 4 5 6 7 8 9 10   1 2 3 4 5 6 7 8 9 10 11 12 13 14 15 16 17 18

Fig. 171.—Chromosome diagrams (idiograms) of maize (left), teosinte from southern Guatemala (center), and gamagrass (right). Small circles, black spots, and shaded regions represent kinetochores, knobs, and nucleolus organizers respectively. (*After A. E. Longley.*)

Fig. 172. The upper chart is a similar representation of the relationships of the genera as conceived under the Engler system of classification. The new scheme differs conspicuously from the old in associating more closely the genera with small chromosomes.

Chromosome Behavior in Crosses.—This type of evidence for relationship has a special value. Chromosomes of two organisms may be similar in form and visible structure and yet be widely different in function. When two organisms are crossed, however, the very fact that a hybrid results shows that the two genomes brought together are sufficiently alike to act in harmony with each other and with the cytoplasm to permit ontogenetic development. This is strong evidence of relationship, for organisms that are obviously very distantly related do not produce hybrids.

A further critical test of relationship comes at the time of meiosis in the hybrid. As already pointed out in previous chapters, synapsis

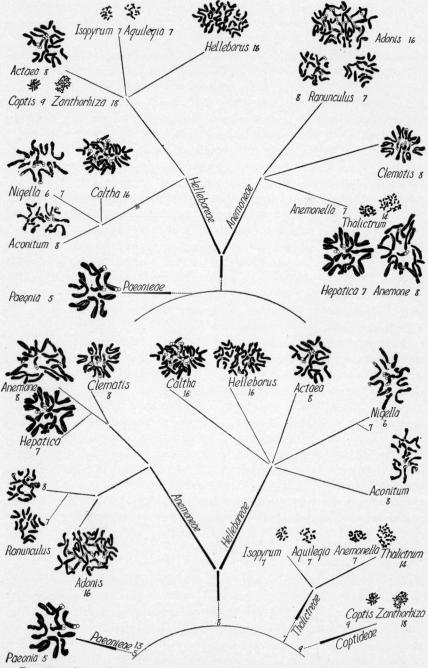

FIG. 172.—Charts illustrating the phylogeny of the Ranunculaceae (buttercup family). Above, arrangement of the genera by tribes according to the Engler system. Below, arrangement of the genera by tribes based on chromosome type, basic number, and the type of fruit. (*After W. C. Gregory.*)

depends primarily upon the homology, or genic similarity, of the chromosomes concerned, any lack of synapsis therefore indicating a lack of close relationship between them (except when it is induced by environmental causes or special mutant genes). In diploid hybrids, synapsis ranges all the way from perfect success to total failure, and in general, though not always, fertility varies with the degree of success. Reverting to *Zea* and related genera mentioned above, it is found that when maize is crossed with either annual Mexican teosinte or teosinte from northern Guatemala the hybrid shows normal synapsis (Fig. 162). In hybrids between maize and southern Guatemalan teosinte, synaptic association shows a few abnormalities due to differences in the linear arrangement of homologous elements. In maize-gamagrass hybrids synapsis occurs only in a few regions of the chromosomes, indicating a low degree of homology. Similar behavior is observed in teosinte-gamagrass hybrids. In triple hybrids containing genomes of all three genera, the *Zea* and *Euchlaena* chromosomes pair, leaving the *Tripsacum* chromosomes unpaired except for an occasional trivalent. These cytological findings are a valuable supplement to taxonomic and breeding evidence for generic relationship. They afford a visible measure of the homology and arrangement of the genes, especially since these plants show the process so clearly.

Evidence comparable to the above is available in certain animal groups also. It has been possible to make the most minute comparisons of chromosomes of related species in the Diptera because of the giant chromosomes in their salivary glands. Years ago the ordinary somatic chromosomes of various species of *Drosophila* were compared, but much more can now be learned from a comparison of their salivary-chromosome maps. In intraspecific hybrids the intimate association of parental elements in the salivary-gland chromosomes permits an even more precise comparison. In this way a point of special interest has been brought out with respect to certain geographical strains of *Drosophila pseudoobscura*. By studying the chromosomes of hybrids between these strains it was found that three of them have the genetical elements in chromosome III arranged in three different ways as the result of inversions: (1) *ABCDEFGHI*, (2) *AFEDCBGHI*, (3) *AFEHGBCDI*. In these arrangements there is a clue to the historical sequence of the races. Two successive inversions could easily give the sequence (1) → (2) → (3) or the sequence (3) → (2) → (1). Also, (2) might have been the precursor of both (1) and (3). On the other hand, it is very highly improbable that an alteration directly from (1) to (3) or vice versa would occur at one step through some more complex aberration. Since the "structural hybrids" between such inversion strains in *Drosophila* tend to be sterile, it has been suggested that such strains, because of the consequent lack of effective interbreeding, might represent early stages in the differentiation of distinct species.

The use of synaptic behavior in analyzing the relationships of polyploid plants has already been described at page 219.

Aberrations in Reproduction.—On several occasions cytology has helped to determine the taxonomic status of certain plants by revealing the presence of an atypical mode of reproduction. An instance of this is seen in the *Caninae* section of the genus *Rosa*. Among these roses are several which had been regarded as true species because of their constancy of type and the lack of intermediate forms. It was found, however, that they were polyploid in constitution and showed the most characteristic type of hybrid chromosome behavior at meiosis. The cause of their true breeding in spite of their meiotic irregularity was revealed in the discovery that they are apomictic: their embryos do not arise from sexual cells but from the nucellus by adventitious budding (page 146). The prevalence of such a mode of reproduction in a genus thus tends to preserve certain hybrids between the species and leads to the establishment of a group of many constant and nearly similar units. Such "agamic complexes" are known in numerous angiosperm genera, including *Rubus, Citrus, Potentilla, Crepis, Taraxacum, Hieracium, Festuca, Poa*, and others.

The Role of Chromosomal Changes in Speciation.—When it is discovered that the number and the morphology of the chromosomes can be used as characters in classification, one cannot pass directly to the conclusion that changes in these chromosomal features have by themselves produced the differentiation of the taxonomic units in which they are found. Visible chromosomal changes, like invisible gene mutations, are factors in speciation, but there are many conditions that must be met if a newly formed chromosomal type is to become established as a distinct species or subspecies in nature. The new type must be physiologically suited to the habitat in which it arises. It must be able to meet competition. It must either have sufficient sexual fertility to maintain itself or be able to reproduce vegetatively. In the latter case further modification through gene mutation would, of course, be much slower than in a plant capable of sexual reproduction. It would be stable and perhaps distinct in type, but not progressive.

A sexually reproducing type should have some degree of isolation from the parental type or types, for as long as it crosses freely with them the production of intermediate types will prevent the attainment of specific distinctness. The isolation permitting the new type to evolve independently through genic variation and selection may be of several kinds. The type may be sexually isolated from the parental or other related types by difference in flowering time, poor pollen tube growth after

cross-pollination, or gametic incompatibility. Its independence may
be almost as complete even when hybrids are produced, for these may be
sterile or otherwise unable to compete with either the new type or its
parents. The genetic mechanisms responsible for hybrid sterility do
not, however, seem to be directly correlated with the genetic changes
producing visible specific differences.

Another form of isolation is that based on adaptability to ecological
habitat. Peculiar physiological characters may not only keep the new
type and its relatives apart within a relatively small region, but they
may lead to very wide differences in geographical range. Examples

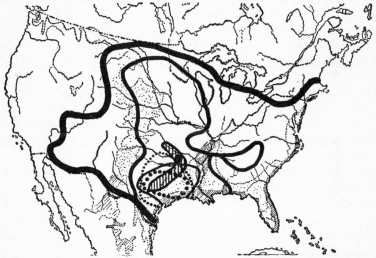

FIG. 173.—Relationship between polyploidy and geographical distribution in the
American species of *Tradescantia*. Outer heavy line: maximum distribution of tetraploid
species. Inner heavy line: maximum distribution of diploid species. Heavy cross-lined
area: minimum distribution of diploid species. Centered about this last area are the
known areas of four diploid species elsewhere tetraploid. (*After E. Anderson.*)

of this are the following. In *Tradescantia virginiana* and its relatives
growing in the United States it is observed that the diploids grow mostly
in the south, while the autotetraploids, which grow in a greater variety
of habitats, have a much wider and more northern distribution (Fig. 173).
It is not thought, however, that autotetraploidy in this genus ranks with
genic differentiation and hybridization as a cause of speciation. In
Biscutella, a genus of cruciferous plants, the derived tetraploid types are
evidently spreading more rapidly in Europe than the diploids. A survey
of the angiosperm flora of Schleswig-Holstein has shown that the percentage of polyploid types is twice as great among northern species as
among southern ones, and that whereas diploids predominate on lime-
poor soils the polyploids constitute 95 per cent of the species found on

lime-rich soils.   In Scandinavia the polyploid types among the Ericaceae are usually more widely distributed in northern and severe habitats. In certain other cases it has been found that polyploids predominate in desert habitats.   In other genera and floras, however, it has been shown that there is no correlation between polyploidy and extremity of habitat; indeed, autopolyploids may be less frost resistant, in part because of their higher water content.   Studies on *Viola, Achillea, Potentilla, Artemisia,* and other genera growing in the Pacific slope region of the United States have shown that although chromosomal differences are commonly associated with different ecological requirements and thus affect distribution, there is no rule as to the kind of region in which a given chromosomal type is found.   Among perennial forage grasses growing in California, however, the drier and hotter regions contain a distinctly higher proportion of polyploids, probably of hybrid origin.

Experimental Taxonomy.—The kinds of facts cited in the preceding section should make it evident that cytotaxonomy is a part of a larger field of investigation.   This more comprehensive field, known as experimental taxonomy, not only adds cytological characters to those ordinarily cited in manuals, but appeals to all other sources that might yield information bearing upon its problems.   The criticism from the geneticist that many species listed in the manuals may be nothing more than intraspecific Mendelian forms is being met by modern experimental taxonomists in their attempts to test their provisional hypotheses by suitable breeding experiments.   Similarly, the criticism from the physiologist and ecologist that certain supposed species may be merely local variants associated with a special habitat is being answered by the use of data from the field of experimental ecology.   Plants of the kinds in question are grown in different soils and in different climatic situations in order to distinguish more surely between physiological variations and the characters truly indicative of relationship.   This often requires observation extending over a period of years.   Furthermore, observation must also be extended in space, for a knowledge of the geographical distribution of species and other taxonomic units is often essential to an understanding of the relative age and advancement of related kinds of organisms.   Taxonomists have long been aware of this and have made use of collections from widely separated localities in formulating their conclusions.   Now that cytological data are being sought in a similar manner, cytologists share with taxonomists the benefits of this broader observational foundation.

It is obvious that conclusions based on such a variety of data can be reached only very slowly, but that when attained they should be far more dependable than concepts reached by shorter routes.   In the meantime we shall have to make use of provisional schemes of relationship devised for immediate purposes, remembering that they, like other concepts based on growing evidence, are always subject to further improvement. It is beyond the scope of this book to discuss experimental taxonomy in detail. Our purpose is to show the bearing of cytology upon biological investigation in a related field and to cite certain instructive examples of the results obtained.

The taxonomy of *Crepis*, a genus of composites, has been intensively investigated for many years with the aid of cytogenetics and geographical studies. The literature is extensive, but the results of widest significance

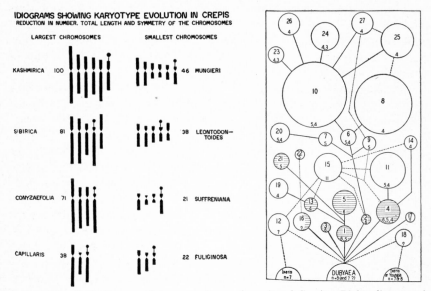

FIG. 174.—Left, diagram of genomes of several species of *Crepis*. Right, diagram of phylogenetic relations of the sections of *Crepis*. Large numerals are section numbers; small numerals are basic chromosome numbers. Shaded sections include the rhizomatous-rooted species. Sizes of circles are roughly proportional to the number of species in the sections. Connections shown by broken lines are less definitely indicated by morphological evidence than those shown by solid lines. (*From E. B. Babcock.*)

can be indicated briefly. The genus comprises about 200 species distributed widely in the Northern Hemisphere and Africa. These evidently constitute a natural group with a common origin and center of distribution. They include a remarkable range of morphological types, and with such evidence of progressive evolution there is associated an orderly and progressive modification in chromosome number and morphology. The trends of karyotype evolution in the genus are shown diagrammatically (Fig. 174). The most recent and thorough treatment of the genus divides it into 27 sections which are not segregated into subgenera. On the basis of comparative morphology, chromosome number, karyotype evolution, and length of life cycle, the sections are numbered in their approximate phylogenetic order. But the phyletic relations between the sections are more clearly shown by a diagram (Fig. 174).

From recent investigations it has been concluded that the most primitive group in the subtribe of which *Crepis* is a member is the genus *Dubyaea* in which the haploid number 8 occurs. Since the evolutionary trend within *Crepis* is from higher to lower numbers, it is assumed that *Crepis* arose from *Dubyaea*-like ancestors with 7 or 8 pairs of chromosomes. The general trend of modification within the *Crepis* karyotype has been from nearly uniform chromosomes with more or less median kinetochores to shorter, distinctly different types of chromosomes with nonmedian kinetochores. Changes in the diploid number of chromo-

Degree of separation External ＼ Internal	Hybrids fertile, second generation vigorous	Hybrids partially sterile, second generation weak	Hybrids sterile or none
In different environment	Distinct <u>subspecies</u> ECOTYPES	Distinct <u>species</u> ECOSPECIES	Distinct <u>species complexes</u> CENOSPECIES
In the same environment	<u>Local variations</u> of one species BIOTYPES	Species overlapping in common territory (with hybrid swarms)	

Fig. 175.—Table showing the concept of species and the terms employed by certain experimental taxonomists. (*After J. Clausen, D. D. Keck, and W. M. Hiesey.*)

somes from 12 to 10, 10 to 8, and 8 to 6 have occurred on several occasions. This was probably accomplished by a series of reciprocal translocations by which the essential portions of certain chromosomes were transferred to other chromosomes, the chromosomes losing these portions then being eliminated. Most of the American species of *Crepis* (section 15) are polyploid with the base number 11 which has not been found in any Old World species. These apparently arose through hybridization and amphidiploidy, followed by further crossing and apomixis. But polyploidy and apomixis are rare among the Old World species. In general, morphologically similar species have similar karyotypes, hence *Crepis* is especially well suited to cytotaxonomic study. The study of hybrids in greenhouse and laboratory has aided in determining the degree of relationship between many of the species.

Five processes of genetic change are regarded as significant in the evolution of *Crepis*. Of primary importance have been (1) the structural transformations of the chromosomes revealed in their number and morphology, for these produce initial intraspecific sterility which makes possible the accumulation of further intersterility along with morphological and physiological divergence. This and (2) gene mutation probably account for most of the progressive specialization within the genus. To these causes of change, (3) interspecific hybridization is secondary in importance, while (4) polyploidy and (5) apomixis have played definite though relatively unimportant roles.

A second series of investigations illustrating the methods and results of experimental taxonomy is that being carried out in the Pacific Coast region of the United States. Following the lead of Turesson in Europe, American botanists are investigating the species of numerous genera with special reference to the influence of climate and ecological habitat. Perennial species including many climatic races in the Pacific Coast region have been placed in gardens at three localities with very different climates: near sea level on the San Francisco peninsula, at 4600 feet elevation near Yosemite National Park, and at 10,000 feet elevation on the Sierra Nevada. In this way it is possible to observe the effects of different climates upon genetically uniform material as well as the behavior of races from different regions when brought into the same environment. The ecological reactions and chromosome numbers of the various races of a species or species group are compared with the purpose of determining whether the differentiation of intraspecific races has a visible cytological basis. In pursuing such studies the investigators have found useful the terminology indicated in Fig. 175. They are, however, quick to admit that one cannot formulate definitions covering all differences between taxonomic units, since species are in all stages of evolution.

Some of the results of these studies are as follows. Three complexes of climatic races (in *Sisyrinchium bellum*, *Potentilla glandulosa*, and *Penstemon procerus*) have become differentiated without change in chromosome number. In two other complexes, involving several other species of *Potentilla*, the chromosomes vary in number and degree of irregularity in behavior, and the plants are evidently apomictic, yet climatic races have been successfully developed as in *P. glandulosa*. In six complexes (in *Zauschneria*, *Viola*, *Aster*, *Artemisia*, *Achillea*, and *Horkelia*) there are differences in chromosome number that prevent free interbreeding and are usually correlated with differences in morphology. Such chromosomal groups can be recognized as taxonomic species, and they usually occupy different climatic regions.

These data and many others have led to the conclusions stated in the following quotation.

This survey and the one conducted by Turesson in Europe indicate that the genetic-physiologic differentiation of a plant group is correlated with the climatic zones it occupies. This follows from the fact that the same kinds of environments are occupied by races that have similar patterns of reaction, even though they belong to unrelated genera or families. This is found to hold irrespective of whether or not the regional forms differ in chromosome number.

The usual pattern of differentiation is purely genetic, with relatively few major steps involved; but superimposed upon this one often finds a cytological differentiation, with one or two changes in chromosome number across the California transect. However, the effects of increases in chromosome number

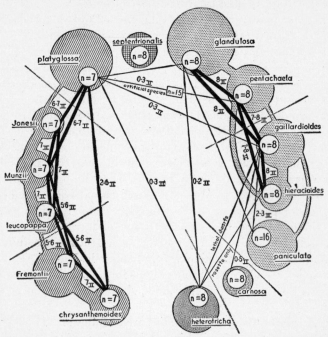

Fig. 176.—Diagram representing relationships in the genus *Layia* as indicated by the combined results of taxonomic, ecological, and cytological studies. Circles represent species with the chromosome numbers shown; shaded connections show degree of genetic affinity; width of solid black lines represents degree of chromosome pairing in interspecific hybrids. The dotted lines indicate major morphological breaks in the genus. (*After J. Clausen, D. D. Keck, and W. M. Hiesey.*)

must have been far overshadowed by the selective influence of the environment in determining the appearance and reactions of plants. From these considerations it appears that it is the genes in the chromosomes, and not the number of chromosomes, which determine the climatic adaptation.

From the point of view of fitness to the environment it is evident that the ecologically important unit is not the species, but the regional climatic race, or, to adopt Turesson's term, the *ecotype*. Several of these may combine to form a species, or a single ecotype may develop an isolating genetic barrier to form a monotypic species. . . . Such monotypic species occupy a narrow climatic belt and show little variation and adaptability. However, it makes little difference whether a given area is populated by a series of ecotypes belonging to one species, or by a series of monotypic species belonging to one species complex, or by a combination of both. The evolutionary past and future differ, however, in the three instances.

Evolutionary processes have left plants arranged in groups of various order and separation, such as populations, ecotypes, species and species complexes. These groups indicate stages in evolutionary differentiation, and they have evolved only where there is a diversity of environments.

There are many mechanisms by which living things can increase their hereditary variation, but regional differentiation requires the discriminating selection offered by unlike environments. We have no evidence that the direct influence of environment produces fundamental hereditary changes in species, but major alterations in environments provide new habitats and refuges for the products of nature's continual experimentation among all the plant species that populate a given area. (Clausen, Keck and Hiesey.)

The above investigations on western plants include detailed studies of interspecific relationships within certain genera, the taxonomic, ecological, cytological, and genetical evidence all being brought to bear upon the problem. One of these genera is *Layia*, of which the analysis to date is summarized graphically in Fig. 176. Inspection of this diagram may serve better than a long description to suggest the complexity of problems of this kind and the amount of time and labor required for their solution. One must choose between solving them quickly and solving them well.

Conclusions.—Cytology has contributed to taxonomy in two important ways. First, it has added a new category of characters to those commonly employed in classification. Obviously, chromosomes are not very useful in the field; nevertheless, they are available and should always be a part of any thorough taxonomic analysis. They do not always prove valuable, but when they do they compensate well for the effort expended upon them. In numerous cases they have enabled workers to decide whether a plant type newly observed in the field is a Mendelian variant, a heteroploid derivative of a familiar species, or a stable and fertile interspecific hybrid. In other words, visible characters of the chromosomes frequently indicate the invisible genic constitution primarily responsible for the external characters.

Cytology's second contribution to taxonomy lies in the clues it gives to the origin of the species and other taxonomic units. Evolution involves the origin of heritable variations, a selective process operating among the variants, and some isolating factor that permits a variant to become modified independently of neighboring types. Darwin began with the variants; now cytology, with genetics, is revealing the inner causes of the variations. It is also revealing some of the internal reasons for the selection of certain variants to the exclusion of others, for cytological phenomena, especially at meiosis, often show why certain chromosomal combinations are viable and stable while others are not. An internal cause of isolation is also evident in cytological behavior which either prevents successful crossing with related types or leads to the sterility of hybrids in case they are formed. Finally, cytological studies sometimes indicate clearly in what order a series of differing types should be read.

Cytology itself has gained greatly from its association with taxonomy. Cytologists have the satisfaction of seeing their subject given wider usefulness in its application to a biological problem of the first rank. They are gaining a greater familiarity with the work of other biologists less confined to the laboratory than they, and through this they are developing a deeper appreciation of the significance of their own subject.

SUGGESTED READING

I. Some General Works on Cytology

CAMERON, GLADYS. Essentials of Tissue Culture Technique. New York, 1935.

CHAMBERS, R. The micromanipulation of living cells. In The Cell and Protoplasm. Lancaster, Pa., 1940.

COWDRY, E. V., ed. General Cytology. Chicago, 1924.

――――. Special Cytology. 2d ed. New York, 1932.

DONCASTER, L. An Introduction to the Study of Cytology. Cambridge (England), 1920.

GEITLER, L. Grundriss der Cytologie. Berlin, 1934.

GRAY, J. A Text-book of Experimental Cytology. Cambridge (England), 1931.

GUILLERMOND, A., G. MANGENOT, and L. PLANTEFOL. Traité de cytologie végétale. Paris, 1932.

KÜSTER, E. Die Pflanzenzelle. Jena, 1935.

PFEIFFER, H. H. Experimentelle Cytologie. Leiden, 1940.

SHARP, L. W. An Introduction to Cytology. 3d ed. New York, 1934.

WHITE, P. R. Plant tissue cultures. Biol. Rev. 16: 34–48, 1941.

WILSON, E. B. The Cell in Development and Heredity. 3d ed. New York, 1925.

II. The Organism and the Cell

ALLEN, C. E. Regeneration, development and genotype. Amer. Naturalist 76: 225–238, 1942.

BAITSELL, G. A. A modern conception of the cell as a structural unit. Biol. Symposia 1: 67–86, 1940.

BERTALANFFY, L. VON (Trans. by J. H. WOODGER). Modern Theories of Development. Oxford, 1933.

BURR, H. S., and F. S. C. NORTHROP. The electro-dynamic theory of life. Quar. Rev. Biol. 10: 322–333, 1935.

CHILD, C. M. Cellular differentiation and external environment. In The Cell and Protoplasm. Lancaster, Pa., 1940.

GILCHRIST, F. G. The nature of organic wholeness. Quar. Rev. Biol. 12: 251–270, 1937.

HARRISON, R. G. Cellular differentiation and internal environment. In The Cell and Protoplasm. Lancaster, Pa., 1940.

KOFOID, C. A. Cell and organism. In The Cell and Protoplasm. Lancaster, Pa., 1940.

LUYET, B. J. The case against the cell theory. Science 91: 252–255, 1940

ROHDE, E. Der plasmodiale Aufbau des Tier- und Pflanzenkörpers. Zeit. f. Wiss. Zool. 120: 325–535, 1923.

SINNOTT, E. W. The cell and the problem of organization. Science 89: 41–46, 1939.

――――. The problem of internal differentiation in plants. Amer. Naturalist 76: 253–268, 1942.

WEISS, P. The problem of cell individuality in development. Biol. Symposia 1: 96–108, 1940.

III. Structural Components of Protoplasts

BEAMS, H. W., and R. L. KING. The effect of centrifugation on plant cells. *Bot. Rev.* **5**: 132–154, 1939.

ELLINGER, P. Fluorescence microscopy in biology. *Cambridge Phil. Soc. Biol. Rev.*, **15**: 323–350, 1940.

FRANCK, J. Some functional aspects of photosynthesis. *Sigma Xi Quar.* **29**: 81–105, 1941.

FREY-WYSSLING, A. Submikroskopische Morphologie des Protoplasmas und seiner Derivate. *Protoplasma Monog.* 15, 1938.

GATES, R. R. Nucleoli and related nuclear structures. *Bot. Rev.* **8**: 337–409, 1942.

GUILLIERMOND, A. (Trans. by LENETTE R. ATKINSON). The Cytoplasm of the Plant Cell. Waltham, Mass., 1941.

HEIDENHAIN, M. Plasma und Zelle. Jena, 1907, 1911.

HUSKINS, C. L. Structural differentiation of the nucleus. In A Symposium on the Structure of Protoplasm. SEIFRIZ, ed. Ames, Iowa, 1942.

KIRKMAN, H., and A. E. SEVERINGHAUS. A review of the Golgi apparatus. *Anat. Record* **70, 71,** 1938.

KNAYSI, G. Elements of Bacterial Cytology. In press, 1943.

KNUDSON, L. Permanent changes of chloroplasts induced by X rays in the gametophyte of Polypodium aureum. *Bot. Gazette* **101**: 721–758, 1940.

LUNDEGÅRDH, H. Zelle und Cytoplasma. Berlin, 1922.

MAXIMOW, A. A., and W. BLOOM. A Textbook of Histology. 2d ed. Philadelphia and London, 1934.

MEYER, A. Morphologische und physiologische Analyse der Zelle der Pflanzen und Tiere. Jena, 1920–1921, 1926.

MÖBIUS, M. Die Farbstoffe der Pflanzen. Berlin, 1927.

————. Pigmentation in plants, exclusive of the algae. *Bot. Rev.* **3**: 351–363, 1937.

NAHM, LAURA J. The problem of Golgi material in plant cells. *Bot. Rev.* **6**: 49–72, 1940.

NEWCOMER, E. H. Mitochondria in plants. *Bot. Rev.* **6**: 85–147, 1940.

RICE, MABEL A. The cytology of host-parasite relations. *Bot. Rev.* **1**: 327–354, 1935.

SOROKIN, H. The distinction between mitochondria and plastids in living epidermal cells. *Amer. Jour. Bot.* **28**: 476–485, 1941.

TISCHLER, G. Allgemeine Karyologie. Berlin, 1921–1922, 1934.

TROMBETTA, VIVIAN V. The cytonuclear ratio. *Bot. Rev.* **8**: 317–336, 1942.

UBER, F. M. Microincineration and ash analysis. *Bot. Rev.* **6**: 204–226, 1940.

WEIER, T. E. The structure of the chloroplast. *Bot. Rev.* **4**: 497–530, 1938.

ZIRKLE, C. The plant vacuole. *Bot. Rev.* **3**: 1–30, 1937.

ZSCHEILE, F. P. Plastid pigments. *Bot. Rev.* **7**: 587–648, 1941.

IV. Protoplasm

BECKER, W. A. Vitale Cytoplasma- und Kernfärbungen. *Protoplasma* **26**: 439–487, 1936.

BENSLEY, R. R. Chemical structure of cytoplasm. *Science* **96**: 389–393, 1942.

FREUNDLICH, H. Some mechanical properties of sols and gels and their relation to protoplasmic structure. In A Symposium on the Structure of Protoplasm. SEIFRIZ, ed. Ames, Iowa, 1942.

FREY-WYSSLING, A. Submikroskopische Morphologie des Protoplasmas und seiner Derivate. *Protoplasma Monog.* 15, 1938.

GORTNER, R. A. Outlines of Biochemistry. New York, 1929.

GULICK, A. The chemistry of the chromosomes. *Bot. Rev.* **7**: 433–457, 1941.

HEILBRUNN, L. V. Protoplasm and colloids. In The Cell and Protoplasm. Lancaster, Pa., 1940.

KIESEL, A. Chemie des Protoplasmas. *Protoplasma Monog.* 4, 1930.

KÜSTER, E. Vital staining of plant cells. *Bot. Rev.* **5**: 351–370, 1939.

MARSLAND, D. A. Protoplasmic streaming in relation to gel structure in the cytoplasm. In A Symposium on the Structure of Protoplasm. SEIFRIZ, ed. Ames, Iowa, 1942.

MEYER, K. H. Protein and protoplasmic structure. In A Symposium on the Structure of Protoplasm. SEIFRIZ, ed. Ames, Iowa, 1942.

MOYER, L. S. Proteins and protoplasmic structure. In A Symposium on the Structure of Protoplasm. SEIFRIZ, ed. Ames, Iowa, 1942.

SCARTH, G. W. Structure and differentiation of cytoplasm. In A Symposium on the Structure of Protoplasm. SEIFRIZ, ed. Ames, Iowa, 1942.

SCHMITT, F. O. The ultrastructure of protoplasmic constituents. *Physiol. Rev.* **19**: 270–302, 1939.

SEIFRIZ, W. The structure of protoplasm. *Bot. Rev.* **1**: 18–36, 1935.

———. Protoplasm. New York, 1936.

———. Protoplasmic streaming. *Bot. Rev.* **9**: 49–123, 1943.

SPONSLER, O. L. Molecular structure in protoplasm. In The Cell and Protoplasm. Lancaster, Pa., 1940.

———, and JEAN D. BATH. Molecular structure in protoplasm. In A Symposium on the Structure of Protoplasm. SEIFRIZ, ed. Ames, Iowa, 1942.

V. Division of the Protoplast

BECKER, W. A. Recent investigations in vivo on the division of plant cells. *Bot. Rev.* **4**: 446–472, 1938.

BERNAL, J. D. Structural units in cellular physiology. In The Cell and Protoplasm. Lancaster, Pa., 1940.

CAROTHERS, E. ELEANOR. Components of the mitotic spindle with especial reference to the chromosomal and interzonal fibers in the Acrididae. *Biol. Bull.* **71**: 469–491, 1936.

CLEVELAND, L. R., with collaboration of S. R. HALL, E. P. SANDERS, and J. COLLIER. The wood-feeding roach Cryptocercus, its protozoa, and the symbiosis between protozoa and roach. *Mem. Amer. Acad. Arts Sci.* **17**: No. 2: 185–342, 1934.

DAN, K., T. YANAGITA, and M. SUGIYAMA. Behavior of the cell surface during cleavage. *Protoplasma* **28**: 66–81, 1937.

FANKHAUSER, G. The development of fragments of the fertilized Triton egg with the egg nucleus alone (gyno-merogony). *Jour. Exp. Zool.* **75**: 413–469, 1937.

HARVEY, ETHEL B. Parthenogenetic merogony or cleavage without nuclei in Arbacia punctulata. *Biol. Bull.* **71**: 101–121, 1936.

KATER, J. McA. Amitosis. *Bot. Rev.* **6**: 164–180, 1940.

LEWIS, F. T. The significance of cells as revealed by their polyhedral shapes, etc. *Proc. Amer. Acad. Arts Sci.* **68**: 251–284, 1933.

LEWIS, W. H. The relation of viscosity changes of protoplasm to ameboid locomotion and cell division. In A Symposium on the Structure of Protoplasm. SEIFRIZ, ed. Ames, Iowa, 1942.

MARVIN, J. W. The shape of compressed lead shot and its relation to cell shape. *Amer. Jour. Bot.* **26**: 280–288, 1939.

MATZKE, E. B.   Volume-shape relationships in lead shot and their bearing on cell shapes. *Amer. Jour. Bot.* **26**: 288–295, 1939.

SCHRADER, F.   The present status of mitosis. *Amer. Naturalist* **74**: 25–33, 1940.

VI. Cell Walls of Plants

ANDERSON, D. B.   The structure of the walls of the higher plants. *Bot. Rev.* **1**: 52–76, 1935.

BAILEY, I. W.   The walls of plant cells. In The Cell and Protoplasm. Lancaster, Pa., 1940.

———, and T. KERR.   The visible structure of the secondary wall and its significance in physical and chemical investigations of tracheary cells and fibers. *Jour. Arnold Arboretum* **16**: 273–300, 1935.

BERKLEY, E. E.   Shrinkage and cell wall structure of cotton fibers. *Amer. Jour. Bot.* **29**: 416–423, 1942.

EAMES, A. J., and L. H. MACDANIELS.   An Introduction to Plant Anatomy. New York, 1925.

FARR, WANDA K.   Formation of microscopic cellulose particles in colorless plastids of the cotton fiber. *Contrib. Boyce Thompson Inst.* **12**: 181–194, 1941.

HOCK, C. W.   Microscopic structure of the cell wall. In A Symposium on the Structure of Protoplasm. SEIFRIZ, ed. Ames, Iowa, 1942.

KERR, T., and I. W. BAILEY.   The cambium and its derivative tissues, X. Structure, optical properties and chemical composition of the so-called middle lamella. *Jour. Arnold Arboretum* **15**: 327–349, 1934.

LIVINGSTON, L. G.   The nature and distribution of plasmodesmata in the tobacco plant. *Amer. Jour. Bot.* **22**: 75–87, 1935.

MARTENS, P.   L'origine des espaces intercellulaires. *La Cellule* **46**: 357–388, 1937.

MEEUSE, A. J. D.   On the nature of plasmodesmata. *Protoplasma* **35**: 143–151, 1941.

———.   Plasmodesmata. *Bot. Rev.* **7**: 249–262, 1941.

PRESTON, R. D.   The wall of the conifer tracheid as a single spiral complex. *Proc. Leeds Phil. Soc. (Sci. Sec.)* **3**: 546–552, 1939.

WISSELINGH, C. VAN.   Die Zellmembran. Berlin, 1924.

VII. The Chromosomes

BUCK, J. B.   Growth and development of the salivary gland chromosomes in Sciara. *Proc. Nat. Acad. Sci.* **23**: 423–428, 1937.

———.   Micromanipulation of salivary gland chromosomes. *Jour. Heredity* **33**: 3–10. 1942.

CLEVELAND, L. R.   Longitudinal and transverse division in two closely related flagellates. *Biol. Bull.* **74**: 1–24, 1938.

GEITLER, L.   Chromosomenbau. *Protoplasma Monog.* 14, 1938.

KAUFMANN, B. P.   Chromosome structure in relation to the chromosome cycle. *Bot. Rev.* **2**: 529–553, 1936.

METZ, C. W.   Internal structure of salivary gland chromosomes in Sciara. *Jour. Heredity* **26**: 491–501, 1935.

———.   Structure of salivary gland chromosomes. *Cold Spring Harbor Symposia on Quant. Biol.* **9**: 23–39, 1941.

NEBEL, B. R.   Structure of Tradescantia and Trillium chromosomes with particular emphasis on number of chromonemata. *Cold Spring Harbor Symposia on Quant. Biol.* **9**: 7–12, 1941.

PAINTER, T. S.   The structure of salivary gland chromosomes. *Biological Symposia* **1**: 215–230, 1940.

Sax, K. An analysis of X-ray induced chromosomal aberrations in Tradescantia. *Genetics* **25**: 41–68, 1940.

Schultz, J. The evidence of the nucleoprotein nature of the gene. *Cold Spring Harbor Symposia on Quant. Biol.* **9**: 55–65, 1941.

Sparrow, A. H. The structure and development of the chromosome spirals in microspores of Trillium. *Canad. Jour. Res.* **20**: 257–266, 1942.

Warmke, H. E. Chromosome continuity and individuality. *Cold Spring Harbor Symposia on Quant. Biol.* **9**: 1–6, 1941.

VIII. Meiosis

Darlington, C. D. Recent Advances in Cytology. 2d ed. New York, 1937.

Kuwada, Y. Studies of mitosis and meiosis in comparison, I. *Cytologia* **11**: 217–244, 1940.

Marshak, A. The effect of X-rays on chromosomes in different stages of meiosis. *Jour. Gen. Physiol.* **19**: 179–198, 1935.

Nebel, B. R. Chromosome structure. X. *Genetics* **21**: 605–614, 1936.

Oehlkers, F. Die zytologischen Grundlagen des genetischen "crossing-over." *Ber. Deu. Bot. Gesell.* **55**: (96)–(118), 1937.

Sax, K., and L. M. Humphrey. Structure of meiotic chromosomes in microsporogenesis of Tradescantia. *Bot. Gazette* **96**: 353–362, 1934.

Schrader, F. The structure of the kinetochore at meiosis. *Chromosoma* **1**: 230–237, 1939.

Wilson, G. B., and C. L. Huskins. Chromosome and chromonema length during meiotic coiling in Trillium erectum L. *Ann. Botany* **3**: 257–270, 1939.

IX. Reproduction in Animals

Agar, W. E. Cytology. London, 1920.

Calkins, G. N. The Biology of the Protozoa. Philadelphia and New York, 1926.

———, and F. M. Summers. Protozoa in Biological Research. New York, 1941.

Cleveland, L. R., with collaboration of S. R. Hall, Elizabeth P. Sanders, and Jane Collier. The wood-feeding roach Cryptocercus, its protozoa, and the symbiosis between protozoa and roach. *Mem. Amer. Acad. Arts Sci.* **17**: 185–342, 1934.

Cleveland, L. R. Origin and development of the achromatic figure. *Biol. Bull.* **74**: 41–55, 1938.

Doncaster, L. An Introduction to the Study of Cytology. Cambridge (England), 1920.

Gray, J. A Textbook of Experimental Cytology. Cambridge (England), 1931.

Hegner, R. W. The Germ-cell Cycle in Animals. New York, 1914.

Jennings, H. S. Chromosomes and cytoplasm in protozoa. In The Cell and Protoplasm. Lancaster, Pa., 1940.

Kofoid, C. A. Cell and organism. In The Cell and Protoplasm. Lancaster, Pa., 1940.

Wenrich, D. H. Chromosomes in protozoa. *The Collecting Net* (Woods Hole) **15**: No. 6, 1940.

Wilson, E. B. The Cell in Development and Heredity. 3d ed. New York, 1925.

X. Reproduction in Angiosperms

Coulter, J. M., and C. J. Chamberlain. Morphology of Angiosperms. New York, 1909.

Ernst, A. Bastardierung als Ursache der Apogamie im Pflanzenreich. Jena, 1918.

FROST, H. B.   Nucellar embryony and juvenile characters in clonal varieties of Citrus. *Jour. Heredity* **29**: 423–432, 1938.

GUSTAFSON, F. G.   The cause of natural parthenocarpy.   *Amer. Jour. Bot.* **26**: 135–138, 1939.

———.   Parthenocarpy: natural and artificial.   *Bot. Rev.* **8**: 599–654.   1942.

MAHESHWARI, P.   A critical review of the types of embryo sacs in Angiosperms. *New Phytologist* **36**: 359–417, 1937.

SCHNARF, K.   Embryologie der Angiospermen.   Berlin, 1929.

———.   Contemporary understanding of embryo-sac development in Angiosperms. *Bot. Rev.* **2**: 565–585, 1936.

SCHÜRHOFF, P. N.   Die Zytologie der Blütenpflanzen.   Stuttgart, 1926.

STEBBINS, G. L. JR.   Apomixis in the Angiosperms.   *Bot. Rev.* **7**: 507–542, 1941.

WEBBER, J. M.   Polyembryony.   *Bot. Rev.* **6**: 575–598, 1940.

XI. Reproduction in Plants Other than Angiosperms

ALLEN, C. E.   Haploid and diploid generations.   *Amer. Naturalist* **71**: 193–205, 1937.

BULLER, A. H. R.   The diploid cell and the diploidization process in plants and animals, with special reference to the higher fungi.   *Bot. Rev.* **7**: 335–431, 1941.

CHAMBERLAIN, C. J.   Gymnosperms.   Structure and Evolution.   Chicago, 1935.

CUTTER, V. M., JR.   Nuclear behavior in the Mucorales.   *Bull. Torr. Bot. Club* **69**: 480–508, 592–516, 1942.

EAMES, A. J.   Morphology of Vascular Plants.   Lower Groups.   New York, 1936.

FITZPATRICK, H. M.   The Lower Fungi.   Phycomycetes.   New York, 1930.

FRITSCH, F. E.   The Structure and Reproduction of the Algae.   New York, 1935.

GÄUMANN, E. A. (Trans. and revised by C. W. DODGE).   Comparative Morphology of Fungi.   New York.   1928.

GEITLER, L.   Reproduction and life history in diatoms.   *Bot. Rev.* **1**: 149–161, 1935.

HALL, R. P.   Cytoplasmic inclusions in Phytomastigoda.   *Bot. Rev.* **2**: 85–94, 1936.

KNAYSI, G.   Cytology of bacteria.   *Bot. Rev.* **4**: 83–112, 1938.

MARTIN, G. W.   The Myxomycetes.   *Bot. Rev.* **6**: 356–388, 1940.

SCHNARF, K.   Embryologie der Gymnospermen.   Berlin, 1933.

SMITH, G. M.   The Fresh-water Algae of the United States.   New York, 1933.

———.   Nuclear phases and alternation of generations in the Chlorophyceae.   *Bot. Rev.* **4**: 132–139, 1938.

STEIL, W. N.   Apogamy, apospory, and parthenogenesis in the Pteridophytes. *Bot. Rev.* **5**: 433–453, 1939.

SVEDELIUS, N.   Alternation of generations in relation to reduction division.   *Bot. Gaz.* **83**: 362–384, 1927.

TAYLOR, W. R.   Phaeophycean life-histories in relation to classification.   *Bot. Rev.* **2**: 554–563, 1936.

XII. Cytology and Mendelian Heredity

ALLEN, C. E.   The genetics of bryophytes.   *Bot. Rev.* **1**: 269–291, 1935.

———.   The genotypic basis of sex-expression in Angiosperms.   *Bot. Rev.* **6**: 227–300, 1940.

BABCOCK, E. B., and R. E. CLAUSEN.   Genetics in Relation to Agriculture.   2d ed. New York, 1927.

BRIDGES, C. B.   Cytological and Genetic Basis of Sex.   In Sex and Internal Secretions (E. Allen, ed.), 2d ed., Baltimore, 1939.

CRANE, M. B., and A. J. C. LAWRENCE.   The Genetics of Garden Plants.   London, 1934.

DAVENPORT, C. B.   Sex linkage in man.   *Genetics* **15**: 401–444, 1930.

GULICK, A.   What are the genes?   *Quar. Rev. Biol.* **13**: 1–18, 140–168, 1938.

LOEHWING, W. F.   Physiological aspects of sex in angiosperms.   *Bot. Rev.* **4**: 581–625, 1938.

LOUIS-MARIE, P.   Hérédité.   *Inst. agricole d'Oka*, La Trappe, Quebec, 1936.

RHOADES, M. M., and B. McCLINTOCK.   The cytogenetics of maize.   *Bot. Rev.* **1**: 292–325, 1935.

ROUSSEAU, J.   Notions élémentaires de génétique.   *Bull. jard. bot. Montreal.* **2**, 1941.

SCHULTZ, J.   The evidence of the nucleoprotein nature of the gene.   *Cold Spring Harbor Symposia on Quant. Biol.* **9**: 55–65, 1941.

SINNOTT, E. W., and L. C. DUNN.   Principles of Genetics.   New York, 1939.

XIII. Chromosomal Aberrations

BLAKESLEE, A. F.   New Jimson weeds from old chromosomes.   *Jour. Heredity* **25**: 81–108, 1934.

CLELAND, R. E.   Some aspects of the cyto-genetics of Oenothera.   *Bot. Rev.* **2**: 316–348, 1936.

DOBZHANSKY, T.   Position effect of genes.   *Biol. Rev.* **11**: 364–384, 1936.

DUGGAR, B. M., ed.   The Biological Effects of Radiation.   New York, 1936.

GOLDSCHMIDT, R.   Chromosomes and genes.   In The Cell and Protoplasm.   Lancaster, Pa., 1940.

GOODSPEED, T. H.   Induced chromosomal alterations.   In The Biological Effects of Radiation.   DUGGAR, ed.   New York, 1936.

———, and F. M. UBER.   Radiation and plant cytogenetics.   *Bot. Rev.* **5**: 1–48, 1939.

KAUFMANN, B. P.   Induced chromosomal breaks in Drosophila.   *Cold Spring Harbor Symposia on Quant. Biol.* **9**: 82–92, 1941.

McCLINTOCK, B.   The production of homozygous deficient tissues with mutant characteristics by means of the aberrant mitotic behavior of ring-shaped chromosomes.   *Genetics* **23**: 315–376, 1938.

———.   The association of mutants with homozygous deficiencies in Zea mays.   *Genetics* **26**: 542–571, 1941.

OLIVER, C. P.   Radiation in genetics.   *Quar. Rev. Biol.* **9**: 381–408, 1934.

SAX, K.   Types and frequencies of chromosomal aberrations induced by X-rays.   *Cold Spring Harbor Symposia on Quant. Biol.* **9**: 93–103, 1941.

STADLER, L. J.   The comparison of ultraviolet and X-ray effects on mutation.   *Cold Spring Harbor Symposia on Quant. Biol.* **9**: 168–178, 1941.

SWANSON, C. P.   A comparison of chromosomal aberrations induced by X-ray and ultra-violet radiation.   *Proc. Nat. Acad. Sci.* **26**: 366–373, 1940.

XIV. Chromosome Numbers and Their Alteration

BLAKESLEE, A. F.   Effect of induced polyploidy in plants.   *Amer. Naturalist* **75**: 117–135, 1941.

CHEN, T.-T.   Polyploidy and its origin in Paramecium.   *Jour. Heredity* **31**: 175–184, 1940.

CLAUSEN, R. E.   Polyploidy in Nicotiana.   *Amer. Naturalist* **75**: 291–306, 1941.

DERMEN, H.   Colchicine polyploidy and technic.   *Bot. Rev.* **6**: 599–635, 1940.

EMSWELLER, S. L., and M. L. RUTTLE.   Induced polyploidy in floriculture.   *Amer. Naturalist* **75**: 310–326, 1941.

FANKHAUSER, G.   Polyploidy in the salamander, Eurycea bislineata.   *Jour. Heredity* **30**: 379–388, 1939.

GOODSPEED, T. H., and P. AVERY.   Trisomic and other types in Nicotiana sylvestris. *Jour. Genetics* **38**: 381–458, 1939.   See also *Proc. Nat. Acad. Sci.* **27**: 13–14, 1941.

HEILBORN, O.   On the origin and preservation of polyploidy.   *Hereditas* **19**: 233–242, 1934.

HUSKINS, C. L.   Polyploidy and mutations.   *Amer. Naturalist* **75**: 329–344, 1941.

LINDSTROM, E. W.   Genetics of polyploidy.   *Bot. Rev.* **2**: 197–215, 1936.

MÜNTZING, A.   The evolutionary significance of autopolyploidy.   *Hereditas* **21**: 263–378, 1936.

NEBEL, B. R., and M. L. RUTTLE.   Colchicine and its place in fruit breeding.   *N.Y. State Agr. Exp. Sta. Circ.* 183, 1939.

RANDOLPH, L. F.   An evaluation of induced polyploidy as a method of breeding crop plants.   *Amer. Naturalist* **75**: 347–363, 1941.

STEBBINS, G. L. JR.   The significance of polyploidy in plant evolution.   *Amer. Naturalist* **74**: 54–66, 1940.

WARMKE, H. E.   Polyploidy and evolution.   *Amer. Naturalist* **75**: 344–346, 1941.

XV. Cytological Aspects of Hybridity

AASE, HANNAH C.   Cytology of cereals.   *Bot. Rev.* **1**: 467–496, 1935.

ALLAN, H. H.   Wild species hybrids in the phanerogams.   *Bot. Rev.* **3**: 593–615, 1937.

GOODSPEED, T. H., and MURIEL V. BRADLEY.   Amphidiploidy.   *Bot. Rev.* **8**: 271–316, 1942.

JONES, W. N.   Chimeras: a summary and some special aspects.   *Bot. Rev.* **3**: 545–562, 1937.

————.   Plant Chimeras and Graft Hybrids.   London, 1934.

MANGELSDORF, P. C., and R. G. REEVES.   The origin of Indian corn and its relatives. *Texas Agr. Exp. Sta. Bull.* 574, 1939.

RAPER, K. B., and C. THOM.   Interspecific mixtures in the Dictyosteliaceae.   *Amer. Jour. Bot.* **28**: 69–78, 1941.

SAX, K.   The cytological analysis of species hybrids.   *Bot. Rev.* **1**: 100–117, 1935.

THOMPSON, W. P.   The causes of hybrid sterility and incompatibility.   *Trans. Roy. Soc. Canada, Ser.* III, **34**, 1940.

WINGE, Ö.   On the origin of constant species-hybrids.   *Svensk Bot. Tidskr.* **26**: 107–122, 1932.

XVI. Role of Cytoplasm in Development and Heredity

DEMEREC, M.   Behavior of chlorophyll in inheritance.   *Cold Spring Harbor Symposia on Quant. Biol.* **3**: 80–86, 1935.

LEHMANN, E.   Der Anteil von Kern und Plasma an den reziproken Verschiedenheiten von Epilobium-Bastarden.   *Zeitschr. Zücht.* A **17**: 157–172, 1932.

MICHAELIS, P.   Über die Konstanz des Plasmons.   *Zeitschr. Ind. Abst. Vererb.* **74**: 435–459, 1938.

RENNER, O.   Zur Kenntnis der Plastiden- und Plasmavererbung.   *Cytologia*, Fujii Jubilee Vol.: 644–653, 1937.

SIRKS, M. J.   Plasmatic inheritance.   *Bot. Rev.* **4**: 113–131, 1938.

WETTSTEIN, F. VON.   Über plasmatische Vererbung, sowie Plasma- und Genwirkung. *Nachr. Gesell. Wiss. Göttingen, Math.-Phys. Kl.*, 250–281, 1926.

————. Die genetische und entwicklungsphysiologische Bedeutung des Cytoplasmas. *Zeitschr. Ind. Abst. Vererb.* **73**: 349–366, 1937.

WINGE, Ö., and O. LAUSTSEN. On a cytoplasmic effect of inbreeding in homozygous yeast. *Compt. Rend. Trav. Lab. Carlsberg, Ser. Physiol.* **23**: 17–38, 1940.

XVII. Cytology and Taxonomy

ANDERSON, E. Cytology in its relation to taxonomy. *Bot. Rev.* **3**: 335–350, 1937.

BABCOCK, E. B. Systematics, cytogenetics and evolution in Crepis. *Bot. Rev.* **8**: 139–190, 1942.

————, and G. L. STEBBINS, JR. The American species of Crepis. *Carnegie Inst. Wash. Pub.* 504, 1938.

————, ————, and J. A. JENKINS. Genetic evolutionary processes in Crepis. *Amer. Naturalist* **76**: 337–363, 1942.

BOWDEN, W. M. Diploidy, polyploidy, and winter hardiness relationships in the flowering plants. *Amer. Jour. Bot.* **27**: 357–371, 1940.

CLAUSEN, J., D. D. KECK, and W. M. HIESEY. Experimental taxonomy. *Carnegie Inst. Wash. Yearbooks* 35–40, 1936–1941.

————, ————, ————. The concept of species based on experiment. *Amer. Jour. Bot.* **26**: 103–106, 1939.

————, ————, ————. Regional differentiation in plant species. *Amer. Naturalist* **75**: 231–250, 1941.

CLAUSEN, R. T. On the use of the terms "subspecies" and "variety." *Rhodora* **43**: 157–167, 1941.

CLELAND, R. E. Analysis of wild American races of Oenothera (Onagra). *Genetics* **25**: 636–644, 1940.

DOBZHANSKY, T. Genetics and the Origin of Species. 2d ed. New York, 1941.

DU RIETZ, G. E. The fundamental units of biological taxonomy. *Svensk Bot. Tidskr.* **24**: 333–428, 1930.

GAISER, LULU. Chromosome numbers in angiosperms. I, II, III. *Genetica* **8**: 401–484; *Bibliog. Genetica* **6**: 171–466; *Genetica* **12**: 162–260. 1926, 1930.

GOLDSCHMIDT, R. The Material Basis of Evolution. New Haven, 1940.

GOODSPEED, T. H. Nicotiana phylesis in the light of chromosome number, morphology and behavior. *Univ. Calif. Publ. Bot.* **17**: 369–398, 1934.

HALL, H. M., and F. E. CLEMENTS. The phylogenetic method in taxonomy. *Carnegie Inst. Wash. Pub.* 326, 1923.

HUXLEY, J., ed. The New Systematics. Oxford, 1940.

LONGLEY, A. E. Chromosome morphology in maize and its relatives. *Bot. Rev.* **7**: 263–289, 1941.

OGUMA, K., and S. MAKINO. A new list of the chromosome numbers in Vertebrata (March, 1937). *Jour. Fac. Sci., Hokkaido Imp. Univ.*, VI, **5**: 297–356, 1937.

SENN, H. A. Chromosome number relationships in the Leguminosae. *Bibliog. Genetica* **12**: 175–336, 1938.

STEBBINS, G. L., JR. Polyploid complexes in relation to ecology and the history of floras. *Amer. Naturalist* **76**: 36–45, 1942.

————. The role of isolation in the differentiation of plant species. *Biol. Symposia* **1.** 1942.

————, and E. B. BABCOCK. The effect of polyploidy and apomixis on the evolution of species in Crepis. *Jour. Heredity* **30**: 519–530, 1939.

TISCHLER, G. Pflanzlichen Chromosomenzahlen, I–IV. *Tabulae Biol.* **4**, 1927; **7**, 1931; **11–12**, 1935–1936; **16**, 1938.

————. On some problems of cytotaxonomy and cytoecology. *Jour. Indian Bot. Soc.* **16**: 165–169, 1937.

TURESSON, G. The genotypical response of the plant species to the habitat. *Hereditas* **3**: 341–347, 1922.

————. The plant species in relation to habitat and climate. *Hereditas* **6**: 147–236, 1925.

WHITE, O. E. Temperature reaction, mutation, and geographical distribution in plant groups. *Proc. 8th Amer. Sci. Cong.* **3**: 287–294, 1940.

INDEX

Numbers in **bold-face** indicate pages bearing illustrations.